God and the Cosmologists

Books by the same author

GOD
and the
COSMOLOGISTS

Stanley L. Jaki

REGNERY GATEWAY
Washington, D.C.

ISBN 0-89526-749-7

Published in the United States by
Regnery Gateway
1130 17th Street, NW
Washington, DC 20036

Distributed to the trade by
National Book Network
4720-A Boston Way
Lanham, MD 20706

Also published in Scotland by Scottish Academic Press Ltd.

10 9 8 7 6 5 4 3 2 1

CONTENTS

Contents

Foreword

The eight chapters of this volume are the enlarged form of the eight lectures which the Farmington Institute for Christian Studies, Oxford, and the Farmington Trust asked me to deliver in November 1988. It is my pleasure to express my appreciation to the Hon. Robert Wills, Chairman of the Trust, and to its Board of Trustees, for the invitation and for the subsidy on behalf of a speedy publication of the lectures.

The lectures were delivered in Corpus Christi College, Oxford. As a Visiting Fellow I would like to thank the President and Fellows of Corpus Christi College for their kind hospitality.

Introduction

The appearance, with increasing frequency, of popularizations of modern scientific cosmology by its professional cultivators, including some of the most prominent among them, should be a sufficient proof of the subject's timeliness.

Of course, the study of the universe as such, or cosmology, has a timeless importance. All great philosophical systems have been cosmologies. This was already true of the systems of Plato, Aristotle, and Plotinus as well as of the systems of the atomists and the Stoics. In Christian thought the special character of the systems of Origen, Augustine, and Aquinas are reflected in their views of the universe in which philosophical and theological notions are mixed with the science of their times. The same is no less true of the systems of Descartes, Leibniz, Hume, and Kant.

Kant claimed that his philosophy rescued thought from Humean scepticism in which there was no room for a universe as a genuine and coherent totality. But there is no place for such a universe in Kant's system where the universe is declared to be the product of the illegitimate cravings of the intellect. The universe as a mere regulative idea in Kant's system regulates nothing and nobody. Hence the rank subjectivism of Kant's immediate followers, and the egocentric pantheism as set forth by Bergson, Alexander, Whitehead, Popper and others. They all turn the universe into an ultimate living entity for which an indefinite unfolding is in store through unlimited spans of time.

Most of these modern philosophers made special efforts to camouflage their message in copious references to science. Not one of them refers to a crucial point, namely, that from the early 20th century on science has achieved, for the first time in its history, a contradiction-free discourse about the totality of consistently interacting things, the only true object of scientific cosmology. Yet, as philosophers they should have at least realized the relevance of this outcome for Kant's contention that the universe, being an unreliable notion, cannot serve as a secure jumping board to the recognition of a Creator. No less ignored by modern philosophers is the set of specificities which the modern science of cosmology has established about the universe. Such a universe cannot help imposing the question: why such and not other?

To this all-important question no reply can be found in the universe itself, however scientifically it may be treated, but only in a factor which is extra-mundane in the deepest metaphysical sense. Modern scientific cosmology does indeed heavily contribute to a re-articulation of the cosmological argument appropriate in an age of science.

Not surprisingly, this re-articulation has failed to come from scientists who all too often make worse the intellectual situation by mixing good science with philosophical fashions or spurious religiosities. The outcome has been even worse whenever theologians mixed second-hand information in science with philosophies and theologies steeped in trendiness. Here too, as in any other area of learning, good intentions could not supply hard studies which, in this case, must include thorough familiarity with the history of scientific cosmology, especially of its 20th-century phase.

These lectures are offered to those whose religion is anchored in the belief in the Creator of all, the Father Almighty. May these lectures help them see that they undermine the very rationality of their stance if they expect their philosophical foundations to come from popularizations of scientific cosmology even if written by first-rate scientists. Rather they must first achieve a firm hold on those foundations in order to see what is gold and what is chaff in modern scientific cosmology.

As to the chaff, amply set forth and documented in

these lectures, they should see it for what it is, a most dangerous form of mental poisoning. As to the gold, it is nothing less than the intellectual assurance about the reality of a true cosmos and, as a consequence, of a Creator worthy of the name. But, as any genuine gold, this too has to prove itself in fire. The fire in this case is the hard-won awareness that truth is an objective that demands continual readiness to conquer it and stand up for it. The worthiness of the effort should be measured by the dimensions of that ultimate standing-up whereby man, in his full reality, enters an eternal life which, in Christ's memorable words, is identical with Truth itself.

Chapter One

UNIVERSE REGAINED

The Universe becomes again a valid conception

W. K. Clifford

Cosmic gain and a cosmos lost

The title can but suggest that at one point in the past, and in fact in the not too distant scientific past, the universe was a lost entity, lost at least for all practical purposes. There is further the title's similarity to Milton's *Paradise Regained* which in turn evokes his *Paradise Lost*. Of the two *Paradise Lost* is by far the best remembered. Its superior artistic quality may have much to do with the fact that the human mind, to say nothing of the heart, resonates more forcefully to the loss of something precious than to its recovery. The outpouring of joy over the finding of a lost coin and a lost sheep, to recall two Gospel parables, may be a human characteristic more unusual than it appears at first sight.

As for the "universe lost," the passing of three centuries has not diminished the gripping strength of John Donne's often quoted line: " 'Tis all in peeces, all cohaerence gone."[1] Donne was born in 1572, the very year when Tycho Brahe was startled on seeing, in a clear November night, a brilliant star near Cassiopeia where none had been observed before. The new star or *nova* created the first major doubt about the heavenly sphere as an unchangeable vault wherein the number and positions of stars were forever fixed. The prospect that the

1

celestial vault was a figment of imagination, however hallowed, meant the loss of that very confine which gave the character of a compact whole or universe to the geocentric ordering of all celestial bodies.

Donne was at the height of his literary powers when Galileo's telescope made the loss of the geocentric universe an irretrievable fact. The telescope showed mountains and craters in the moon, so many pockmarks in an allegedly perfect incorruptible body. Through revealing the phases of Venus, the telescope also served evidence that the earth could not be the center of planetary orbits. The chief victim of the telescope was, of course, the celestial sphere whose apparent uniformity had been the main reason for viewing all things as parts of a coherent whole or universe. The telescope showed in a narrow and irregular band of the sky, the Milky Way, incredibly many more stars than the two thousand visible to the naked eye in the entire celestial vault.[2] Since already in Galileo's life every improvement of the telescope only increased the number of stars seen, the heavenly sphere itself seemed to evaporate. And so did the universe insofar as it was taken for a totality deserving the name of cosmos or beauty par excellence. Whereas a spherical shape seemed to provide a configuration of things that formed a universe, that is, a convergence of all into one coherent totality, the ever-receding cosmic depths steadily weakened man's grip on a possibly universal shape.

None of the foregoing astronomical reasons were mentioned by Donne. This merely shows that relatively few major scientific discoveries need to be known if one is to sense the general message carried by science. In warning that in vain

> We thinke the heavens enjoy their Sphericall,
> Their round proportion embracing all,

Donne   offered one specific reason, the all too large number of eccentrics that were needed to account for the mention of planets even in the Copernican system. Donne may have been short on information about the latest in science, but he saw very deeply into the new mentality it generated. He registered the loss of coherence, and with it the implicit loss of the universe with reference to the rising popularity of atomism:

> And freely men confesse that this world's spent
> When in the Planets, and the Firmament
> They seeke so many new; then see that this
> Is crumbled out againe to his Atomies.

But for Donne the real issue was not the atoms, so closely connected in the early 17th century with the name of Epicurus, that chief antique spokesman of cosmic incoherence. Donne saw that for many the primary usefulness of atoms lay in the support they seemed to give to sheer utilitarianism, an attitude centered on mere counting. This is what lies behind Donne's most penetrating remark and complaint: "all just supply, and all Relation." In this light alone can be seen something of the depth of Donne's registering the loss of the universe:

> For the worlds subtilst immateriall parts
> Feele this consuming wound, and ages darts.
> For the world beauty is decai'd, or gone,
> Beauty, that's colour, and proportion.

There is less groping for real depth in Milton's portrayal of the same loss in Books VII and VIII of *Paradise Lost*. In Book VII chaos is turned into a universe by God's taking from His "Eternal Store the golden Compasses . . . to circumscribe this Universe and all created things."[3] But, as it turns out in Book VIII, doubts arise in the newly created Adam whether things, as described in the six-day creation story, are truly circumscribed or coherent and form thereby a universe.

Of course, even before his fall, Milton's Adam is a mid-17th century man. He is disturbed by the vast empty spaces in the heavens, by the uselessly fast rotation of the starry sphere as contrasted with the "sedentarie earth."[4] No less of mid-17th-century-make are the answers which Archangel Raphael offers to Adam's reverential doubts. The answers indicate a state of mind which has no assurance that the mind can ever achieve a hold on the universe. On the one hand, Archangel Raphael admits that Adam's thirst for understanding everything in the heaven is justified: "Heav'n is as the Book of God before thee set." On the other hand, Archangel Raphael takes the fideistic position befitting Milton, the Puritan. Man can learn "the Seasons, Hours or Days, or Months or Yeares," that is, all the information necessary to cope with his genuine needs. To satisfy those needs it matters not to know whether the Heaven or the Earth moves. In the same vein Archangel Raphael, that is, Puritan Milton, also declares that Almighty God can be much better admired by man if many things in heaven remain forever removed from his ken.[5] God, so Archangel Raphael argues, placed the heavens very far from the earth so that man might not be bogged down in speculations which are but so many sheer formalistic means "to save appearances."[6] Much less should man concern himself with

> other Worlds, what Creatures there
> Live; in what state, condition or degree.

In sum, Milton not only admits that the universe is lost for man's mental grasp but also counsels perpetual resignation to that loss. His reasons, which are partly theological with a fideistic touch and rational with a touch of scepticism, are important to note in order to understand the attitude of modern Western man toward the universe during the next three hundred or so years. Fideism is the kind of flame that readily consumes itself. Within a generation after the Puritan revolt that commanded Milton's sympathies, deism, which has no room for faith, was very much in ascendency. Newton, for one, still believed in biblical miracles, but not in the greatest biblical miracle which is God's incarnation in Christ.[7] From his Christian childhood's faith Newton kept no more than the reference in the Nicene Creed to God as the Pantokrator to whose periodic interventions he entrusted the stability of the solar system. He listed half a dozen features in the planetary and stellar universe that could not be derived from natural laws.

In the limbo of infinity

In doing so Newton the cosmologist could seem to favor Christian rather than deist perspectives in which God never intervenes in the universe. It was still to be learned, though not from Leibniz, that the *Christian* Pantokrator does not leave the universe to itself even though it is in no need of periodic repair work on His part. Newton proved himself to be even less than a deist on the only point raised in his time about the universe as such. The point was called to his attention by a divine, Richard Bentley, about ten years after the publication of the *Principia*. The case is all the more interesting because the first edition of the *Principia* contains nothing on the universe as such and certainly nothing on the question whether the universe is finite or infinite. This was the question which Bentley tried to exploit in the last of the eight lectures he delivered in 1692 as the first of the Boyle-lecture series.[8] Before printing the lectures Bentley asked for Newton's comments on what almost two centuries later became known as the gravitational paradox of an infinite universe. Without offering any mathematics, Bentley argued qualitatively that in an infinite homogeneous universe of stars the net effect of gravitational pull is zero because its pull is the same in every direction.

In his reply Newton lectured Bentley, his future Master in Trinity College, on the art of adding and subtracting infinities. Newton gave no mathematical details, nor did he put himself on record whether the universe was finite or infinite. Bentley stuck to his qualitative reasoning that a real universe obeying the inverse square law of gravitation had to be finite. In that cosmic finitude Bentley saw a clear proof of a limitation to specific size or quantity which could come only from the Creator's hands.

Newton's reluctance to come out openly on behalf of an infinite universe is significant for three reasons. One, and not so important, is that he would have thereby repudiated an essay of his, written in 1672, in which he emphatically stated that the universe is finite in an infinite space.[9] Another and more important reason could be some apprehension on his part that by advocating an infinite universe he might incur theological censure. In the circle of his friends and associates he seemed to have kept saying that the universe was finite. Otherwise Addison would not have asserted in the *Spectator* in July 1714 that the universe was strictly finite.[10] This was also the view which Voltaire gathered during his stay in 1726 in London where he often mixed with Newtonians. Ten or so years later, when Voltaire came out with his *Elémens de la philosophie de Neuton*, a book that went through almost thirty editions before 1800 alone, Voltaire emphatically stated that the universe was finite according to Newton and reason, in that order.[11]

The third reason for mentioning the Bentley-Newton debate is that its part relating to the gravitational paradox is ignored in A. Koyré's *From the Closed World to the Infinite Universe*, a book which in the eyes of many is the last word in scholarship on the history of cosmology from Nicolas of Cusa to the death of Newton.[12] Only one explanation can be given about Koyré's astonishing silence on a point of which he could not be unaware. Had Koyré referred to the paradox, he would have destroyed the very message of his interpretation of the astronomical revolution. According to Koyré the astronomical revolution had two major impacts on the Western mind. One was that the dissolution of the closed geocentric universe seemed to deprive mankind of the cosmos. Although the loss was inconceivably profound, for centuries it was grasped only by a few (Pascal being one of them) and "even now is often misvalued and misunderstood in its true bearing."[13] As with most historians of scientific ideas, Koyré too overlooked the obvious, namely, that in the *Pensées* it is the free-thinker and not the Christian who is frightened by the eternal silence of infinite spaces. For the Christian there was no problem on noting that "the whole visible world is only an imperceptible atom in the ample bosom of nature" and that nature is "an infinite sphere, the centre of which is everywhere, the circumference nowhere." In the Christian perspective, to continue with the same *pensée*, it is "the greatest sensible mark of the almighty power of God that imagination loses itself in that thought."[14] Had he sympathized, however slightly, with Pascal, the Christian, Koyré could have also found noteworthy the *pensée* that "physical science will not console me for the ignorance of morality in the time of affliction. But the science of ethics will always console me for the ignorance of the physical sciences."[15]

In short, the dissolution of the geocentric cosmos meant a crisis only for those who put mere physics before sound metaphysics. Koyré clearly ignored all but the few unbelievers and agnostics of the 17th century as he specified the second impact of the dissolution of the geocentric cosmos: An infinite universe did not seem to call for a Creator. Or, as Koyré put it, the infinity of the world proved that God, or rather the Christian God, was a "Dieu fainéant," a "do-nothing God," who could quietly depart from the scene as one not needed by the universe.[16]

Such an interpretation of the astronomical revolution may have rhymed with Koyré's Weltanschauung, a pantheism mixed with agnosticism, but not with the historical record. Few around 1700, or even later, suggested an infinite universe, with only one scientist or cosmologist among them. He was Edmond Halley, well known for his atheism as well as for his roundabout defense of an infinite homogeneous universe. Those, mostly philosophers, who endorsed the idea of an infinite universe, almost invariably saw in it a convenient excuse for dispensing with a truly transcendental God. Unlike the Cambridge Neoplatonists, Spinoza spelled out this excuse with commendable openness, though with no reference to science. Before him Giordano Bruno and Jacob Boehme had coupled their defense of the infinity of the universe with dicta bordering on irrationalism and sheer antiscience. A hundred years after Spinoza, German enlightenment, idealism, and romanticism became so many breeding places for advocates of cosmic infinity as well as of pantheism. Bruno was reinstated in honor by Schelling, a virulent pantheist. But even a Novalis, sympathetic to positive Christianity, could write rather naively: "Nothing is more accessible to the mind than the infinite."[17]

The writings of Schelling do not echo the instructiveness which graces, between the lines, the article on "Infini" that appeared in 1764 in Volume V of the *Encyclopédie*. In that article, which attested the fear of theological censors, Diderot, its most likely author and always ready to pour scorn on theology, reserved infinity to God as the only being who could properly possess it.[18] But what were the grounds for the theologians, seated either in the Sorbonne (or in Lambeth Palace and in Oxford, for that matter) to see a threat in the idea of an infinite universe? The threat of such a universe could not come from the scientific literature. There the idea of an infinite universe found its first thematic appearance in article form as late as 1823, and in book form only in

1847.[19] The threat came from philosophers who themselves did not formulate it with sufficient clarity. Partly because of this theologians still have to recognise in the alleged homogeneity of an infinite universe the true source of that threat.

The cosmic barter

One of those philosophers was Kant who certainly saw the pivotal role which is played by one's acceptance of the universe in one's appraisal of belief in the Creator. As Kant tried to demolish the cosmological argument, he put forward about the universe an apparently scientific claim, which in fact had little to do with science. According to Kant the universe was an unreliable notion (the bastard product of the metaphysical cravings of the intellect) because science could not establish whether the universe was finite or infinite, atomistic or continuous. Or in Kant's very words: "If the world is a whole existing in itself, it is either finite or infinite. But both alternatives are false (as shown in the proofs of the antithesis and thesis respectively). It is therefore also false that the world (the sum of appearances) is a whole existing in itself."[20]

Kant rested on this conclusion the truth of "transcendental ideality," that is, his entire philosophical system. Moreover he hinted in the same breath at the ultimate benefit to be derived from that truth. It was an artful understatement on his part that "this remark is of some importance." For as the reader of the *Critique* was to find out, a self-centered individual remained the only entity of any importance if he took Kant for guide. But he could not say that he had not been forewarned: "For when the arguments of reason," Kant continued, "are allowed to oppose one another in unrestricted freedom, something advantageous, and likely to aid in the correction of our judgments, will always accrue, though it may not be what we set out to find."[21] Any astute reader of the

Critique could at that point suspect that the advantage in question was the establishment of man as a fully autonomous being, though only at the greatest conceivable price. His absolute autonomy (at the safest remove even from a special revelation of God) could be purchased only by losing the real universe. He was left with its regulative idea which, being a mere idea, could not regulate any real being and certainly not the ego.

Kant's bartering the universe for an ego free of any subjection to a Creator, who can only be known if there is a real universe, started a rampage of subjectivism in which, as already the writings of Fichte and Hegel were to show, universe and science fared very badly. Here too Kant set the pattern. In Kant's lengthy lucubrations about the first and second antinomies one would look in vain for any reference to statements by scientists on matters cosmological.[22] As to the first antinomy, he did not even refer to Bentley's book, available in German translation since 1714. He also ignored Voltaire's book on the basics of Newtonian philosophy (available in German since 1741) as well as Euler's *Lettres à une princesse d'Allemagne*, in both of which the finitude of the universe was firmly stated. Shocking should seem Kant's failure to refer in the *Critique* to Lambert's *Cosmologische Briefe* the publication of which in 1761 started their lengthy correspondence. Kant's chief interest in Lambert's book related to the explanation there of the Milky Way which he found very similar to the one he had proposed in 1756 by borrowing heavily on the ideas of Wright.[23] Kant simply ignored Lambert's pointed reference to the impossibility of an actually realized infinite quantity as a major reason for endorsing the finitude of the universe.[24] In sum, insofar as science or scientists could be invoked in the 1770s, when Kant wrote the *Critique*, their testimony was well-nigh unanimous about the finitude of the universe. From the viewpoint of contemporary science the first antimony of Kant did not exist.

Worse for Kant, there could be no first antimony even on the basis of the premises of his epistemology. They derived from his contention that the categories of the mind acted as so many filters for data obtained by the senses about the external world. In fact even that world's existence became a function of the mind. One of the categories of the mind was perception in a three-dimensional manifold which did not include boundaries. Had Kant been logical, he should have recognized that far from having a ground for setting up an insoluble alternative between a finite and infinite universe, he should have declared that the universe had to be infinite.

That in arguing the first and second antinomies Kant shifted from empiricist to idealist grounds and back, has often been noted. He shifted so often as to turn those antinomies into sheer sophistries. No less a sympathetic student of Kant than Norman Kemp Smith reached the devastating conclusion that "his proofs [about the antinomies] are in every instance invalid."[25] Whatever the readiness in philosophical circles to accept well-argued conclusions, it is still to be widely recognized that in regard to the first antinomy, which is under direct discussion here, Kant had no ground to appeal to science. More importantly, it is still to be perceived that Kant demanded from his readers the highest price that any rationalist philosopher can demand. The price was the universe. It had to be lost if one was also to find specious excuses for parting with one's rational belief in God. In that respect Kant's strategy did not differ from the one Hume set forth in his *Dialogue on Natural Theology*. Hume, another so-called Newtonian philosopher, ended up with a portrayal of botched up and aborted universes, universes produced in spiders' bellies.[26]

In a style that was an exercise in nebulosity, Kant declared the universe to be a notion unworthy of reason. He did not see the irony when, a decade or so after the publication of the *Critique*, he gladly accepted congratulations from his circle of admirers, invariably amateurish in matters scientific. They celebrated Kant for his having divined by the sheer powers of the mind what Herschel could discover only by building huge telescopes. The discovery in question had two aspects: one related to the Milky Way as a lentil-shaped confine of countless stars, the other to the nature of nebulous stars as so many other Milky Ways or galaxies. In respect to both Kant's originality was less than he claimed in his *Universal Natural History and Theory of the Heavens*, published in 1756.[27] There Kant set forth the genesis of an infinite universe as the only universe that could come forth from the hands of the Creator with infinite powers. The real creator of that universe was Kant's own mind, obsessed with the idea that an apparently homogeneous primordial cosmic state could contain in germ a most specific actual universe. Herein lay the real threat for theologians, a threat of which more later and especially in the second chapter.

Hand in hand with that threat went another one, set forth by Kant in a still earlier work of his in which he argued that there should exist an infinite number of universes because the mind can imagine an infinite number of dimensions.[28] It is this blissful step from mere concepts to reality which turns, as will be seen in another chapter, not a few recent writings on cosmology into an antitheological tirade. What all this should illustrate about Kant is that, from the start of his career to its very end, his universe was the universe of his mind, the worst trap in which to lose the universe. He was in fact so self-centered as to write repeatedly, "I am God," in his last great work, the *Opus postumum*.[29]

Schizophrenia bred by infinity
The latter work could not, of course, be known to those who received their university education in the last decades of the 18th century when Kant suddenly loomed

large, in Germany at least, as one of the greatest intellects ever. Influenced also by the pietistic strain of the German scene, they readily espoused Kant's claim that God would not be worthy of His infinite powers had He not created an infinite universe. The most fateful entry of that "pious" claim of Kant into science came with Wilhelm Olbers, the famed discoverer of asteroids. He used it as a peremptory argument on behalf of the infinity of the universe in his now classic paper on the "Transparency of Cosmic Spaces," published in 1823.[30] There Olbers wanted to dispose of the paradoxical problem which the darkness of the night poses in an infinite universe filled homogeneously with stars. To resolve the paradox he assumed (possibly through a subconscious recall of the solution proposed by Chéseaux in 1743)[31] that much of the starlight was absorbed in the interstellar ether. Whatever the infancy in 1823 of thermodynamics, Olbers should have realized that bodies steadily exposed to radiation would eventually heat up to the temperature of the sources emitting that radiation. The laws of thermodynamics were still to be strictly formulated when in 1847 the younger Herschel exposed for precisely that reason the fallacy of Olbers' solution of the paradox.

By the mid-19th century the Hegelian left took for a fundamental tenet the infinity of the material universe together with the eternity of matter. The Hegelian right in its Neo-Kantian form also did its best to nurture the idea of an infinite universe as a precious Kantian bulwark of rationality. Only a few scientists dared to challenge the Kantian steamroller decked out in scientific nomenclature. One of them was the prince of mathematicians, Gauss, who noted with an eye on non-Euclidean geometry that Kant's dicta on categories were sheer trivialities.[32] Most scientists readily espoused the encomium which Helmholtz offered on Kant, the scientist, in 1871.[33] The victorious Second Reich needed cultural heroes as well. By the end of the 19th century the idea of the infinite universe had eaten itself so heavily into the minds of scientists as to make them insensitive to patent fallacies implied in it. One of those fallacies had for its victim Lord Kelvin when, in a direct reference to the universe, he identified Euclidean infinity with intelligibility:

> I say *finitude* is incomprehensible, the infinite in the universe *is* comprehensible. Now apply a little logic to this. Is the negation of infinitude incomprehensible? What would you think of a universe in which you could travel one, ten, or a thousand miles, or even to California, and then find it came to an end? Can you suppose an end of matter or an end of space? The idea is incomprehensible. Even if you were to go millions and millions of miles the idea of coming to an end is incomprehensible.[34]

The other form of insensitivity expressed itself in a reasoning bordering on schizophrenia that divided the universe into two parts: One part consisted of the Milky Way which at that time was believed to be much larger than other galaxies. As the latter were spotted in very large numbers around the two galactic poles, they seemed to constitute with the Milky Way an essentially spherical mini-universe. Outside that mini-universe lay the other part, infinite in every direction with an infinite number of homogeneously distributed galaxies. By declaring with fallacious arguments that this outer infinite universe could not sensibly affect the interior mini-universe, scientists, with Kelvin in the van,[35] condemned the universe to be lost forever. Agnes M. Clerke, the leading historian of astronomy of the 19th century, voiced in 1905 the consensus when in her great monograph, *The System of the Stars*, she declared: "With the infinite possibilities beyond [the Milky Way] science has no concern."[36]

Large as the mini-part (or the Milky Way Galaxy) of the universe was in itself, its limitedness, surrounded as it was by a presumably infinite number of galaxies, could not suggest a finite universe. The idea of a finite universe made a scientifically spurious comeback through thermodynamics, or rather through the heath-death of the universe which seemed to be implied in the law of entropy. Of course, when at the November 26, 1906, meeting of the Société Française de la Philosophie Perrin steered the discussion of the foundations of thermodynamics toward the heath-death of the universe, he merely paraphrased an idea of Clausius, already more than three decades old. At that meeting George Sorel made a remark that a decade or so later could have been made for genuinely scientific reasons, but was not:

> I am very much struck by the fact that modern physics has restored, without apparently perceiving it, the old notion of a finite closed world, entertained in antiquity, a notion that was discarded in the 17th and 18th centuries by those who accomplished the scientific revolution by shattering the confines of the world. Whereas they were fully conscious of their innovation, modern physicists returned to the idea of a finite universe without justifying it and without even taking account of the counter-revolution they had achieved.[37]

An engineer by education, but a social philosopher by profession, George Sorel illustrated with his remark a pattern, by then centuries old and very valid even today: The evaluation of what fundamentally happens in science is a business more philosophical than scientific.

Universe regained and overlooked
A proof of this was the development, already under way when Sorel spoke (though not for the right reason), that led to the recovery of the universe in a genuinely scientific sense. A scientific answer in the affirmative was in

the making to Sorel's introductory question: "Does one have the right to speak of the universe, of the ensemble of things?" About that development, which started with a suggestion of Riemann and was first worked out in 1872 in a sketchy form by Zöllner,[38] the observation made at the beginning of this chapter certainly applies. Whatever joy there was about the great prospect of regaining the universe, it was very muted in comparison with the loud lamentations offered in the 17th century about the universe lost. Only one scientist of note, W. K. Clifford, at the Imperial University of London, remarked on a jubilant note that through being appraised in a four-dimentional manifold "the universe, as known, becomes again a valid conception."[39] In the context Clifford did not refer to Kant. But his statement, very anti-Kantian in itself, should seem to be an explicit rebuttal of Kant. Clifford was one of the first British academics to pay close attention to the German intellectual scene, and to its Neo-Kantianism in particular, as it developed during the second half of the 19th century.

That Neo-Kantians in Britain, or elsewhere, failed to take note is understandable. No philosophy implants schizophrenia so deeply in the mind with respect to external reality as do Kantian idealism and its progenies. The silence of the scientific community about Zöllner's great breakthrough is more difficult to explain. There was no jubilation when Schwarzschild worked out in 1900 the space-time curvature of the mini-universe which he, of course, believed to be *all* the observable universe.[40]

Still to come was the supreme touch of irony, a touch all the more ironic as it was provided by Einstein. the supreme scientific genius of the 20th century. Ten years of extreme mental concentration preceded the publication of his fifth and concluding memoir on General Relativity that dealt with its cosmological consequences. That memoir meant nothing less than the universe regained, or rather gained for the first time in the history of science. No explicit reference to this was made by Einstein who perhaps could excuse himself on the ground that his memoirs were heavily technical. He also set for himself a pattern with his first non-technical book on Relativity by not calling attention to the enormous novelty of the fact that General Relativity allowed a contradiction-free scientific treatment of the totality of gravitationally interacting things. His brief reference there to the gravitational paradox that plagued the idea of the infinite Euclidean universe[41] was not followed up by as much as a hint that by laying a true hold on the universe, science, which is always cosmology, has finally come into its own.[42]

The universe as the greatest prize for science was nowhere in sight at perhaps the most dramatic meeting of the Royal Society that took place on November 14, 1919. The meeting had for its principal subject Eddington's report on the results of the famed expedition he had led earlier that year to West Africa to measure the bending of starlight around the eclipsed sun, the most celebrated consequence of General Relativity. Whitehead, who was to come up eventually with a rival form of Relativity, certainly kept millions in the dark about the real achievement of Einstein as he recalled that meeting in perhaps the finest passage he ever penned:

> The whole atmosphere of tense interest was exactly that of the Greek drama: We were the chorus commenting on the decree of destiny as disclosed in the development of a supreme incident. There was dramatic quality in the very staging — the traditional ceremonial, and in the background the picture of Newton to remind us that the greatest of scientific generalizations was now, after more than two centuries, to receive its first modification. Nor was the personal interest wanting: a great adventure in thought had at length come safe to shore.[43]

Never was a great adventure more thoroughly misread and the jubilation over it more effectively shifted from its true reason. Yet nothing would have been easier than to state that the universe, that could not be caught with the nets of Newtonian gravitation, has now been captured by a recasting of Newton's work.

Oversight of this point was well nigh complete in books, all of them now classics, written by Pauli, Born, Weyl, Bertrand Russell, and Eddington on General Relativity within half a dozen years of its completion.[44] The professed philosophical interest of most of them makes their oversight all the more inexcusable. They certainly showed no urge to call their readers' attention to the special tie between General Relativity and the universe. A mere look at the subject index in those books tells a baffling dislocation of appraisal. If the word universe (or world, or cosmos) occurs there, it does so only with one or two entries. Usually, one finds there the entry "world line" as the sole and vague reminder that General Relativity has an all-important consequence for the scientific understanding of the totality of things, or the universe.

Insensitivity to that consequence often shows up in the principally philosophical character of the evaluation of what really takes place in science. When philosophers signally fail in that evaluation they have little excuse in the fact that scientists fail to alert them. Philosophers, who had been in the habit of slighting the universe or of entertaining spurious ideas about it, would have been warned in vain by scientists. It is in this light that one should reflect on that famous occasion at the Sorbonne when in early April 1922 the elite of French philosophers, with Bergson in the lead, questioned Einstein on Relativity. They failed to raise the basic subject of the human inquiry which is the universe. Time was the only topic on which Bergson and Einstein exchanged views, though not fruitfully. Einstein claimed immunity from pressing philosophical questions about time on the ground that his interest in time was merely that of a physicist. Such was a polite evasion on the part of Einstein, all too ready to reduce the reality of time to what his Relativity allowed one to say about it. Had Bergson queried him on the subject of the universe, a most revealing exchange of ideas might have followed.[45] To be sure, Bergson's idea of the universe as the ultimate living entity, driven by an *élan vital* and never running out of new possibilities, had no common points with what General Relativity implied about the universe. Yet a reference by Bergson to his pantheistic universe might have prompted Einstein to air his espousal of Spinozism as a cosmic philosophy. There the cosmos or the universe could not be discovered, let alone regained.

Clearly, the philosophy must be the right one if the universe as restored by science is to be done justice. A further illustration of this is the handling of the subject by Bertrand Russell and Alfred North Whitehead, in both of whom keen philosophical interest was united with eminent competence in mathematical physics. Yet the universe remained for Bertrand Russell a "brute fact," about which he wanted no further questions.[46] The universe could but make uneasy the one who converted to philosophical realism only as a form of empiricism. As for Whitehead, he distanced himself from the scientific universe in the measure in which he got entangled in an evolutionary recasting of Kantian epistemology. No wonder that the center of Whitehead's cosmic view was man as a co-creator with God of the universe, all three imperfect, all three evolving.[47]

Such a view had little room for exact science but plenty for unbridled fantasies. Whitehead heedlessly spoke of universes, of infinite possibilities in a universe to which science had just denied infinity.[48] Scientific sobriety fared poorly when on touching a small mahogany stand Whitehead declared that there may be in it

civilisations as complex and diversified in scale as our own; and up there, the heavens, with all their

> vastness, may be only a minute strand of tissue in
> the body of a being in the scale of which all our uni-
> verses are as a trifle. Man has only just begun to
> understand, not this vastness, for we cannot grasp
> it, but that such vastness exists, and that it throws
> out all his previous calculations.[49]

Introductory to this extraordinary peroration, that flew
in the face of modern scientific cosmology, was Whitehead's emphatic abolition of natural laws: "There *are no*
natural laws. There are only temporary habits of nature."

Whitehead never explained how science, especially
the science of cosmology that spans so many magnitudes
in space and many more in time, can be cultivated on
that very "temporary" basis. There could, however, be no
doubt as to the true nature of a religion that alone could
issue from a cosmology that had for its object a cosmos
full of quasi-conscious volitions. The great conclusion of
Whitehead's *Process and Reality* that "cosmology is the
basis of all religion,"[50] should be read in that light. The
religion in question is radically different from any religion, especially orthodox Christianity, in which the
object of worship is an infinitely perfect Creator of a universe which can be perfect only in a strictly limited sense.
Still unclear is the true reason for the break of Whitehead, the son of a Church of England clergyman, with
Christianity. He himself gave as reason his reflections on
the gallant self-sacrifice of countless younger British
academics in the bloody battlefields of World War I.
Whitehead believed that they could have died only "for
the worth of the world."[51] A proof of this he never
offered, although proofs to the contrary he might have
gathered from any of the padres assisting many of those
gallant men.

Einstein's perplexity
The broader picture of modern scientific cosmology
would be much clearer if recent leading cosmologists

had imitated Whitehead's readiness to offer glimpses
into the deepest recesses of their minds. Still revealing
should seem the slighting of the universe in such recent
and prominent discussions of the cosmology of General
Relativity as S. Weinberg's *Gravitation and Cosmology*,[52]
C. Lanczos' *Albert Einstein and the Cosmic World Order*,[53]
and A. Pais' *Subtle is the Lord: The Science and Life of Einstein*.[54] Against their slighting of the universe within the
framework of General Relativity Einstein would have
been rather slow to protest. The reason for this is to be
sought in his religion where the object of worship was, in
his own words, Spinoza's God, or Nature in short.[55] And
just as Spinoza and most other pantheists, old and new,
Einstein too found it embarrassing to address himself to
the world or universe insofar as he placed it on a divine
pedestal. Once on that pedestal the universe cannot do
what God is supposed to do, namely, to answer as a person to that personality which turns man truly into a
human being. As a champion of cosmic religion[56] Einstein was at least logical by pouring scorn on personal
immortality while ascribing immortality to the universe.

Such an immortal universe seemed to him to lurk
between the lines of his memoir on the cosmological
consequences of General Relativity. It was a universe
basking in the glory of an apparently perennial immo-
bility and having that spherical shape which all ancient
pantheists loved to predicate about the universe. No
wonder that Einstein reacted not with the cool detach-
ment of a scientist but with the deep involvement of a
"believer" when he learned that his cosmos was shown to
be subject to that transitoriness which is the chief characteristic of all mortals. Einstein's distinctly non-scientific and markedly religious reaction to that news, of
which more in another chapter, proved his often quoted
words that the man of science is a poor philosopher. For,
as will be seen, the specter of transitoriness, cosmic or
other, may be a pyschologically powerful pointer to God,

though not a philosophically reliable pointer. Most reliable philosophically is, however, the message of modern
scientific cosmology that the universe is real and that it is
no less specific than any real thing. Both these points
were glaring in Einstein's fifth memoir which contains
formulas for the total mass and radius of the universe.
But if the universe is so specifically real, nothing could
have been more logical than to ask: why is the universe
what it is and not something else? With that question one
would have, of course, placed oneself within the perspective which shows not a divinized universe, impotent to
answer that question, but a personal God free to choose
to create one among an infinitely large number of possible universes.

In trying to avoid that perspective Einstein made one
of his most elementary philosophical blunders. It is part
of his letter of March 3, 1952, to Marcel Solovine, his
friend from their Zurich student days. The letter, largely
devoted to the religious bearing of cosmology, was
prompted by Solovine's inquiry whether rumors were
true about Einstein's becoming a believer and a Catholic
to boot. While flatly denying these rumors, Einstein tried
to steer a middle course between atheism and belief in a
personal God. He held high the miracle of the universe,
a miracle of a high degree of order in an objective world
"which we are in no way entitled to expect *a priori*." But
then he added: "Curiously, we have to be resigned to recognizing the 'miracle' without having any legitimate way
of getting any further."[57]

Enormous as was the philosophical instructiveness of
these words, it remained hidden to the one who wrote
them. Einstein failed even to note that Immanuel Kant,
the philosopher-hero of his youth, would have been the
first to protest his claim that "there is no legitimate way
of getting any further," that is, going beyond the miracle
of a universe existing in its specifically ordered reality.
For the real strength of Kant's strategy lay precisely in
his claim that in order to make impossible the step from

the universe to God, one had to destroy access to the universe itself by declaring it a notion unworthy of the intellect.

Divines who failed to divine

Herein lies the first crucial contribution of modern scientific cosmology to the issue about God's existence. That cosmology has for its object the universe itself which only half a century ago did not yet figure in first-rate books having in their titles the words cosmology or cosmogony. Those books were about the evolution of stars, of planetary systems, and of galaxies. They had not a chapter, not even a good paragraph, on the universe as such. Nothing illustrates better this strange misuse of those words (cosmology and cosmogony) than two vast monographs by James Jeans. One, which earned him the prestigious Adams Prize for 1917, was entitled, *Problems of Cosmogony and Stellar Dynamics*. The other, also a quarto volume, was published in 1928 and had *Astronomy and Cosmogony* for its title but no cosmos in its contents. The four references in it to Einstein had nothing to do with the cosmology made possible by General Relativity.[58]

Within three years Einstein's cosmological work was in the full center of scientific attention through a blue-ribbon panel discussion sponsored by the Royal Society.[59] None of the speakers noted that all their discussions presupposed that owing to Einstein's work the universe had become a reality for science. What was not noted by scientists studying the universe itself and by philosophers afraid of the reality of the universe, failed to be noted even by philosophers and divines whose very message depended on the ability of the mind, scientific or philosophical, to achieve a valid grasp of the totality of things. One of them was the Abbé Lemaître, a member of that panel, who through his affiliation with the University of Louvain was amply exposed to Thomistic philosophy.[60] Moreover, he never dallied with modernism, which certainly cannot be said about another member of that panel, E. W. Barnes, not only a well-trained mathematician but also the Anglican bishop of Birmingham and the *enfant terrible* of his Church at that time. The finitude of the universe, as called for by General Relativity, meant for Bishop Barnes only the opportunity that such a universe can be discussed by science.[61]

Had Bishop Barnes referred in that connection to Einstein and General Relativity, Archbishop Temple might have had second thoughts on his espousing in his Gifford Lectures Whitehead's evolving universe diffused with Mind. Confusion waited in the wings. It was adumbrated in the Archbishop's concession to Hume's "devastating suggestion" that all the mechanical order of the physical universe cannot remove the possibility that "this world, for aught (any man) knows, is very faulty and imperfect compared to a superior standard; and was only the first rude essay of some infant deity, who afterwards abandoned it, ashamed of his lame performance."[62] A decade or so later Archbishop Temple offered to a correspondent the following statement as the logical unfolding of his Gifford Lectures:

> What we must completely get away from is the notion that the world as it now exists is a rational whole; we must think of its unity not by the analogy of a picture, of which all the parts exist at once, but by the analogy of a drama where, if it is good enough, the full meaning of the first scene only becomes apparent with the final curtain; and we are in the middle of this. Consequently the world as we see it is strictly unintelligible. We can only have faith that it will become intelligible when the divine purpose, which is the explanation of it, is accomplished.[63]

Once more theology ran the risk of appearing as an advocacy of blind faith. Temple's was the elementary philosophical failure to see the difference between the rationality of a quantitative pattern, which science can provide, and an understanding which also implies the grasp of purpose about which science can say nothing.

No less telling cases of oversight of enormous opportunities for theological cosmology proved to be the well-known public lectures given by E. T. Whittaker in the 1940s.[64] No one in his time, and even in our time, has had such a grasp as Whittaker did on what had taken place in physics from Newton to Einstein. He too made the first serious effort to show the bearing of the new science of cosmology on the proofs of the existence of God. Only he missed the crucial point, the reality of the universe, for which he could have blamed authors of Scholastic manuals on cosmology, had he consulted them. In those cosmologies, a point that deserves to be studied in detail, the universe as such is not discussed.[65] No wonder that Whittaker's attention was dominated by the temporality of the universe as revealed by its expansion, the topic of another lecture. And so did the temporality of the universe dominate a famous address of Pope Pius XII, who had Whittaker as his chief advisor in matters scientific.

The Pope's address, given on 21 November 1951 to the Pontifical Academy of Sciences,[66] received world-wide publicity. In fact, its text was carried almost *in integro* in the next-day issue of *The New York Times* and introduced there by a front-page summary.[67] Einstein in Princeton could not remain unaware of it, nor could most of Einstein's friends. The glowing words of the Pope about modern scientific cosmology may indeed have started rumors about Einstein's possible "conversion". But on reading the Pope's address Einstein could not find in it what he needed most for a conversion, philosophical if not religious.

What Einstein the philosopher-scientist needed above all was a momentous reminder that Kant's central claim, that the universe was a bastard product of the metaphysical cravings of the intellect, had no chance in the court of modern scientific cosmology. Had he been reminded of this he might not have concluded his letter to Solovine with a remark resounding with hollow confidence: "I have to add the last point [namely, that there is no way of going beyond the universe], lest you think that weakened by old age, I have fallen into the hands of priests."[68] At any rate priests, divines, and Christians in general, still have to become aware that the most fundamental development in modern scientific cosmology is its witness that the universe has been regained. The erstwhile lamentation about the "universe lost" will not be exceeded by jubilation about the "universe regained" unless there is a full realization of the measure of what has been regained in the context of modern Western intellectual history.

Chapter Two

NEBULOSITY DISSIPATED

The universe is a single jewel . . . peerless and
priceless, for there cannot be another one

G. K. Chesterton

Cosmic jewel in retrospect
It happens all too often that whenever something is very
much expected not to happen, contrary developments
may already be under way. Einstein certainly hoped that
the universe would never show a large-scale motion.
This hope of his was expressed in a roundabout way at
the very end of his memoir on the cosmological consequences of General Relativity. There he defended the
introduction into the field equations of a new term that
later came to be called the cosmological constant: "The
term is necessary only for the purpose of making possible a quasi-static distribution of matter, as required by
the fact of the small velocities of the stars."[1] The term,
which he many years later referred to as the "biggest
blunder" he had made,[2] stood for a repulsive force whose
role it was to prevent all matter in the universe from
being pulled by gravitation into one single lump.
　Einstein soon learned from De Sitter that even from
the purely theoretical viewpoint his quasi-static universe
was less threatened by a possible contraction than by a
possible expansion. The supreme irony was provided by
Einstein's remark that he would not discuss whether the
introduction of the new term was tenable "from the
standpoint of present astronomical knowledge,"[3] that is,

from the standpoint of observational evidence that ultimately decides whether a theory is right or wrong. Rarely did a scientist read more incorrectly the signs of the times or, in this case, portents already visible in the astronomical sky.

While individual stars showed a great variety of motion, such was not the evidence that began to accrue from the early 1910s on about spiral galaxies. By and large their spectra showed a red shift indicative of recessional velocity. In the early 1920s this could mean that those galaxies might not be permanently subordinate parts of the Milky Way. In other words, the mini-universe revealed itself as possibly being in the process of fragmentation, the very opposite to what a universe has to be. Also, the Milky Way itself had to be removed from its exalted status as the main part of that mini-universe to one among tens of thousands of spiral galaxies. This happened when around 1924 Hubble observed Cepheid variables in the Andromeda nebula which enabled him to establish its true distance and size. The distance turned out to be two million light years, or twenty times the diameter of the Milky Way. This showed the Andromeda nebula to be roughly equal in size to the Milky Way, and a true rival to the supposedly chief body in the visible universe.

But when the observable or mini-universe had to be divided into tens of thousands of equally big parts and cease thereby to appear as a coherent whole, another development came to the rescue of cosmic coherence. The result was nothing short of dramatic in that it gave an unsuspectedly precise grasp on the universe itself. This major breakthrough in cosmology occurred when in 1927 the Abbé Lemaître derived from Einstein's cosmological equations the expansion of the universe and correlated that rate with data on galactic red-shifts already available.[4] Lemaître's conclusion should seem especially daring when contrasted with the diffidence with which Hubble and Humason published, about that time, their first analysis of those red-shifts. Even four years later, with many more data on hand, they voiced their constraint "to describe the 'apparent-velocity-displacements' without venturing on the interpretation and its cosmological significance."[5] Yet the velocity-distance-law contained not only the revolutionary implication that the whole universe is subject to an over-all dynamics of expansion, but also that far back in the cosmic past all things, or the universe, had to be a very small thing.

This latter point found its first elaboration in Lemaître's famous hypothesis of the early universe as a "primitive atom."[6] He did not, however, seize on the principal philosophical opportunity which this view of the universe offered. Not that the exploitation of that view demanded scientific expertise or professional training in philosophy. What was demanded could have conceivably been found in those Catholic and Thomistic circles in which Lemaître moved. Yet even in those circles where Chesterton had for some time been eagerly read, no attention was given to his most penetrating analysis of scientific laws, widely available in his *Orthodoxy*, first published in 1908.[7] It also contained what in view of late-20th-century developments in scientific cosmology should pass for a profound anticipation of their very gist:

> The universe is a single jewel and while it is a natural cant to talk of a jewel as peerless and priceless, of this jewel of the cosmos it is literally true. This cosmos is indeed without peer and price; for there cannot be another one.[8]

But if the universe was to reveal convincingly what precious things reveal in their smallness, namely, its exceedingly specific features, its expanding motion had to be followed up in the reverse direction.

For a long time, however, another aspect of cosmic expansion, the transitoriness of the universe, exercised above all the minds of cosmologists. As will be seen in the next chapter, that transitoriness may be taken for something more than it is, unless attention is first focused on cosmic specificity, as revealed by the expansion of the universe. Cosmic specificity was already part of the chief lesson that has been provided by the regaining of the universe in terms of Einstein's cosmology. In addition to its primary outcome, the re-instating of the universe in its intellectual respectability, that cosmology also disclosed important particulars about the universe as such. As noted in the first chapter, the total mass and maximum radius of the universe are particulars to specifics about the universe that point to its contingency, that is, to the possibility of its existing with different specificities. To appreciate that primary outcome it had to be seen outlined against its historical background, the record of references to the gravitational and optical paradoxes of an infinite universe. In connection with the specificity of the universe, too, a recourse to history may turn out to be highly instructive.

The infinite Euclidean universe resisted a unitary scientific grasp only in part because of its infinity, about which Eddington once soberly said: "That queer quantity, infinity, is the mischief and science must not do anything with it."[9] Another and no less important reason lay in the presumed homogeneity of that universe. The more homogeneous an object is, the more it resembles a slippery fish that readily escapes one's hold on it. As for the infinite universe, its homogeneity first meant but a homogeneous distribution of stars, so many non-homogeneous and indeed most specific objects. Even so, that homogeneous distribution of non-homogeneous specific objects gave rise to debilitating paradoxes, optical and gravitational, whereby the universe slipped through the scientist's fingers. A far more sinistrous homogeneity, that of a primordial matter, began to raise its threatening head in science only after Herschel found that certain luminous patches in the sky could not be resolved into stars. But Herschel, who loved to speak of the realm of galaxies as a luxuriant cosmic garden with all sorts of plants and all in various stages of growth,[10] never referred to irresoluble nebulous patches as an evidence of a primordial matter that needs no explanation.

Nebulosity and homogeneity

This dubious honor went to Laplace, the archetype of those modern scientists who survive most different political systems and even flourish in all of them. They exemplify the species of intellectual (and at times moral) invertebrates that err only in catching up a bit late, now and then, with the changing ideological climate. Laplace, who began to rise in the *ancien régime* and served with equanimity the Jacobins and the Directorate, did not notice soon enough that Napoleon, for purely political reasons, was already edging toward religion and Church when Herschel made his famous visit in Paris in the summer of 1802. As an illustrious guest, Herschel had to pay, in Laplace's company of course, a visit to the First Consul who quickly turned the conversation to Laplace's theory of the evolution of the solar system. The theory was already six years old and was available in two editions of the *Exposition du système du monde*, a popularization of the main features and dynamics of the solar system.[11] There Laplace hinted that the origin and evolution of the solar system as described by him could very well be true of other stars and by implication of the whole universe as well.

The theory, that subsequently dominated 19th-century scientific and popular imagination under the name of nebular hypothesis,[12] began with a rotating nebulous matter. As it contracted, it also cooled in its outer regions which, according to the Laplacean scenario, separated in successive rings from the central part and coalesced into individual planets. The chief drawback of the theory was that it came from a first-rate expert in Newtonian mechanics. The theory implied elementary oversight of such a basic law of mechanics as the conservation of angular momentum. Laplace, of course, had the right to assume that the original nebula was rotating but he had no right to suggest that he had scientifically explained that assumption. In fact from start to end the theory needed repeated interventions by some external agent capable of supplying what Laplace's physics could not deliver. While the lopsided distribution of the angular momentum in the solar system in favor of the planets is still a problem for celestial dynamics,[13] the physics of turbulent motion in gases and liquids may account for the original rotation. Yet even then one still has to resort to an even better physics for the explanation of why the gas or liquid is constituted in the first place of such material particles whose interactions produce vortices.

Clearly, more than physics had to be at work in Laplace's mind as he presented his theory as one that made unnecessary Newton's recourse to divine interventions to explain various features of the solar system, and especially of its genesis. Napoleon must have been familiar with this aspect of Laplace's theory; otherwise he would not have asked, and in Herschel's presence, why there was no mention of God in his genesis of the solar system. Such is the background of Laplace's often quoted, and almost invariably out of context, reply, "Sire, je n'ai pas besoin de cette hypothèse," as recorded by Herschel.[14] This dictum of Laplace, repeated and paraphrased on countless occasions by advocates, professional and amateur, of the nebular hypothesis throughout the 19th century and beyond, has a touch of hubris, but this is not its most instructive feature.

Laplace's self-assurance, so unmindful of obvious scientific difficulties, has an explanation only if seen in its philosophical foundations. One need not dig too far to find their deepest level. The nebulous celestial fluid, found everywhere by Herschel in the sky, seemed to be simple enough to dispense with further questions. That such had to be Laplace's reasoning may be gathered from a pattern long antedating Laplace and reasserting itself at regular intervals to this very day. The pattern was noticeable in both main trends of Greek cosmological thinking, the Platonist and the atomist. The simplicity of the sphere, or the apparent homogeneity of a boundary layer, was taken by Plato and the many he inspired as the reason for the necessary existence of a spherical universe. No questions were asked either by Platonists or by Aristotelians why the universe had to be a sphere with a very specific size. As to the atomists, the apparent homogeneity of a chaotic state warded off further questions. That second thoughts might not have been altogether absent from their minds can be gathered from a story about young Epicurus. As he read to his grammarian preceptor from Hesiod's *Theogony* that "eldest of being, Chaos first arose, thence Earth wide stretched," he stopped and asked: "And Chaos whence?" His preceptor replied that for answer he must turn to the philosophers.[15] Possibly Epicurus remembered this incident when he became a philosopher and posited, somewhat animatedly, the chaotic concourse of atoms as the ultimate from which everything else developed.

The nebulous fluid that gave rise to everything else developed in Laplace's cosmogenesis, satisfied the thinking of both traditions. It was not, however, at the apparent chaotic simplicity or homogeneity of that fluid that Whewell aimed his criticism as he took up, in 1833, the nebular hypothesis. He rather noted that Laplace's hypothesis assumed things to be in motion. Were that notion to be traced to the configuration and properties of previously existing matter, "these configurations must have resulted from some still previous cause," be it the nebulous fluid, and that therefore the first Cause "which is not Mechanical" (here Whewell echoed Newton) could not be evaded.[16] One trouble with this argumentation was that its ontological substance was hidden in a mechanical garb that appeared the more shapeless the further it led back in the past. The science of the day was powerless to offer anything specific about those configurations that petered out into sheer nebulosity for not having exact figures (geometrical or numerical) assigned to them.

Absence of scientific specificity in matters cosmological heavily contributed to that philosophical myopia that set the tone of Herbert Spencer's famed cosmogenesis. That it contained little science should not seem surprising. No solid scientific training was needed for laying out railroad tracks whereby Herbert Spencer earned his living before he took up philosophy as a profession.[17] In this latter capacity he quickly awed many, with a generous sprinkling of eminent scientists among them. One of them, Charles Darwin, soon spoke of Herbert Spencer as one of the greatest philosophers ever.[18] This extravagant praise has since cast a sad reflection on both Darwin and the author of *First Principles*. Herbert Spencer's shift from a most unphilosophical profession to that of a professional philosopher was easy and effective because he had a great facility with phrases. As almost always, here too excellence of style could carry on its coat-tail a heavy load of dubious reasoning. The converse of this, of course, is the ineffectiveness of incisive arguments when the style carrying them demands more concentration than a dazzling TV serial or a coffee-table book in which every paragraph is followed by pages of splashy illustrations.

There were no illustrations in Herbert Spencer's *First Principles* which contains his claim that the present most un-homogeneous state of affairs, characteristic of our own backyard as well as of the stellar reaches, is an evolution from a perfectly homogeneous state. Had he added no qualifications, he would have lowered himself from the rank of a bad philosopher to that of a very bad one. Perfect homogeneity he would grant in principle at least only to matter. The action of forces on matter could never be homogeneous. Consequently, a destabilization

of the homogeneous original state was a foregone conclusion. One could, of course, find countless cases in the
actually unhomogeneous world about non-homogeneous forces, but this would not be enough for the purposes of Spencerian cosmogenesis. Its truth had to be an
a priori verity:

> It is still to be shown that this general truth is dem-
> onstrable *a priori*. We have to prove specifically that
> the instability of the homogeneous is a corollary
> from the persistence of force. Already this has been
> tacitly implied by assigning unlikeness in the expo-
> sure of its parts to surrounding agencies, as the
> reason why a uniform mass loses its uniformity.
> But here it will be proper to expand this tacit impli-
> cation into definite proof.[19]

The definite proof did not amount to more than the
declaration that the force acting on homogeneous bodies
was always localized and therefore non-homogeneous in
space. "The part with which the striking body comes into
contact, receiving the whole of the communicated
momentum, is driven in towards the centre of the mass.
It thus compresses and tends to displace the more cen-
trally situated portions of the mass."[20] Herbert Spencer
did not care to consider why the force has been
"dehomogenized" from a perfectly symmetrical form
into a specifically localized one so as to issue in the dis-
placement described above. His was a curious oversight
because such main physical forces as gravitation and
electricity were known to act symmetrically. With his
cavalier approach to the problem on hand Herbert
Spencer could even dispense with the postulate of initial
homogeneity: "No demurrer to the conclusions drawn
can be based on the ground that perfect homogeneity
nowhere exists; since whether that state with which we
commence be or be not one of perfect homogeneity, the
process must equally be towards a relative heterogeneity."[21]

Clearly, Spencerian cosmogenesis was saddled with a double fault. One was the inconsistency that he did not consider the case of perfectly homogeneous force, although both philosophically and scientifically the case was obvious. The other was that although he professed no absolute need for perfectly homogeneous matter, he endlessly spoke of it. This is why his cosmogenesis was taken for the development of all non-homogeneous from the homogeneous. As such, that development gave a much-needed assurance to countless admirers of his, especially in the United States, that Social Darwinism had a safe cosmological basis.[22] But the same development also proved to be the Achilles' heel of Spencerian cosmogenesis. Since the latter had for its forte Herbert Spencer's fluent prose, its effective criticism demanded a first-rate stylist.

H. G. Wells, the man of letters in question, was not a philosopher, much less was he free of wishful thinking. For decades he made a very good living by immersing himself in a world of fantasies that freely ranged across cosmic spaces. But as time went on, H. G. Wells' sense of the real took a measure of his imagination. This is not to say that wishful thinking is entirely absent from Wells' philosophical testament, *First and Last Things*. Indeed, it is so philosophical as to turn now and then into a cosmology because H. G. Wells meant to offer an explanation of the full range of existents. Having grown up at a time when Spencer's cosmogenesis was the rage of the day, H. G. Wells naturally took it for the target of his sharp pen. He most likely did not perceive that his devastatingly short critique hit Spencer's cosmogenesis by hitting all its millions of enthusiastic readers first. They almost to a man saw in that cosmogenesis a ground for ignoring questions about the universe that can be answered only if one is ready to look beyond it, that is, beyond the very totality of consistently interacting things. The criticism offered by H. G. Wells is as short as it is scathing: "He [Spencer] believed that individuality (heterogeneity) was and is an evolutionary product from an original homogeneity, begotten by folding and multiplying and dividing and twisting it, and still fundamentally *it*."[23]

Possibly nowhere else has so much been described by *it*, perhaps the most nondescript among all English words. H. G. Wells endorsed *it* with a weight all the heavier, because he made *it* convey the utter nullity of the enterprise of getting something from that nothing with which the word "homogeneous," if taken literally, is synonymous. That such is the case received an incisive support only a few years after Wells' remark appeared in print. Moreover, the alleged perfectly homogeneous starting point of the cosmic process was the very target of Eddington's words: "To my mind undifferentiated sameness and nothingness cannot be distinguished philosophically. The realities of physics are unhomogeneities, happenings, change."[24] Those realities will remain radically unhomogeneous even when they appear "very simple."

The mirage of simplicity
Simplicity too can exist and be the object of a discussion only if it is a very specific simplicity. Herein lies the gist of that second and more important consequence of the expansion of the universe mentioned earlier in this chapter. The consequence is that for the first time in the history of science speculations about the early state of the universe have become scientifically respectable insofar as they relate to invariably very specific entities and processes. So early is that state as to precede by a billion years the formation of stars and the formation of most chemical elements. Speculations about that state are part of an ever more intense theoretical and experimental research about the primordial state of matter. The vast and tightly interlocking evidence gathered so far gives a resounding lie to pseudophilosophical

schemes that make the origin of the cosmos appear as if it were a mere *it* and therefore an apparently valid excuse to brush aside further questions about it.

A modest familiarity with human nature should be enough for seeing in those schemes a more than purely logical matter. The superficiality to which human thinking can readily fall a victim is the only explanation of a detail in the life of I. I. Rabi, typical of many other scientific lives. The son of deeply believing orthodox Jews, teenager Rabi parted with belief in a personal God on being exposed to the simplicity of the heliocentric arrangement of planets. "Who needs God?" quipped young Rabi[25] whose resolve and talent made him subsequently see features of the realm of the nucleus that were simple only in appearance. His experimental demonstration of the nuclear spin, for which he received the Nobel Prize, is a case in point. A proton with such a specific spin was no more simple than an exquisitely cut diamond. Yet Rabi never came around to being impressed more by stark specificities in the realm of the nucleus than by their apparent simplicity. This is why Rabi developed no second thoughts about that quip of his, except insofar as it deeply offended his devout parents.

Only a factor deeply at play in human nature can account for the readiness with which the physicists' philosophical blindness to the specific is espoused by non-physicists as a respectable posture. A case in point is the argumentation in *The Blind Watchmaker* by the Oxford biologist, Richard Dawkins. His professed reliance on physics went far beyond a purely methodological one. In that latter case he would have restricted himself to saying that as a biologist he takes "the facts of physics, the facts of the world of simplicity, for granted." Indeed, it was not the biologist's problem, to quote Dawkins, "if physicists still don't agree over whether those simple facts are yet understood." But Dawkins was totally wrong in thinking that physicists *as*

such provided the assurance for what constituted the ultimate ground for his rank materialism:

> The fundamental original units that we need to
> postulate, in order to understand the coming into
> existence of everything, either consist of literally
> nothing (according to some physicists), or (accord-
> ing to other physicists) they are units of the utmost
> simplicity, far too simple to need anything so grand
> as deliberate Creation.[26]

Whether there can be a creation, properly so called,
which is not deliberate, may seem possible only to those
intellectuals who do not take most seriously their own
freedom to choose among various theories.

At any rate, Dawkins accurately reported the thinking
of most physicists as he put them in two categories. They,
as will be discussed later, either claim that "the nothing"
has in fact become part of physical research, or they take
the lazy view that what "appears" utterly simple can exist
without being created in the first place. In both cases
sloppy philosophizing is grafted onto strictly scientific
data that have nothing in common with the former. Anyone who delved into technical books and articles on
those "simple" particles can quickly register the overriding features in them. They show time and again that
those particles have sharp numerical properties and also
that their very specific interactions can only be expressed
in formulas that should appear the very opposite to simplicity. A cursory glimpse into any recent issue of *Particle
Properties Data Booklet* with its well over a hundred pages,
all bursting with exact data, should be enough even for a
layman to purge himself of confidence in brave statements of physicists about the "simplicity" of the foundations of the physical world as they *actually* see it. That at
one point or another those particles have, during the last
sixty years or so, appeared as a fairly simple set should
impress only those unmindful of the invariable vanishing of those simple sets.[27] So much in a way of warning

about the apparent finality of the actual "standard" model consisting of three layered sets of leptons and quarks. Of course the physical world may ultimately be reduced, as far as the physicist's account of its properties goes, to a single formula with a couple of constants.[28] Even that simplicity would not lack stark specificities which then would provoke, except in deliberately inert minds, the question why those specificities are of this and not of some other magnitude.

Such a question, with its patently cosmological bearing, is legitimately provoked even by the actual bewildering multiplicity of fundamental particles. The reason for this is that for the past twenty years or so every advance in fundamental particles research meant a forward step in investigating the very early states of the universe. The chief impetus in that respect came with the discovery of the 2.7°K cosmic background radiation in 1965. At first it was mostly spoken about as a rebuttal of the steady-state universe of which more in another chapter. A rebuttal it certainly was but much more than that. The real import of the discovery of that radiation failed to be pinpointed in a truly seminal phrase that brings to a conclusion Weinberg's fascinating account of the chain of near-misses (theoretical as well as experimental) that preceded it: "The most important thing accomplished by the ultimate discovery of the 3°K background radiation in 1965 was to force us all to take seriously the idea that there *was* an early universe."[29]

It may be that too many, including Weinberg himself, took too seriously the steady-state theory in which there can be no "early" universe and, what is much less realized, not even a universe.[30] Yet even the principal observational reason, on which the steady-state theorists staked so much, had a shaky and short-lived foundation. Following the recalibration of the galactic red-shifts by W. Baade in 1952, there remained no serious reason for taking the earth's past to be longer than the past of the universe shown by its expansion. Indeed, the 2.7°K back-ground radiation ultimately proved not so much that there was an *early* universe (if this needed a proof at all in 1965), but that even in its earliest stages the universe was what a universe had to be: a most specific totality of all things that, because they were things, could only be specific.

Radiating specificity
In itself that 2.7°K radiation could be taken for the very opposite of specificity as it came uniformly from all directions. But once more there lay behind apparent simplicity a stark specificity. The radiation's name, 2.7°K, was in itself a proof of this. It designates a black-body radiation whose intensity peaks at a so-called char-acteristic temperature and whose intensity-versus-wave-length curve has a characteristic, that is, specific shape. As such, the 2.7°K radiation could be recognized as the surviving evidence of a very specific state of affairs at a time stretching through the second and third minutes after the start of the actually observed expansion of the universe. Tellingly, already when around 1950 Gamow and others made the first inconclusive suggestions about the early universe as a place for the formation of the ele-ments, it appeared very different from a state of non-descript nebulosity. Not only the neutrons, with which Gamow started, were known to have very specific properties, but they had to be bathed in a very specific flux of photons that outnumbered each neutron by about one billion. Moreover it was already then noted that such a radiation density should have cooled by now in such a way as to correspond to a black-body radiation with a peak at about 5°K.[31]

After that radiation was, with no lead from theorists, detected by Penzias and Wilson in 1965, enormously much has been learned about the physical conditions appropriate for the formation of hydrogen (H), deuter-ium (^{2}H), tritium (^{3}H), and helium (He). And as always happens in physics, here too the exploration of a particular phase quickly led to the investigation of the conditions that preceded and followed it. In both directions, and especially in the direction leading farther and farther back in time, the advances have been far-reaching. Within the last twenty years or so, science pushed far beyond the first two hundred seconds in which the formation of those light elements has to take place. Today, the hottest field of research relates to times that preceded those two hundred seconds, a mere two orders of magnitude, by 35 to 43 orders of magnitude, that is, fractions of a second compared with which a billionth, a trillionth, or even a quadrillionth of a second should seem to stand for eternity. Owing to the importance of that rarified research, popular accounts of it, some of them first-rate, some of them mere bogus, quickly followed. In the former, reliable scientific discourse is often mixed with interpretations that amount to wading into deep philosophical waters as if it meant a mere frolicking on the shore.

Indeed, as will be seen in the subsequent chapters, cosmologists and fundamental particle physicists found themselves time and again out of their depths even in respect to fairly elementary matters of philosophy. Ocean shores that seem flat as one strolls along the water's edge, can quickly turn into steep slopes. There, with a single step one can lose touch with the ground, and what is worse, be exposed to treacherous undercurrents. The analogy with wading deep into philosophy should be obvious. Its depths, currents, and eddies can easily claim for easy victims even professional philosophers, let alone amateurs, be they Nobel laureates in physics. Those high-level popularizations contain, as will be seen later, many examples of this. The mere appearance of the word "creation" in their titles should be a reason for concern. Misunderstandings were not effectively forestalled when Gamow offered the rare warning that in his book, *The Creation of the Universe*, the word creation meant no more than "making something shapely out of shapelessness as, for example, in the phrase, the latest creation of Parisian fashion."[32] For by trying to shed thereby some light on the very different philosophical notion of creation out of nothing, Gamow fell back on a notion, "shapelessness," which, however unphilosophical or not, has no place in physics.

Since physics can only deal with shapes or quantitative specificities, it is all the more regrettable that those books, which contain so many inappropriate and at times brazenly self-defeating reflections, do not contain the one which would have been entirely within the competence of physicists, in fact which is their very competence. For as is the case with any series of advances in any area of physics, there has been one overriding characteristic of advances in the investigation of the states of matter from its conditions in the first three minutes to its state in the first microseconds and far beyond in the inconceivably smaller fractions of a second. That characteristic consists in the fact that the quantitative specificity of a particular state (or phase or shape) of matter can be traced only to another state no less specific in its quantitative characteristics.

This fact retains its philosophical significance even if the quantitative features in question should appear trivial or nondescript. It is a mere psychological fallacy to see in the numbers 11111 or 12345 or 12321 something more specific than in numbers such as 37825 or 74952, that show no obvious pattern. Taken in itself any number is as specific as any other number or numerical quantity. Those playing the lottery know this all too well. They never choose "nicely" looking numbers. Winners of very big prizes often admit that their choice of lucky numbers was left to patently non-numerical considerations, such as the date of birth of a special relative or friend, or the reading backward of the middle portion of one's telephone number.

Many are unwilling or unable to appreciate that *any* number or *any* quantitative relationship is very specific. They seem to think that only a very "special" looking number can be the carrier of a philosophical message, of which more later. They have no such excuse when it comes to the earliest states of matter. There, time and again, one has on hand correlations that should give a shock treatment to minds that have almost completely lost their philosophical sensitivity. Such minds have invariably been desensitized by latter-day versions of Laplacean or Spencerian nebulosity or homogeneity, such as Gamow's "shapelessness," or some "simple" looking numerical symmetries. Those minds might still think themselves to be in seventh heaven or riding on cloud nine if indeed the formation of H and ^{2}H would be the result of a primordial mixture of protons, neutrons, electrons and photons, all in equal number, that is, one neutron, one electron, and one photon for each and every proton. This equality would provide them with a semblance of "perfect" symmetry or homogeneity that in turn might seem to dispose of further questions that are troublesome for being plainly metaphysical. Those minds would not easily be puzzled by the fact that of those four ingredients only the proton and neutron are reasonably similar to one another, whereas the electron and the photon are very different from the two others in addition to being very different from one another. The blissful un-metaphysical repose of those minds should, however, be gravely threatened by the fact that for each proton, neutron, and electron there should be almost exactly 40 billion photons present in that primordial mix. This shocking imbalance, or asymmetry, or non-homogeneity should appear even more shocking if instead of "almost exactly 40 million" one would say 39,999,213,350,15. Such a numerical disproportion would forcibly show the stark physical unhomogeneity in that primordial mix, which by that very fact would cease to appear "primordial".

Protons, neutrons, and electrons are particles of the so-called ordinary matter. In asking the question about their immediate origin, that is, the phase that gives rise to their formation, one has to include considerations about their antiparticles. The very fact that particles and antiparticles "annihilate" themselves once within each other's range makes it impossible to start with an equal number of them, for in that case one would be left with radiation alone. The inequality that secures matter turns out to be its most surprising kind, that is, the one which is a hair's breadth removed from complete equality. The first clue came from the investigation, about 25 years ago, of the decay of K°_2 mesons. This particle is one of those few particles that are identical with their antiparticles. Therefore if matter and antimatter were equal, one would expect that when an electron appears as a decay product, a positron too would appear. But this is not the case. The slight anomaly in the decay of K°_2 mesons can only be explained if the production of ordinary matter outpaces that of antimatter by a factor of one part in 10 billion, a hair-raisingly slight departure from that "perfect" balance or symmetry that seems to dispose of further questions.

In a sense it is true that the detailed account of that process is such as to justify the comments of the discoverers, Val Fitch and James Cronin. The former was quoted as saying that "it's really arcane," whereas the other said: "I find it difficult to convey to my family just about what it is I have been doing."[33] Yet the matter should seem plain simplicity itself in the sense that it plainly shows nature not to be simple in a trivial sense. That slight asymmetry, of ten billion antiprotons against ten billion plus one protons, should bring home to the most uninitiated that subtle specificity is a basic feature of the cosmos. This is revealed with a blunt force by the early phase of the cosmos where, owing to its smallness, it can almost be literally grasped by the mind. Utterly trivial may appear the difference already between a hundred and a hundred and one matches, let alone the difference between a million and a million and one. Yet anything but trivial should that difference appear if the extra match alone would produce the spark leading to a general conflagration. But it is precisely the presence of that one *additional* proton, additional to the ten billion already on hand, that can make the universe itself go at a particular stage of its early development.

This proton-antiproton imbalance is at work at the trillionth of the first second, the trillionth standing for twelve orders of magnitude. Even further back in time, 25 orders of magnitude further back, that is, in inconceivably short fractions of a second, is that state in which exactly the opposite occurs. The process is connected with the moment (10^{-35} sec) where the strong or nuclear force becomes the second force that "freezes out" or appears as a separate force while the electroweak and electromagnetic forces still are indistinguishable. (The freezing out of the gravitational force precedes that of the strong force by eight orders of magnitude on the time scale, as it takes place at 10^{-43} sec). Prior to the freezing out of the strong force the scene is dominated by $\overline{X}$-bosons and their antiparticles ($\overline{X}$-bosons). The decay of both issues in quarks and antiquarks of which the nucleons (protons and neutrons) would later be composed. In both cases the ratio of products is 1 to 2 and 2 to 1 respectively. But unless that ratio, which in itself would produce the same amount of matter and antimatter, is not slightly modified, real matter would not dominate in the later stages of cosmic evolution. Actually, because of the similarity of $\overline{X}$-bosons with K°_2 mesons, each of them produces one billion plus one quarks, whereas each of their antiparticles produces only one billion antiquarks.

Specific imbalances

At this point it would be tempting to think that there is a way of taking the metaphysical sting out of those two very specific imbalances, both hair-raising because they are so close to perfect balance. Don't they cancel out one another and suggest thereby that primordial homogeneity may be lurking somewhere in a phase still further back in time? Such a thought would be sheer foolhardiness for more than one reason. First, homogeneity, which oscillates between two states of imbalance, however close to a perfect balance, must have an imbalance within it in order to start a swinging, so to speak, back and forth around a point of perfect equilibrium. A perfect homogeneity, let it be remarked in passing, can have no center, be it a center of balance or of anything else. Second, not only the X particles but all so-called fundamental particles are exceedingly specific and esoteric, too. No wonder that physicists had to resort to such labels as color, charm, truth (top), and beauty (bottom), each with several varieties, to designate those arcane properties.[34] Third, the state of interaction, of which the X particles are the chief carriers, can only be traced to a quantitatively most specific state. That state, or the stage of superunification, has for its chief specificity the reduction of all forces into a single one, with perhaps a single set of numerical constants.

Before taking a look at that stage, still wholly hypothetical, it would be worthwhile to consider the main stage of the development of the very early universe. If represented on a single diagram with the entire development of the universe, that early phase would correspond to a practically vertical line representing a huge temperature drop from $10^{26}°$K degrees to a few thousand within the first two hundred seconds and with much of that drop occurring during the first thousandth of a second. The rest of the development of the universe would correspond to a practically horizontal line standing for 15 billion years. If that scale were to be divided into 12 parts, each corresponding to a cosmic "month" of little more than a billion years within one cosmic "year," the formation of the sun would fall somewhere in "September."[35] The unusually high ratio of heavy elements in the sun indicates that it may be a third-generation star, that is, a star formed from the remnants of an exploded supernova (possibly a second-generation star), a typical place for the formation of heavy elements. The first-generation stars formed in "mid-January," after galaxies had arisen from a material that by then had been completely transformed from plasma (in which nucleons and electrons are not yet firmly united) into light elements. The latter, as was already noted, began to form during the first three minutes. It is there that the curve begins its sharp temperature rise that at present can be traced up to about $10^{26}°K$ (a temperature a quadrillion times higher than the one in the center of the sun) and back in time to 10^{-43} seconds.

The principal feature of the practically vertical part of the curve is that it is broken at three specific moments (and temperatures) as if in each case the cosmic fluid, falling downward with respect to its temperature, were to hit a narrow ledge. The similarity with a cascade should be obvious, but so should be a most important difference. In an ordinary cascade the collision of the water with the irregular rocky ledges produces a "chaos" of bubbles and vapor that does not lend itself to precise quantitative evaluation. The very opposite happens in the cosmic cascade. There each ledge stands for a very specific phase-transition, the results of which are particles, interactions, and the emergence of previously hidden forces — all with very specific properties in the strict quantitative sense.

The science of cosmology has indeed come a long way from a nebulous prehistory. The early phases of the cosmos look rather like a finely chiseled cascade on whose ledges successive generations of particles form until the ordinary set of light elements takes over. Most of those particles are derivable from one another, but only through very specific processes, all governed by strict selection rules that allow only the occurrence of exceedingly few possibilities out of a very large number. No different will be the situation when the tracing of those primordial processes will be carried beyond Planck's time or 10^{-43} seconds, which implies the exploration of conditions at temperatures higher than $10^{26°}$K. Only above that temperature will gravitation appear identical with the three other forces, electromagnetic, electroweak, and nuclear.

This outcome assumes, of course, the success of longstanding efforts to quantize the gravitational force. The success depends on the existence of gravitons, another kind of those very fundamental particles (such as electron, proton, and photon) whose physical magnitudes do not, for the moment, seem to be derivable from anything else whatever the possible tracing of the four known forces to a single manifold. The latter may be on hand through the latest hot-pursuit in cosmology, the superstring theory, facetiously called TOE, or the Theory Of Everything.[36] It may or may not turn out to be the theory that will "lead to a new understanding of what space and time really are, the most dramatic [understanding] since general relativity."[37] Yet its potentials should seem very great if it could make Weinberg respond to the news about the so-called anomaly cancellation: "I dropped everything I was doing, including several books I was working on, and started learning everything I could about string theory. . . . The mathematics is very difficult."[38]

The mathematics involves a ten-dimensional manifold that should seem startlingly specific in itself. Originally proposed by John Schwarz as the explanation of the strong or nuclear force, the string theory first disclosed its cosmological potential in 1974 as a low energy approximation of Einstein's General Relativity. Later it became clear that the four known forces could be made to appear the derivatives of a ten-dimensional manifold, four ordinary, that is, recognizable by the senses, and six imperceptible to them. Ordinary matter would then ultimately consist of strings that are 10^{-35} cm long. As to the imperceptible dimensions, they curl up into knots of the same dimensions which, because of their extreme smallness, must be ascribed enormous energies in terms of Heisenberg's uncertainty principle. The great turning point in the fortunes of superstrings came when in 1984 Schwarz and Green showed that the "handedness" or *chiral* character (a most specific asymmetry) of the electroweak forces is not an anomaly. For all that it remains a specificity within a theory that should appear enormously specific. A universe represented by it will hardly look "a universe that is the ultimate in simplicity."[39] That its "simplicity" is self-explaining deserves the comment prompted by the assumption that an eternal universe is self-explaining. Such an assumption "is to evade, rather than illuminate, the issues of its origin and *quantum numbers*"[40] (italics added).

It should be easy to see what all this has to do with philosophical cosmology. In investigating those very early processes in the physical universe, the object of the physicist is not merely this or that particular process but the entire universe. That such is the case may easily be gathered from the fact that already at the proton-antiproton stage, where the K°_2 decay is all-important, the universe is not bigger than a large ball. At the phase where X particles dominate, the universe is as small as a pinhead, a comparison which is good insofar as size is concerned. Apart from that a pinhead looks like a dull sphere that prompts no further questions. It is doubtful whether anyone, except a criminologist or someone madly in love, was ever intrigued by a particular pinhead.

Cosmos in a grain of sand
Quite different should seem the case with the early universe if it can be likened to a diamond. In that case not so much the size, but the specific features of the object would hold one's attention. The cuts that make a dia-

mond resplendent are so many exact quantitative operations. That science can establish quantitative properties
about the universe as such was already a chief result of
the first chapter dealing largely with the cosmological
consequences of Einstein's General Relativity. But those
properties — total mass, maximum radius or minimum
curvature of the permissible paths of motion — refer to a
fully developed universe, an entity which can be studied
by General Relativity but which is too large to be visual-
ized, however vaguely. Quite different is the case with the
quantitative properties established by modern scientific
cosmology about the early universe. Those properties
bring the universe within ordinary comprehension as if
to fulfill Blake's prophetic vision about the universe
revealed by a grain of sand.[41]

Blake could have referred to an ordinary microscope
that would show each grain of sand as a specially cut
stone. Far more interesting "cuts" would be revealed
through that "microscope" which is the cosmological
bearing of fundamental particle physics. That physics
keeps unfolding the truth of Einstein's unconditionally
affirmative reply to the question: "Supposing it were possible to discover *all* the properties of *a grain of sand*,
would we then have gained a complete knowledge of the
whole universe?"[42] Information about all those properties
would include accurate details about all the basic constants of nature. It has now been known for some time
that knowledge of the numerical value of those constants
can provide such details as why the sky has to appear
blue, why the size of stars must fall between well defined
limits, and why mountains on the earth cannot be much
higher than the Himalayas.[43] A grain of sand can
through its numerical specificity evoke to ordinary comprehension the universe in small as if it were an exquisitely cut jewel.

Contemplation of the cosmic jewel may prompt in
cosmologists the kind of reflections that are akin to a
mystical experience. One of them introduced his survey

of recent cosmology with the caption taken from one of the sixteen visions of Jesus seen by Juliana of Norwich, the great late-14th-century English mystic. He (Jesus), she wrote, "showed me a little thing, the quantity of a hazelnut, in the palm of my hand, and it was as round as a ball. I looked thereupon with the eye of my understanding and thought: What may this be? and it was answered generally thus: it is *all* that is made"[44] (italics added). Interest in such captions will be sparked only in those who have not yet gone philosophically blind by giving exclusive attention to quantities. For the primary purpose of the specificities of things is not to make possible mere quantitative games with them, but to help one recognise the very reality of things and the Reality that makes them real.

A reality, insofar as it is recognized through its specificity, will never appear a nebulous thing. If modern physical science has achieved anything of basic importance, it is the dissipation of that nebulosity in which scientists weak in philosophy and philosophers imbued with scientism have since Laplace enveloped the origin of the universe. A universe, which science shows to be real and specifically so, will not fail to point beyond its specific phases to an origin which has to be a factor metaphysically beyond the universe. The alternative is to be trapped in regress to infinity and to use the word universe without meaning by it the very totality of consistently interacting things.

With this the very essence of this book has been spelled out. With the exception of its next chapter, all the subsequent ones will deal with various objections that may be raised against the chief claims of the first two chapters that also form the gist of the so-called cosmological argument about the existence of God. Modern scientific cosmology provides no basis for that lingering agnosticism that seeks support in science for a jaundiced look at the universe. That cosmology contradicts the claim that the universe cannot be fully investigated and that the complete rationality of the universe is always a hypothesis and not a fact.[45] Both these claims are philosophical and as such stand or fall with the philosophy, a brand of Kantianism, that inspires them. Since the contrary of those claims is also philosophical, science, be it the modern science of cosmology, cannot prove them either. But if there is any sane and overriding trend in modern scientific cosmology it is the deep-running conviction, revealed by the practice if not the thinking of its cultivators, that the universe is a reality which, owing to its specificities is in its entirety and in its particulars fully investigable by science.

Modern scientific cosmology strongly supports the age-old philosophical conviction that there is a universe. Furthermore, modern science also shows the universe, whether very young or fully developed, to be exceedingly specific in its totality as well as in its very constituent particles and forces. Such a specific universe reveals its contingency by its being limited to a specific form of physical existence. As will be shown later, that specific form of existence certainly cannot be taken, on scientific grounds, for a necessary form of existence. The specificity of the universe, which is an evidence of its reality, is also the evidence of its contingency, namely, that it is but one of many possible universes. Such is the essence of the contribution, and a most precious one, which science can make to philosophical cosmology.

To appreciate philosophical cosmology one needs that philosophy which is worthy of its name or etymology, namely, love of wisdom. As in other cases, here too love begins with wonderment which is genuine only if it leads to a real love of its object in a philosophical sense. That wonderment has no need of that pseudo-cosmic background on which Aldous Huxley fell back in order to support his deterministic view of human history. Yet to a far more specific extent than he might have gathered from cosmologists in the late 1920s, when he wrote his *Grey Eminence*, it has become true, through modern scientific cosmology, that "any given event in any part of the universe has as its determining conditions in all previous and contemporary events in all parts of the universe."[46] Without being entitled to say anything about determinism insofar as it means ontological causality, modern scientific cosmology certainly reveals the stunning degree of the specific coherence of all across space and time. To feel a sense of wonder in registering that specificity, and with the appreciation of genuine love for it, should be within the reach of any ordinary mind. Nothing extraordinary seems indeed to have gone into a poem of four lines:

> How infinitely odd —
> Just think of it — that God
> Should place at Immensity
> A stark specificity.[47]

True love, of course, should be the exact opposite of selfishness or self-centeredness. This kind of love can hardly be assumed to be a general commodity in that academia, well typified by Oxbridge, if there is any truth in the saying that Oxford dons and students walk around as if the whole universe belonged to them, whereas those in Cambridge don't seem to give a damn as to whom the universe belonged.[48] The difference between these two stances cannot be too great. Both places nowadays boast of first-rate cosmologists who speak and write as if they were the masters of the universe.[49] Apart from that, in both places the preponderant part of the population is made up, for at least the academic year, of those who are between their eighteenth and twenty-first years. About these nobody made a better observation than the Rev. Albert Samuel Barnes, usually referred to as "Mugger" Barnes, who was Ronald Knox's predecessor in the Catholic chaplaincy in Oxford.

A leap in the dark or a luminous step
Unlike Monsignor Knox, "Mugger" Barnes was never

perturbed by his charges' various failings. His view was
that between the ages of eighteen and twenty-one most
men (and women, "Mugger" Barnes would add today)
give up the practice of their religion but most come back
to it later. Undergraduates, "Mugger" Barnes used to say,
last only three years.[50] Some time after graduation,
though at times only decades later, those young men and
women become, if not ardently religious, at least latently
philosophical. Not because they are seized by the
specificity of existence, a perennial task even for good
philosophers, who should blame themselves if their
charges show diffidence toward the cosmological proof
of God's existence. If that proof is to prove anything, it
has to start with a drill, so to speak, of the mind so that it
may see in any ordinary thing, however trivial, that
specificity which reveals its contingency, namely, that it
could have been something else. Having undergone that
drill, the mind will reverberate with the readiness to use
each and every thing as a springboard to something else
and will find it most natural to use the universe too as a
board that catapults one to mental heights where one
recognizes the Maker of the universe.

In the absence of a preliminary drill the mind will see
in the cosmological argument a leap in the dark, a leap
for which a faith largely devoid of intellectual compo-
nents will be needed. Those who invoke Kierkegaard as
an assurance about the advisability of such a leap
should pause. First, that advisability should have better
support than the invariably vague demonstrations of
Kierkegaard's "decisive" influence on Bohr as he worked
out his theory of the hydrogen atom.[51] Second, the leap
advocated by Kierkegaard cannot be a leap from the cosmos into a dark beyond where God is to be found. The
universe could not really exist for Kierkegaard who
made the contradictory claim that "the universe is a system but only God knows the system."[52] For if only God
knows the system of the universe, how can man know
that the universe is a system? Whatever excuse

Kierkegaard might have had in the "scientific" cosmology of his day, no such an excuse can be claimed today. Modern scientific cosmology has shown that as a physical reality the universe is indeed a most tightly interlocking system and that man can know that system or the world.

Man, of course, has to be something of a philosopher in order to know that the system is contingent, that is, it might have been otherwise. Man has to be a philosopher to realize that if a thing is found to be what it is, because it was produced by another specific thing or state of affairs, the point of contingency has thereby been pushed only one stage back. As a good philosopher, man will realize that there is only a limited number of such stages available in a universe limited to one overall specificity which reveals its contingency. Those unwilling to admit cosmic contingency can, for a while, take refuge in the dream that has regress to infinity as its cherished object. For a while, to be sure, because as the years go by grey strands in their locks become more visible. Then they might realize that their lives could have been different, and at times very different. They would reach this most philosophical conclusion by being seized by the fact that human existence is most transitory. And since all thinking, even the best philosophical one, is somewhat egocentric, from this experience of theirs they might go on to perceiving that all things could have been very different. No more and no less is needed to start on the road to become impressed by cosmic contingency and to turn thereby into a first-rate philosopher. Here too modern scientific cosmology provides its own instruction by the piercing light it has shed on the transitoriness of the universe, the topic of the next chapter.

Chapter Three

TIME'S SPECTER

The grand Instructor, Time

E. Burke

The trap of eternalism

The history of modern scientific cosmology, not much older than two generations, contains more items of startling novelty than do comparable phases of intellectual history. Yet in at least one respect it does not differ from other aspects of human history — individual and social, political and cultural. In all of them heroes and common folks, great powers and puny organizations are cut to the quick when forced to face up to the perspective of inevitable transitoriness. Herein lies a clue to the first reactions to the scientific cosmology made possible by General Relativity. When Einstein stated in 1918 that the scientist "makes this cosmos and its construction the pivot of his emotional life,"[1] he did not refer to his General Relativity which he had just completed with a memoir on its cosmological consequences, as a means whereby the universe could be turned into a valid object of science. Even when shortly afterwards he disclosed to his friend, A. Moszkowski, in more personal terms his awe of the universe, he did not deplore as a contrast the dubious fashion that had by then for three generations taken the universe to be synonymous with infinity.[2]

Not that unlike materialists and some mistaken believers, who for very different reasons insisted on the infinity of the universe, Einstein found attractive a possi-

57

ble saving of infinite matter. Nor did he find in the obvious limitedness of a spherical universe a noteworthy pointer toward a factor transcending the cosmos. Much the same is true of cosmologists who more recently noted that there arose no gravitational paradox if infinite matter was allocated in a hyperbolic space-time.[3] The strange infinity of such a universe can easily be spotted by reducing it to ordinary three dimensions. Then it appears as a saddle with no edges but still with very specific slopes. In such a universe ordinary things, a human body or a star, would be reduced to an infinitesimally thin coin that can move only on the surface of that cosmic saddle but can never move either above or below it. Such is a freedom of movement which, though without limits in a sense, implies strict finitude or limitation in another. Although that strangely infinite saddle should have awakened metaphysical awareness, it has acted as a gentle rocking horse that dulls that ability whereby one sees beyond the physical.

Quite different reactions took place insofar as the universe revealed itself in the specter of time or transitoriness. On yielding to De Sitter's argument that cosmic space was a function of time, Einstein quickly noted the special status of a zero point along the cosmic time parameter. "This point," he wrote on June 22, 1917, to De Sitter, is thus *de facto* preferred. . . . Naturally this does not constitute a disproof, but the circumstance irritates me."[4] Behind that irritation, which is hardly a "scientific" reaction, there lay a religious outlook which had for its object of worship an unchangeable universe. Einstein cast his lot with that religion when his youthful though intensive belief in the biblical Creator could not cope with a materialist rehash of the nebular hypothesis.[5] He began to drift toward a Spinozean veneration of Nature or Universe that has to be infinite as well as timeless, as befits an entity that emanates necessarily from God. Years later Einstein expressly specified the God of his belief as Spinoza's God or Nature writ large.

Like countless other admirers of Spinoza, Einstein too was taken in by Spinoza's sophism in the *Ethics* where the creation of a specific universe is held incompatible with divine omnipotence: From God's nature

> an infinite number of things . . . have necessarily flowed forth in an infinite number of ways, or always follow from the same necessity in the same way as from the nature of a triangle it follows from eternity and for eternity that its interior angles are equal to two right angles . . . . Otherwise, we are compelled to confess that God understands an infinite number of creatable things, which he will never be able to create, for, if he created all that he understands, he would . . . exhaust his omnipotence and render himself imperfect.[6]

Like countless other pantheists, Spinoza too failed to ponder a debilitating consequence of that eternalism for the scientific investigation of the universe, although Oldenburg, secretary of the Royal Society, had called his attention to it: "If the nature of the universe is not limited, its parts are by this nature of infinite power infinitely modified, and compelled to undergo infinite variations."[7] Apart from the impotency of science to cope with truly infinite variations that endlessly go on, there was the even more fundamental problem of pantheism. Spinoza could not hide his perplexity when confronted with the question: How can an allegedly divine Nature or world — immortal, infinite, and infinitely perfect — appear in very finite, very imperfect, and indeed very mortal, forms. The name of Tschirnhausen, who posed this question to Spinoza,[8] does not appear even in lengthy surveys of the history of philosophy. This only shows that in order to recognize fundamental problems in philosophy one does not necessarily have to be a professional philosopher and not even a philosopher-scientist, a new and dubious brand of sages.

Another reason for recalling Einstein's advocacy of Spinozean pantheism relates to its timing. By the late 1920s Einstein had already dismissed as "mere speculation" a paper which Friedmann in Leningrad published in 1922 on the cosmology of general relativity. There Friedmann noted that once Einstein's world model was disturbed, it could not only contract or expand but also oscillate, that is, go through an apparently endless series of contractions and expansions.[9] A Spinozean pantheist, Einstein should have immediately seized on Friedmann's idea of an oscillating universe as a means whereby time's specter could be dispelled from the "divine" universe. But Einstein began to see merit in Friedmann's paper only in the early 1930s and suddenly he took a very appreciative view of it.[10] Clearly, something very important must have taken place in scientific cosmology between 1922 and 1931. Indeed, the development could only cut to the quick any pantheist like Einstein. For nothing less important took place in those years than the discovery, experimental and theoretical, that the universe was indeed subject to a specific overall motion, and in fact to an expansion which (it should be enough to think of the growth of one's own body, especially when that growth is excessive) is always the sign of transitoriness. The universe has ever since been under the specter of a scientifically verified passing of time. In fact the most loudly publicized efforts in modern scientific cosmology aimed at the dissipation of that specter.

Scientific cosmologists who worked in Marxist regimes, especially in the Soviet Union, had no choice but to tow the line of Party ideology. There the eternity of matter had been a "scientific" dogma ever since the publication of the first authoritative communist interpretation of science, Engels' *Anti-Dühring*. There Engels declared that "matter without motion is just as inconceivable as motion without matter. Motion is therefore uncreatable and indestructible as matter itself."[11] Engels, amateur though he was in matters scientific, served to

the end as Marx's scientific advisor and missed no
opportunity to decry as imbecile the creators of thermodynamics, Clausius and Thomson (Lord Kelvin) for
their claim that the universe was running down.[12] Lenin
praised both Marx and Engels as "partisans in philosophy from start to finish" who were "able to detect the
deviations from materialism . . . in each and every new
tendency."[13]

Eternity of matter and the passing of time
The cruel treatment of Soviet cosmologists in the mid-
1930s may very well have been motivated by the Party-
ideologues' apprehension that a finite and expanding
universe may pose a double threat to the dogma of materialism. Quite possibly V. A. Ambartsumian, a member
of the cosmology-panel at the 1978 Düsseldorf World
Congress of Philosophy, declared under duress that science served experimental evidence about the eternity of
matter.[14] Compliance with dialectical materialism still
could motivate materialist recastings of cosmology in the
Brezhnev and Andropov era. It was then that A. D.
Linde of the Lebedev Institute in Moscow came to the
rescue of the inflationary theory whose original propo-
nent, A. H. Guth of MIT, still has to throw off the last
thin veil from around his brazen materialism.

The readiness with which many Western cosmologists
endorsed, though often in covert forms, the eternity of
matter cannot, of course, be a reflection of fear of political reprisals. Their readiness rather reflects the logic
whereby a progressively de-Christianized Western
World naturally opts for materialism in which, as was
noted in the heyday of 19th-century materialism, "the
essential axiom is the eternity of matter, namely, that it
has no origin and will have no end."[15] Espousal of materialism naturally generates the wish to hear the "scientific" news that the universe has been around since eternity and will never be subject to a doomsday. Implicit in

that news, eagerly picked up by the media and no less eagerly read by the public, is that there will be no day of Judgment either. If the de-Christianized modern man looks for immortality he does so only with the expectation that he will be forever free of the specter of an eternal life which might turn out to be a consciously experienced eternal death. One is indeed to show utter insensitivity to the vast evidence, pagan as well as Christian, ancient as well as modern, about moral consciousness (guilt-feeling) and expectation of inevitable punishment,[16] if one were to take for abstract philosophizing a rarely quoted statement of Einstein:

> Immortality? There are two kinds. The first lives in the imagination of people, and is thus an illusion. There is a relative immortality which may conserve the memory of an individual for some generations. But there is only one true immortality, on a cosmic scale, and that is the immortality of the cosmos itself. There is no other.[17]

It should not therefore be surprising that Einstein's work was time and again invoked by fellow scientists in support of cosmic eternalism. Thus W. Nernst assured on February 23, 1929, a distinguished audience that in addition to radioactivity as a "deteriorating process" there are also "great constructive energies at work in the universe, or else the universe would speed to its death. Radioactive destructive energies are counterbalanced by radioactive constructive energies." And as if to save this incredible declaration from ready objections, Nernst invoked the authority of Einstein as one who "has found a formula for these facts that alone would have sufficed to make that physicist immortal." Nernst must have thought that once cosmic immortality was on hand, a sort of personal immortality would be a cinch. His philosophical bravado was matched by plain irresponsibility in matters scientific: "According to his [Einstein's] formula we must suppose that cosmic masses may without emitting any rays submerge in the ether of light, which is the mother of all energy, there to condense and become a part of a new world system."[18] The formula in question was the famous mc^2 which Nernst invested with magic powers. He had no excuse to forget that by then the ether had been laid to rest for twenty-five years through Einstein's work on special relativity that contained that very formula as its essential consequence.

Had Einstein offered a disclaimer, its echoes would have kept reverberating. His connivance with cosmic eternalism on pseudo-scientific grounds could not be of interest to most of his biographers who as a rule portray him as an exemplary character without guile and with no fault. Only on occasion do in Einstein biographies appear lines revealing for their brevity, such as the ones in A. Pais' *Subtle Is the Lord*, a vastly documented monograph. There it is stated, fleetingly though, that Einstein "disgracefully failed" two women, his first and second wives, and that he showed anything but a "rebellious attitude" against Hitler.[19] Obviously, such failings are far easier to live with if instead of the individual soul, the cosmos is believed to be immortal. One should not therefore ask specifics about the personal failings of that still living cosmologist who described the non-eternity of the universe, suggested by its irreversible expansion, as a "march towards a graveyard of frozen darkness" and added that "it would make the whole universe meaningless. If it were true, I would quit and spend my life raising roses."[20]

Unscientific price of a "scientific" eternity
The remark was prompted at a conference in late 1975 where prospects looked meager for detecting the so-called missing mass that would turn the expansion of the universe into a contraction and, hopefully, into a perpetual repetition of this process. The search for the missing

mass, of which more later, is the less extravagant form of a frantic escape from the ominous specter of cosmic transitoriness. The more extravagant form is the postulating of the emergence of matter out of nothing. It began to be proposed no sooner than the expansion of the universe had become widely recognized in the late 1920s. Already at that blue-ribbon panel on cosmology, sponsored by the British Association for the Advancement of Science in 1931, two speakers — James Jeans and Robert Millikan — postulated the emergence of matter across cosmic spaces that came suspiciously close to postulating the spontaneous emergence of atoms out of nothing. Fairly transparent was their expectation that in spite of its expansion the universe kept its density the same and therefore remained exempt of the passing of time.[21]

This postulate did not enter the mainstream of scientific discussions until 1947 when Thomas Gold and Hermann Bondi proposed the steady-state universe. But even then something more than detached scientific reasoning was needed to turn that theory into one of the three main rival theories of cosmology.[22] One of those extra factors was "the flair for popular broadcasting" which Fred Hoyle, a Cambridge astronomer and the third father of the steady-state theory, displayed with great success. Another was the effectiveness with which the theory seemed to satisfy a craving for the eternity of matter. Clearly, one is entitled to look for non-scientific reasons when just about the same time two leaders of British astronomy voiced radically conflicting appraisals of the theory. The Astronomer Royal, Sir Harold Spencer Jones, found the theory "attractive," a British understatement for "praise at a high level."[23] Herbert Dingle, President of the Royal Astronomical Society, minced no words in the opposite sense. According to him the perfect cosmological principle, whereby the steady-state theorists meant an always perfect or essentially unchangeable world, called for calling a spade a spade, that is, for denouncing it as "the perfect agricultural principle."[24]

The first proponents of the steady-state theory tried to appear purely scientific in pursuing their ultimate objective. They presented as their concrete goal the resolution of a specific scientific problem: In 1947 the age of the earth, as appraised by the radioactive decay of uranium, appeared to be twice as great as the past time of the recession of galaxies, often taken for the age of the universe. Yet within five years the conflict found an easy solution through a better measurement of the luminosity of several galaxies and, consequently, by a recalibration of Hubble's constant. This fact may in itself suggest that the problem was disproportionately small to the full thrust of the steady-state theory embodied in the perfect cosmological principle. In its mere phrasing alone the principle should appear to convey more metaphysics than physics. Perfection as such is not within the purview of scientific method that deals only with the correlation of the quantitative aspects of things and of their interactions.

The steady-state theory was in fact the most metaphysical among all modern physical theories inasmuch as it touched on things in reference to the very source of their existence. For if it was true that hydrogen atoms kept emerging at a steady rate out of nothing so that ever fresh galaxies may form in the spaces left empty by the recession of galaxies from one another, a perspective arose that was more metaphysical than physical. Physically, the perspective assured a steadiness or essential unchangeability to the physical universe, though through a maneuvre that was profoundly metaphysical inasmuch as it subverted all ontology or the study of being. Within that antiontological perspective all things, the whole universe, owed their existence to an arbitrary assertion about the emergence of real things out of nothing as if the nothing could be a spontaneous ontological source of existence. The ultimate support of such an assertion was a sheer insensivitity to elementary rules of reasoning or, more specifically, an utter disregard for the dictates of sufficient reason.

In writing in 1952 that the emergence of hydrogen atoms should be taken not for a transformation of energy (radiation) into matter but for a true emergence out of nothing, H. Bondi, who certainly did not care to invoke the Creator, dispelled any doubt about the true wellsprings of the steady-state theory.[25] Tellingly, most scientific critics of the steady-state theory seemed to grant that the continual and spontaneous emergence of matter out of nothing can be the part of a good scientific theory. Debates centered on two chief observational predictions of the theory. One was an extra amount of 21 cm radiation characteristic of free hydrogen in intergalactic space. The other implied the absence of a larger than average number of galaxies at very great distances. For according to the steady-state theory the universe could never be smaller than it is today.

All those scientific critics ignored the fact that the steady-state theory implied not only an eternal but also an infinite universe, with its consequent paradoxes. In addition to postulating a continual creation of matter out of nothing since eternity, the theory also implied the continual piling up of an infinite amount of matter just beyond the edges of the observable universe. The theory provided no explanation to the problem that all matter (particles or galaxies) passing through that edge could do so only by doing what is impossible, namely, by acquiring the speed of light and therefore becoming infinite in mass. Impossibilities of this kind were regularly encountered by those among modern scientific cosmologists who tried to ward off the specter of transitoriness by giving a scientific glitter to the cause of cosmic eternalism.

At any rate, authors of papers[26] critical of the steady-state theory failed to raise even more fundamental questions such as these: Can any physical phenomenon be ascribed on observational basis to emergence out of

nothing? Is not emergence out of nothing a strictly metaphysical proposition wholly impervious to the methods
of physics? Was Hoyle taken to task when he described
as "the most important problem of present-day astronomy, indeed one of the most important problems of all
science" the task of elucidating the question of the
ontological and temporal origin of the universe?[27] Nor
did the scientific community raise the question whether
it was rationally respectable to obtain the resolution to a
purely quantitative problem at the price of playing a
most arbitrary game with reality. Again there was a complete silence on the question whether scientists are entitled to hide under scientific cover their personal unease
about a universal transitoriness that readily evokes
metaphysical and spiritual perspectives. Nor was it
asked whether, if science is truly an open reasoning, the
scientist should not openly state his motivations as he
makes his option in topics that, indirectly at least, may
have a bearing far beyond a purely "scientific" understanding of the universe. Long before Hoyle stated that
for him God was by definition the Universe and the Universe was God,[28] he should have declared that this was
the very message of the steady-state theory as he
understood it in 1947. He and his colleagues should have
made it clear right there and then that the cosmological
principle they advocated was "perfect" because they
wanted to ascribe to the universe that ultimate perfection
of perennial endurance which has been invariably
ascribed to it by all pagan, pantheist, and materialist
thinkers.

Within the scientific community these points have not
been aired for various reasons. One is the philosophical
poverty reigning in scientific circles. Einstein was rarely
so much to the point as when he remarked that the
man of science is a poor philosopher.[29] Another reason
was that because they deal with quantities, scientists are
tempted to think that all their thinking about science is
free of non-quantitative judgments, ontological and ethi-

cal. Last but not least, scientists are part of their cultural and social ambiance which, in its 20th-century Western form, has become increasingly pragmatic. A general manifestation of this is a carefree indulging in selective indignation. Genocides, racial discriminations, and political oppressions are made to form different classes of which only some, but not others, are judged worth being decried in the highest decibels. Within such a milieu the only real concern about transitoriness aims at its temporal mitigation for the purposes of privileged individuals, classes, and nations. Underlying this selectivity is the presumption that all is over with this life. This, however, can be so only if the universe is not subject to transitoriness. Such a universe is in no need of being created. It may keep emerging forever out of nothing if it needs at all that supreme trick which is to lift oneself by one's own bootstraps above that greatest conceivable difference that separates non-being from being.

Such considerations should present an opportunity, largely unexplored so far, for historians and philosophers of science who have now for three decades been mercilessly probing the "social" background of scientific theories. Not, of course, for the "leading edge" among them. They, as was noted with accurate acidity, would readily condemn "all present and future philosophers of science to the torments of the damned: that is, to reading the sociology of science" and nothing else.[30] The torment should seem doubled if only those scientists would then belong to the "science-society" who claim to have no religion, whereas those professedly religious would be psychoanalyzed as if they professed something else. (Some always know better than others.) The torment is tripled by those few philosophers of science who see the irony but shy away from the subject of the religion of scientists, and, of course, of the religion of philosophers of science, and of the even more revealing lack of it in most cases.[31] At any rate, one should not expect from mostly pragmatist historians and philosophers of science the probing into antireligious and antimetaphysical motivations as possibly underlying pragmatist attitudes. They are in fact still to probe into the curiously speedy process whereby the steady-state theory established itself in the 1950s as one of the three rival cosmologies.

The speed is all the more telling because cosmologists and astronomers — to say nothing of science popularizers — could claim only one experimental or observational reason prior to 1952[32] and none whatever after 1952. Wholly postulational remained the chief predictions of the steady-state theory, such as the extra amount of 21 cm radiation of hydrogen atoms and the absence of increase in the number of galaxies at very great distances, prior to their being observationally disproved in the early 1960s. Did the theory recommend itself on purely esthetic grounds? Was the idea of a single expansion (Big Bang) less esthetic or less encumbered by the specter of perpetual monotony (the very denial of esthetic value) than was the theory of a perpetually oscillating universe? Can something truly esthetic be contained in a theory which denies limits whereas in all artistic masterworks limits are essential? Why do even the best paintings look better when limited by a frame? The answers to these questions should be obvious. It should therefore be most realistic to look for the popularity of the steady-state theory in a motivation that goes beyond pure science and also beyond that estheticism which is a mere distraction from metaphysics and religion.

Such motivation (always typical of pantheism, the only religion compatible with pragmatism) may be the effort whereby one tries to compensate for one's personal transitoriness with hopes about a non-transitory cosmos. Part of that motivation relates to the prospect that such a cosmos does not call for a Creator whose reality alone can turn one's transitoriness into an eternally irrevocable proposition. Although the cultivation of that prospect is very much of a private and personal nature, the printed record is not altogether void of evidences that it is at work in reference to cosmological theories. A memorable instance is Nernst's reaction to the calculations which the young theoretical physicist, Friedrich von Weizsäcker, made in 1938 about the age of the universe. Far from taking in stride the results of several billion years, Nernst was visibly upset. He warned Weizsäcker that the universe could not be temporal or transitory because cosmic eternity was the very foundation of science.[33] Clearly, more than science has to be involved when a scientist has so much at stake in the eternity of the universe as to become agitated on seeing it contradicted by science.

That extra factor will not appear less "religious" when its avowed religious character is contrasted, as done by Hoyle, with "the crude ritualistic survivals from the Stone Age that pass for religion in our modern communities." Religion has always implied answering to esthetic impulses as any survey, however summary, of art history would readily show. That religion is ultimately a matter of esthetics, let alone that mere esthetics is more religious than religion itself, is a transparent play with words. Hoyle engaged in such a game when he declared in the same breath that "it is to the structurally elegant and beautiful laws which govern the world that the modern scientist looks for in his religious impulses."[34] He may have indeed protested too much. At any rate, cosmologists are still to be found who would lay down their lives for the Milky Way, or for black holes, or for the missing matter.

Missing matter and eternity missing

Actually, the search for the missing matter may have grown very intense during the last fifteen years or so because of a "religious" motivation at work. The presence of religion may be suspected when a scientific search prompts the remark on the part of one most sympathetic to it that "never in the history of scientific endeavor have so many laboured so hard to measure so little."[35] As for the true nature of that religion it consists in the assurance that one is forever freed from the religious duty to lay down one's life for truths and moral precepts pointing far beyond physical existence. This is not to suggest that cosmological, let alone religious, perspectives were at work when in 1932 Jan Oort reached the conclusion that in order to explain the motion of stars outside the disk of our galaxy, the disk had to have twice as much matter as the total mass of visible stars there. Nor could "religion" be yet suspected when shortly afterward Fritz Zwicky found only one hundredth of the total mass that was needed to explain by Newtonian gravitation the stability of large clusters of galaxies.

But in the early 1970s the presence of "religion" could not be easily discounted as search for the missing mass suddenly got into high gear. By then even Hoyle admitted the futility of his effort "to tough it out" in the face of the discovery of the cosmic background radiation. The latter dealt a devastating blow to the "perfect" cosmological principle according to which the cosmos has no history because one cosmic epoch cannot be different from another cosmic epoch. In other words, science undercut once more the "religious" veneration of the universe as an eternal, and by inference, a self-creating entity. Revealingly, Hoyle sought an escape hatch in postulating a "very large number of *undetected sources*, sources of very low intrinsic emissions." He, however, admitted that "most astronomers find it unpalatable to assume the existence, not just of a new class of source, but of a class with a very large number of members". He put that number at 10^{14} or 100,000 times the total number of visible galaxies.[36] A large order it was, but suggestive of a great faith that can move much more than mountains.

Since the steady-state theory failed as a support of cosmic eternalism, astronomers fond of it had to make a go of the next best, or the idea of an oscillating universe.

That the universe may be closed, that is, oscillating, was a ready inference from the moment when at the Spring 1974 meeting of the American Physical Society J. P. Ostriker claimed to have found much extra mass in galactic halos. Had the alleged discovery lacked cosmic implications, the media would not have become excited about it. Frustrated eternalism blared forth in E. H. Harrison's remark, already quoted, when a year and a half later a re-examination of the galaxy density in the Coma cluster failed to turn up more than a fraction of the missing mass. At any rate, the media have not ceased to greet with headlines alleged discoveries of the missing mass while downplaying persistent failures. The connexion between this and the media's distinctly negative attitude towards the religion that refuses to be downgraded to mere estheticism is hardly a coincidence.

Stated in dry figures the problem of the missing mass grows exponentially as large units of the cosmos are investigated in their dynamical behavior. Whereas in the center of our galaxy, and also in our own neighborhood, the observable luminous mass is only three times less than the one required on dynamical grounds, the same factor is between ten and twenty at the edge of our galaxy. In smaller groups of galaxies the factor is already between fifty and a hundred, and becomes about three hundred in large clusters of galaxies. Insofar as the uniform rotation of galaxies and the stability of clusters are real physical phenomena, these discrepancies represent *real problems*. For their solution there seem to be only two avenues: either to detect the mass missing or to assume that the inverse square law of gravitation is not valid at great distances. Opting for the latter alternative is not to the liking of most cosmologists. They are obviously aware of the self-defeating efforts, now about a hundred years old, to explain the advance of the perihelion of Mercury by a slight modification of the exponent in the inverse square law.[37] Yet the inverse square law is modified in a different way in General Relativity and may be in need of modification when it will be tested over very great, that is, galactic and intergalactic distances. Still, any parting, however slight, with the inverse square law will infringe on the universal validity of the theory of central forces, a theory too successful to be given up lightly.

Whatever the apparently sacrosanct character of the inverse square law, many cosmologists are all too ready to look for very large amounts of extra matter both inside and outside the galaxies. Their readiness is noteworthy for more than one reason. One is the very large amount of matter needed to resolve genuinely scientific problems posed by the rotation of galaxies, by the orbits of binary galaxies, and by the stability of clusters of galaxies. Another reason is the persistent failure to detect that missing mass. While in the early 1980s there could yet be no imperative reason to turn the quest for the missing mass into an inquest,[38] the moment for a reconsideration may not be too far. Still a third is the problem posed by self-defeating consequences of the case were particular forms of that matter to be found. This latter point deserves to be looked at in some detail.

Thus if red or black dwarfs (stars never large enough to have nuclear processes in their interior) were to be in large numbers in the halos of galaxies, they would have very large random velocities and as such would be easily detected. Yet only one percent of the required number has been found so far. Also, such dwarfs would, if present in the requisite number, make the galaxies "sticky," that is, cause them to be lumped into dense clusters which then would turn into huge lumps. Another class of candidates for the missing matter is composed of white dwarfs and neutron stars, both remnants of stars that burnt up their nuclear fuel. Their presence in very large numbers is not, however, conceivable without a high concentration of heavy elements in interstellar gas which does not, however, show that characteristic. A third group of candidates, black holes, do not fit the bill either. Their primary or first generation kind would have long ago evaporated by the emission of photons. Their secondary generation would, in galactic halos, constantly trap matter, a process accompanied by strong emission of X-rays that are not, however, observed. In addition, they too would pose the "stickiness" problem. As to black holes outside galactic halos, they would produce huge tidal effects resulting in the systematic distortion of elliptical and spiral galaxies, a feature rarely observable in them.

The fourth class of candidates, the heavy neutrinos, are directly involved in the larger or cosmological problem of the missing mass. They were first postulated in the mid-1970s and allegedly observed in the early 1980s. Of course the discovery, if true, would have justified Carlo Rubbia's exuberant remark: "The cosmological consequences are absolutely fantastic."[39] Although the masses ascribed to neutrinos, by themselves massless particles, were in the range of a dozen to three dozen eV (the mass of an electron is about half a million eV), the enormously large number of neutrinos would have provided the matter needed for the solution of the foregoing scientific problems, that is, the ones posed by the rotation of galaxies and by the stability of galactic clusters. As it turned out in 1984, heavy neutrinos too would be a fly in the cosmological ointment. With these neutrinos present, our universe would look very different because they would have greatly postponed the formation of galaxies and the formation of stars within them.[40] It is in this light that one should look back at the euphoria which around 1980 took heavy neutrinos for that factor that would cause the present expansion of the universe to come to a halt and turn it into a contraction.

Qualification of those problems as scientific may make appear unscientific the search for the quantity of matter that would close the universe in the sense of turning its present expansion into a contraction. But a search cannot be unqualifiedly scientific if a heavily a priori factor is also at work in it. Apriorism dictates the view that the universe should be closed rather than open, although observational evidence heavily supports its openness whereas there is no reason why the universe should not be open. The search is less than unqualifiedly scientific also because its promoters take lightly the enormous empirical difference, a factor of 100, which is between the actually observed matter density and the one postulated. Or in more technical terms the observed value for Ω is about 0.01 as opposed to 1 which by definition is the critical density that would just turn the expansion into a contraction. That observed value has more than enough support in the data offered in the latest review article to let its cautious reader question its facetious conclusion: "Those of us who are not directly involved in the fray can only suppose that the universe is open ($\Omega < 1$) on Wednesday, Friday, and Sunday and closed ($\Omega > 1$) on Thursday, Saturday, and Monday. (Tuesday is choir practice.)"[41]

It is hardly scientific to gloss over that difference on the ground that in astronomy and cosmology a difference of several magnitudes hardly makes much difference. (It is well to recall that a difference of only one fifth of a magnitude was taken by the champions and erstwhile admirers of the steady-state theory for an overriding justification of their truly extravagant claims.) Nor is it scientific to argue that the idea of a closed universe resembles the great theories of physics, such as the work of Copernicus, Newton, Maxwell, and Einstein. In all these cases direct experimental verifications were crucial for eventual success. Copernicanism made little headway until Galileo's telescopic observations. Speedy acceptance of Newton's work largely depended on the measured identity between the rate of fall of the moon and of bodies on the earth's surface. As to Maxwell's theory, it overcame strong and valid criticism not so much because of its intrinsic beauty, but because of Hertz's experiments. General Relativity became really victorious only after the observation of the bending of starlight around the sun in connection with the 1919 solar eclipse.

No similar observational or experimental advantage goes with the advocacy of a closed universe, while a great many observational evidences militate against it. Fortunately, its advocates admit that its chief appeal is esthetic. Is not that admission a cover-up for other motivations at work? The esthetic appeal should seem rather unconvincing on the basis of esthetics alone. Beauty, as was noted, is inconceivable without the presence of some overarching limit which is precisely what is absent in the closed universe theory in spite of the word "closed" in its name. But before probing into the wider background of the closed universe theory, one may legitimately ask: Why is a universe with a single expansion and contraction more esthetic than a universe with a single expansion? Or why should a Big Bang followed by a Big Crunch appear more esthetic than a single Big Bang?

Cycles: linear and dogmatic

The allegedly more esthetic character of the closed universe will appear in its true light as soon as one asks: Is the Big Crunch the end of all? It seems that for some the Big Crunch is merely needed to give plausibility to the idea of an endlessly oscillating universe. In discussing the grave problems posed for theoretical physics by a possible rebounce from a Big Crunch, I. D. Novikov and Ya. B. Zel'dovich noted in a matter-of-fact style that the possibility suggests the appealing picture of a cyclic universe, persisting indefinitely into the past and the future.[42] By evoking the prospect of indefinite cosmic endurance the idea of an oscillating universe may effectively ward off the specter of cosmic transitoriness. More than mere esthetics goes therefore with the advocacy of a closed universe and with the search for the extra matter needed by it. Far more powerful than esthetics may be the belief that the eternity of the universe would dispose of questions about any reality transcendental to the universe as its very cause.

A direct proof of the presence of such belief would require a plain disclosure on the part of cosmologists concerning their philosophical beliefs. This is, however, available only in a very few cases. Moreover, philosophical (or indirectly religious) matters offer little hope for coming to a generally shared understanding of their basic terms, let alone for agreeing about them. It should seem therefore more profitable to go on with a scientific analysis of the advocacy of the missing mass and, by implication, of an eternal universe.

First to note is the frequent silence about a most scientific aspect of an oscillating universe. Its oscillations must be viewed as gradually dying out as long as one retains a modest respect for the law of entropy. The point is all the more worth considering because it was already made half a century ago and in a most prominent scientific context: Richard C. Tolman's *Relativity, Thermodynamics, and Cosmology*, first published in 1934.[43] The idea of a perpetually oscillating universe might not have turned into a ready cliché had the majority of that book's scientific readers paid serious attention to a diagram in it. The diagram shows the eventual dying out of the oscillating universe and is noteworthy for an additional reason. In the diagram the subsequent curves standing for subsequent oscillations are not connected. The reason for this is that in 1934 nothing was known (and *pace* Hawking and others still nothing is known in 1988) about the kind of physics which prevails in that inconceivably dense state where the Big Crunch allegedly turns into another Big Bang.

This total ignorance is glossed over in the diagram which graces *The Physics of Time Asymmetry* of P. C. W. Davis.[44] There four successive cycloidal curves, with decreasing amplitudes, illustrate the fate of the oscillating universe. The book deserves to be mentioned also because reference there to Tolman's discussion of the problem is furtive to say the least. In fact the reference is so inconspicuous that a world-renowned cosmologist failed to note it. As he called my attention to Davis's discussion of the problem, he did not want to believe my reply that Davis merely repeated what Tolman had already set forth and in greater detail.

All this is characteristic of the fact that most references to the oscillating universe do not contain about it a most important information. The latter relates to the fact that the difference between a universe with single expansion and a universe with many expansion-contraction cycles is far smaller than generally imagined. Since in an oscillating universe the energy peaks of successive cycles are smaller and smaller, a line connecting those peaks would graphically evoke that linearity which is the obvious characteristic of a universe with a single expansion. Both are in fact subject to the gradual diminution of the intensities of all physical processes in them. In the case of the simply expanding model such quantitative details are available as the extinction of all small stars at 10^{14} years or thousand times the present age. At 10^{19} years stars in the central regions of the galaxy will collapse into a black hole. At 10^{32} years all ordinary elements will disappear through the disintegration of protons and neutrons. Beyond that the main events would consist of the fall of miscellaneous particles into black holes accompanied with emission of X-rays. Such a state would last until 10^{65} years. It would be followed by the occasional evaporation of black holes into mere radiation while the temperature of the universe would continue to fall.[45] As for the oscillating universe, estimates can be made about the number of cycles it would perform were it to possess that enormously large amount of extra mass.

The idea of an oscillating universe, once conceived in terms of real physics and not in terms alien to it, differs not so much from the idea of a single expanding universe as from that age-old idea of eternal recurrences

Symbolized by the ever-rotating wheel, or swastika, that idea of the cosmos was responsible for the stillbirths of science in all ancient cultures, including Hellenic and Hellenistic Greece.[46] In that respect too, the word swastika contradicts its etymological meaning which is "to be well." The straitjacketing of science in Nazi Germany[47] which took the swastika for its symbol is a powerful modern instance of that painful lesson of scientific history. (The same is also true of Marxist realms[48] whose symbol, the combination of the hammer and the sickle, has a curious resemblance to the swastika). Science escaped from the syndrome of its invariable stillbirths in all ancient cultures only in the Christian Middle Ages. There the eternalism of Greek cosmology was discarded with an eye on the Christian dogma of creation out of nothing and in time that imposed a linear framework on cosmological thought. In particular, the shift implied a replacement of the Aristotelian laws of motion with the law of inertial motion as conceived by Buridan and Oresme, a fact that greatly helped the work of Copernicus and all the early Copernicans.[49]

This is mentioned for two reasons. One is that the great turning points of scientific history deserve to be kept in focus if its crucial errors are not to be repeated. The other is that in this chapter a plea has been made for openness, that is, for a laying of all of one's cards on the table. The cards of this author are those of a physicist, of a historian of science, and, last but not least, of a Catholic theologian. As such he professes no sympathy for Hegelianism and Jamesian pragmatism. He has no use for Eastern philosophies in which there is no room for the doctrine of creation out of nothing and in time, a doctrine that served as the wellspring of a linear view of cosmic and historical processes. Therefore he finds most satisfying the cosmic linearity as strongly suggested by the observational fact of cosmic expansion and all its vast theoretical support. He, however, is not bound by his Roman Catholic faith to endorse the single expansion model. Professor Hawking merely hatched a new fallacy about the Catholic Church by claiming that she "seized on the big bang model and in 1951 officially pronounced it to be in accordance with the Bible."[50]

Transitoriness as specificity

What a Roman Catholic or any genuinely believing intelligent Christian should find most satisfying about the slow dying down of the universe, both in the single expanding and in the oscillating case, is that it can be cast into specific quantitative terms. In other words, whether one follows up the history of the universe into its earliest phases or into its most distant future, one sees that quantitative specificity is the invariable rule. That quantitative specificity — strictly defining the physical universe in its present, its past and its future — should be a constant reminder of its contingency, namely, that it could have been otherwise. This is the only strict argument that can be drawn from the specter of the transitoriness of the universe.

From that argument one can easily infer the createdness of the universe, if one's eyes are not blocked by idealist or empiricist philosophies or by that recent parody of philosophy which takes human thinking for a mere game and does it in the name of science. But the same argument cannot provide a specification of the time or moment of cosmic beginning. In other words physics, by showing everywhere the quantitative specificity of the universe, can be of great support in articulating the cosmological argument or the creation of the universe out of nothing. Physics is also of great help insofar as it gives a most impressive, though not absolutely final, assurance that energy is quantized. Consequently, the total number of physical interactions would have to be finite in a finite universe. In that sense, physics strongly suggests a temporal finiteness for a physically "active" universe. This point may be greatly

strengthened with badly needed qualifications about the
true meaning of Cantor's work on transfinite numbers.
Far from giving support to the idea of an actually realized infinite quantity, transfinite infinity, to recall a
pointed remark of Hilbert, "is nowhere to be found in
reality."[51]

Physics in no way contains a proof of a temporal
beginning of the universe. The method of physics always
means an inference from one observable state to
another. Observability in turn implies that the thing
observed is not absolutely inert and therefore can interact with the observer and its instruments. This is why
any talk about an eternal inert universe preceding the
actual universe has no place in physics. As for those who
speak of esoteric fluctuations in the vacuum prior to the
actual physical processes that can be traced back to 15
billion or so years, they either mean real physical
processes or they do not. In either case they build an illusory screen against the specter of cosmic transitoriness.
Much less does physics provide basis for an inference to
a non-existing state that conceptually has to precede a
creation in time out of nothing. After three hundred
years of Newtonian physics and after a near century of
modern physics the truth of creation in time is best left
with supernatural revelation where Thomas Aquinas
assigned it.[52] A Christian can indeed no more effectively
undermine his cosmological view than by espousing this
or that latest headline about the spotting by astronomers
of the moment of creation ten, fifteen, or twenty billion
years ago.[53]

Although cosmic transitoriness, as established by science, provides no ground for a strict philosophical argument, it remains a powerful reminder, indeed more powerful than many strict arguments, about the true ground
of existence which is God. How powerful that reminder
is can be judged from the readiness with which some scientists resort to most improbable schemes to assure eternity to the universe. The latest of them was brought to the

attention of the wider public under the caption "Renegade Physicists Challenge the Big Bang."[54] The caption, "Illogical Scientists" would have better fitted the bill in view of the reasoning of their leader, Hannes Alfvén, a Nobel-laureate for his work in plasma physics and an unabashed eternalist. "If there were a Big Bang," he was quoted as saying, "you had to have the Hubble expansion. But it does not follow that because there's an expansion, there was a Big Bang, That's the same logic that says, all dogs are animals, and therefore all animals are dogs."[55] As he cautioned against faulty reasoning, he simply mistook what is a strictly individual case for a case of individuals in a class.

It may be that the gravitational force may not explain the clustering of supergalaxies into still larger units of billions of light years in diameter within the 15 or so billion years that have elapsed in the actual expansion. It may also turn out that plasma physics, in which electromagnetic forces dominate, should be invoked to explain long filaments in the center of the Milky Way if they are there and if the $2.7°K$ cosmic background radiation has, indeed, more energy than predicted by Big Bang theories. But even then no plasma cosmology, in which even the formation of single galaxies may take hundreds of billions of years, can prove that the universe "has existed forever, without a beginning and with no end in sight."[56] The only proof of such a universe is a pagan dogma which is indirectly asserted in Alfvén's remark that the proponents of Big Bang, aware as they are of some of its problems, "are cautious. A Christian does not go to Mecca and become a convert overnight."[57] If most cosmologists, who have little to do with Christianity, will not quickly convert to plasma eternity, it is because they have not yet thrown all logic to the winds.

Another of those recent eternalist schemes in cosmology is the idea that at the end of each oscillation the universe scoops up out of the vacuum the very same amount of energy which it has just dissipated by doing the work of expansion and contraction.[58] The idea is best called the theory of cosmic gasoline station where no cash, not even a credit card, is necessary. The theory is of no more worth than the huge concave ether walls which Rankine conjured up a hundred years ago everywhere in space for the reconcentration of dissipated starlight.[59] Those walls are just as fictional as the probability calculation offered by Boltzmann shortly afterwards. He began by trying to give plausibility to the idea that because all atoms in a table may have their random motions directed at a given moment in the same upward direction, the table may suddenly rise above the ground. On that basis he proposed that this or that part of the universe, nay the entire universe too, may as a phoenix rise from its ashes.[60] It would have been more scientific for him to recall in the first place that the phoenix is a purely fictional bird.

A hundred years after Rankine and Boltzmann the same idea of getting something for nothing is making the rounds in a far more seductively scientific garb which calls for a specific treatment in another chapter. Before discussing it, attention should be given to another facet of modern cosmological speculations. The facet has two sides to it, though on a deeper than psychological level, just as was the case with the alternative between transitoriness and eternalism. Nothing goes indeed so much to the root of thinking about cosmic existence as the decision between the alternatives whether the cosmos necessarily is what it is, or whether its existence is contingent upon a choice transcending that totality which the cosmos ought to be by definition.

Chapter Four

GÖDEL'S SHADOW

> Even the Great March had to begin with a
> first step
>
> Mao Tse-tung

Under-standing and some pantheists
The contingency of the universe, which forms the subject of this chapter, is a philosophical and, indeed, very metaphysical topic. But so is the purpose of all these chapters. They are meant to provide the kind of understanding that can only be had if it is possible to do metaphysics, that is, to go beyond the entire physical realm, or the universe, without leaving it physically. That possibility is the very condition of true metaphysics. Metaphysics taken in that sense is not a discourse about ideas about the universe or about a universe of ideas or about our ideas about those ideas. True metaphysics implies a series of assertions about a Reality beyond the universe, as the cause of the reality of the universe itself.

This causal, ontological dependence of the universe on that extra-universe reality is its contingency, a term of which more shortly. Taken in that sense the truth of the contingency of the universe implies that, although the universe is, by definition, the totality of consistently interacting things, it is possible to spot something beyond the universe. Whether this is possible or not, it is certainly not possible for physics. Whatever understanding physics can offer, it cannot see beyond the universe and much less can it take up an observational stand outside the universe. The understanding of the universe in terms of its contingency depends on whether there is in man an ability to get, so to speak, "under" the universe and to ponder from there its very existence.

The metaphor of "standing under," which one resorts to in conveying the fact that one understands, will intrigue only those who have not yet entirely succumbed to the positivist illusion that all understanding has to do with what is on the surface.[1] To look metaphysically beyond or beneath the universe can hardly appeal to most physicist-cosmologists who as a rule refuse to take a serious look at the very foundations of physics lest they come across plain philosophy. If prompted by prominent philosophers to take such a look, they often offer in reply a variant of Rutherford's rebuff of Samuel Alexander: "Well, what have you been talking all your life, Alexander? Just hot air. Nothing but hot air."[2] That Alexander's evolutionary idealism may have justified such a reply does not dispose of questions about what may be beyond that plain physical reality which Rutherford championed in graphic terms.[3] He did so at a time when many physicists waxed "metaphysical" by seeing mere wave packets in atoms and nuclei as if physical reality depended only on their thinking. Most of them failed to see that once a physicist grants existence to a very real universe, existing even when he does not think about it, he leaves open questions about its contingency, that is, about its ontological dependence on a Reality which is "beyond" it or "beneath" it.

The reality ontologically underlying the universe cannot be really different from it if a necessary connection is claimed between the two, namely, that neither can exist without the other. Illustrations of this are all pantheistic or emanationist theories of the universe. Whatever understanding could be gained about the universe in those theories, it has been invariably useless for the purposes of science. By not making a clear distinction between the Prime Mover and the sphere of stars, Aristotle erected a supreme justification for his view that the mover must be continuously in contact with the moved thing. He therefore brushed aside hints that pointed toward the idea of inertial motion or Newton's first law. Furthermore, a pantheistic world view in his case too invited a thinking about the universe as if it were a quasi-living organism.[4] He found it therefore most tempting to speak of the motion of its main and small parts as being driven by "volitions". The result was that Aristotelian discourse about the physical world which, to recall a phrase of E. T. Whittaker, is "worthless and misleading from start to end."[5] The fact that references to the actual physical universe are exceedingly rare in Plotinus' system is perhaps the only saving grace in his extremely abstract emanationism.[6] The emanationism that dominates medieval Jewish cabbalistic literature prompted a flood of obscurantist speculations there about the creation of the world,[7] speculations so much at variance with the lucidity of the biblical message.[8] If Giordano Bruno made a parody of Copernicus' system, it was because its precision and specificity made "with the file of geometry," as deplored by Bruno,[9] countered his effort to fuse everything into everything else.[10]

After Bruno one comes to the scientific age proper. Marin Mersenne, probably the best contemporary judge of what was good and bad in early 17th-century writings about science, was very much to the point as he denounced Robert Fludd, a notoriously pantheist cosmologist, as an "evil magician."[11] The pantheist Spinoza did not notice the irony hidden in his resolve to be a pantheist to the point of emphatically declaring that "nothing in the universe is contingent, but all things are conditioned to exist and operate in a particular manner by the necessity of the divine nature."[12] This could only mean that things necessarily were what they were and could not even in theory be something else. Such was a hostility to the contingency of things and deprived Spinoza of that sympathy for things without which physical science cannot thrive. The one who excelled in lens-grinding never ventured farther into physics than writing a treatise on the rainbow.[13] It contained nothing really new about the geometry of rainbows, a fairly old shoe by then, and not a hint about the physics of that very physical phenomenon. As pantheism gained respectability from the late 18th century on, it propelled a new tide of obscurantist interpretations of science. Emanationist pantheists, such as Schelling and Hegel, form a list ominous for science and for scientists.[14] That the classics of Marxist literature — such as the writings of Marx, Engels, and Blanqui[15] — are full of stultifying dicta on science, is closely tied to materialist dialectics. According to its principal tenet there is nothing to look for beyond or under matter because matter, being a necessary existent, is the very opposite to a contingent being.

Varieties of contingency

The contingency of the universe as defined above is not the meaning that would be familiar to a typical traveler browsing, say, in the highbrow section of an airport bookstore. (The reason for choosing that locality will be clear in due course). The traveler in question need not unduly blame himself. Nor should he blame the English language for its unusual ability to tie most divergent meanings to the same word. Long before the words contingency and contingent became standard parts of English during the 17th century, they had already meant, in Latin and early Romance languages, something accidental, haphazard or random, under the broad umbrella of chance, the special topic of another chapter.

The meticulous listing with many illustrations, in the Oxford Dictionary of the English Language, of the various meanings of "contingency" and "contingent" is dominated by the shades of "randomness" or the accidental.[16] In connection with contingency the list begins with brief references to nearness, contact, and affinity, as the first of the two main groups of meanings. The second and much longer group of meanings comprises uncertainty of occurrence, fortuitousness, freedom from predetermining necessity, the condition of being at the mercy of accidents, conjecture of events without design, a merely possible future event, and finally a thing or outcome incident or dependent upon an uncertain event.

Even longer is the list of the shades of meaning that can be attached to the word contingent, an adjective. It is there that one encounters, in addition to the meanings already listed in connection with contingency, the meanings of not being determined by necessity in regard to existence, and the meaning of not existing of itself but in dependence on something else. These additional meanings are rather different from that of chance occurrence which, as will be discussed in another chapter, is often taken for the absence of cause and undoubtedly so in modern physics and scientific cosmology. Those additional meanings are also different from that of a necessary connection. It is between these two meanings that one finds sandwiched that notion of contingency which it is the aim of this chapter to find embodied in the universe.

Such contingency means the thorough dependence of a thing on another factor, without assuring a necessary existence to that thing or, in our case, the universe. About this contingency, a profoundly philosophical notion, modern scientific cosmologists often imply its opposite, namely, the necessary existence of the universe. At the same time they also often suggest that the universe is a haphazard or chance occurrence in the sense of having no cause. This may surprise scientific cosmologists, often strangers to the main patterns of intellectual history. One of those patterns shows that a philosophically extremist position can easily generate the belief that full advantage may be taken of the opposite position as well. With the coming of Hegelians, pragmatists, and complementarists, this arbitrariness, if not plain intellectual recklessness, received the halo of highest respectability.

Scientific cosmologists are prompted to endorse philosophically contradictory claims for more than one reason. One is that they honor reasoning in the breach insofar as they make those claims more rhetorically than philosophically. They hardly ever state in a categorical manner that the universe is necessarily existing and therefore non-contingent, that is, non-dependent on any other extra-cosmic factor, such as God. Rather they speak of their urge to construct an all-encompassing physical theory which, because of its beauty or simplicity, should make the universe appear self-explaining. Such is their excuse, steeped more in rhetoric than in logic, not to look for a cause of the universe. The rhetoric is all the more misleading because its references to esthetics camouflage an ultimately philosophical message.

The real thrust of "ultimate" theories

There is much more than meets the eye in Dirac's celebration of an intuitive sense for beauty as the source of crucial ideas in theoretical cosmology. "You just have to try and imagine what the universe is like," he said ten years ago after making the point that beauty in a theory is just "like beauty in a picture or beauty in music. You can't describe it, it's something — and if you don't feel it, you just have to accept that you're not susceptible to it. No one explains it to you."[17] But if one takes a non-communicable sense of beauty for the ultimate arbiter among cosmic views, it can also protect one from facing up to philosophical questions about the universe on the ground that they are not beautiful. In an age of science, philosophers talking about the beauty of their own insights may be at a great disadvantage in respect to scientists who by talking about their own sense of beauty set it up as an anesthetic against that other kind of beauty.

Less futile may therefore be the scrutiny of statements that are dominated not so much by references to the beauty of theory as by its quality of giving a "complete understanding of the universe." Such a theory, in Prof. Hawking's words, is also a means "to understand whether the universe has a meaning, and what our role is in it . . . [and] to know why the universe exists at all, and what was there before the beginning."[18] He left unspecified the respective competence of physics and philosophy as he implied that physics can answer the questions of why and for what purpose. His curiosity about what happened before the beginning has for its sole justification a vague use of the word "beginning". It is not rigorous not to take rigorously a beginning which is meant to be taken rigorously if it is really a beginning. At any rate, his quest for the ultimate or complete theory cannot truly be an all-consuming ambition. In the same breath he also declared the eventual finding of that theory to be a source of disappointment. He gave as his reason that man needs not so much the truth but a quest for it:

> There may be ultimate answers, but if there are, I would be sorry if we were to find them. For my *own* sake I would like very much to find them, but their discovery would leave nothing for those coming after me to seek. Each generation builds on the advances of the previous generation, and this is as it should be. As human beings, we need the quest.[19]

It is rather sad to find a great cosmologist who is unable to see that such a view of the quest for truth is in itself a truth and that physics cannot prove, if it can be proved at all, that the finding of the truth of a complete theory is a lesser truth than the truth of searching for it.

At any rate, the quest for truth, rather than the finding or possessing it, is not held supreme in the closing remark of Hawking's *Brief History of Time*. There he speaks about the complete theory as knowing God's very mind[20] which is something very different from a never-ending quest for that knowledge. The context contains other instances too of the absence of rigorous reasoning. One is Hawking's blast at philosophers interested only in the analysis of language[21] and his plea for a return to the great philosophical tradition stretching from Aristotle to Kant.[22] Hawking merrily overlooked that Kant's chief aim was to bring about a complete and irrevocable break with the realist tradition initiated by Aristotle. Yet this point, as was argued in the first chapter, is of crucial significance for the status of the notion of the universe and consequently for the status of scientific cosmology as well. In fact so great is the difference between Aristotle and Kant that no meaningful discourse has ever been possible between their genuine followers.

For Kant the shape of external reality is determined by a sort of introspection. Kant and many of his admirers readily took that introspection for an easy a priori means whereby one can dispense with hard and exact studies in investigating the external world or universe. Aristotle (and certainly Thomas Aquinas) held that even the so-called categories of the mind are the fruits of abstraction from concrete knowledge.[23] The same difference underlies another point which may seem particularly telling in this age of science. Kant acknowledged only such metaphysics and theory of knowledge that could be patterned on the exactness of physics, Newtonian physics that is, about which he knew very little. Aristotle, however, never ceased to warn about the difference between mathematics and metaphysics or rather the manner in which man knows reality regardless of whether it displays mathematical properties or not.

Of course, if that difference can be overlooked, then it is possible to entertain with Hawking some fanciful ideas about that ultimate theory. He spoke of that ultimate theory as being "so unique as to be understandable in broad principle by everyone, not just a few scientists. Then we shall all, philosophers, scientists and just ordinary people, be able to take part in the discussion of the question of why it is that we and the universe exist."[24] He gave absolutely no proof on behalf of his claim that questions about the cause of existence of the universe can be raised only after all its mathematical or quantitative properties have been found out. The claim is fanciful, to put it mildly, but it is in that fanciful perspective that one should see Hawking's wish to have his book available in airport bookstores.[25] Often one goes there in utter frustration for having been informed about the true amount of time whereby the departure of one's plane is being postponed. Answers to philosophical questions are invariably postponed in the *Brief History of Time*, although it is bursting with such questions precisely because it is about the search for the ultimate theory. That theory is the most philosophically loaded theory among all physical theories because a complete account of *all* quantitative features of the universe brings up the question about the cause of so specific a universe.

No answers could be wrested from Prof. Hawking by someone most privy to his thinking. The words of Jane Wilde (Mrs. Hawking) are on record:

> There is one aspect of his thought that I find increasingly upsetting and difficult to live with. It's the feeling that, because everything is reduced to a rational mathematical formula, that must be the truth . . . You can't actually get an answer out of Stephen regarding philosophy beyond the realms of science. He is now postulating a theory in which the universe is . . . with no beginning and no end and no need for God at all. What I can't understand is whether — and this is something in the whole 22 years of being married to him that I haven't been able to understand — he is working within the bounds of maths and science and saying: 'This is what the theory predicts; if you have other interpretations that's up to you.' Or whether he is saying: 'This is the only concrete evidence we have of anything.' I can never get an answer, I find it very upsetting.[26]

The clarity and poignancy with which the crucial difference between mathematics and philosophy is stated by one who above all wanted to be a devoted wife puts to shame most occupants of chairs, prestigious and other, of physics, mathematics, and astronomy. They are still to acquire the profound yet elementary insights in Mrs. Hawking's poignant words. There the only relapse into present-day academic obfuscation is the equating of rational with mathematical, a relapse fully remedied by the splendid context.

The poignancy of Mrs. Hawking's words gained further emphasis by the reporter's paraphrasing of what was obviously a part of the interview: "What she does get, when the conversation reaches a point beyond which he [Prof. Hawking] will not go, is the Hawking grin. Moving when first glimpsed, this [grin] can clearly also be infuriating. For Mrs. Hawking, a devout Anglican, it seems like an agnostic door slamming in her face."[27] Grin is not philosophy, nor is there much philosophy in agnosticism. Yet all this is all the more frustrating because Prof. Hawking is fully aware, at least in some moments, of what a physical theory is, even if it is a complete theory. To quote his very words: "Even if there is only one possible unified theory, it is just a set of rules and equations."[28] These words deserve to be posted over the entrance of each and every department of physics and astronomy.

Prof. Hawking's stark and sound definition of physical theory becomes even more so by his contrasting it to physical reality: "What is it," he asks, "that breathes fire into the equations and makes a universe for them to describe?" His question, reverberating with common sense, gains in philosophical stature by his admission that "the usual approach of science to constructing a mathematical model cannot answer the question of why there should be a universe for the model to describe." But the philosophical soundness, which then would evoke something beyond the universe as its underlying cause of existence, suddenly vanishes. This is already intimated by that innocuous looking reference to the "usual approach of science." It seems to imply that an "unusual" or rather "unusually" good physical theory can answer Prof. Hawking's question in which formal metaphysics is conjured up by colloquial informality: "Why does the universe go to all the bother of existing?"[29]

But as proposed by Prof. Hawking this question is more rhetorical than philosophical. For he thinks that the truly unified and complete theory is not a usual theory. Otherwise his question, "Is the unified theory so compelling that it brings about its own existence?" would not be followed by questions in which rigor yields to flippancy: "Or does it need a creator, and, if so, does he [the Creator] have any other effect on the universe? And who created him?"[30] Flippancy stems not so much from the agnostic cosmologist's readiness to poke fun at the Creator, but from his inability to take seriously two points, his occasional lip-service to both notwithstanding. One is that the universe exists even when the cosmologist does not write esoteric equations about it. While those equations may marvelously account for all quantitative specificities of the universe, they suppose its existence instead of assuring it.

The other point is that the universe constitutes a true and specific totality of *all* consistently interacting things. Therefore if the cosmologist feels the urge to trace that totality to some other factor, he no longer does physics but metaphysics. For that other factor cannot be a thing that interacts with the universe in the manner of things. In all interactions among things a specific thing modifies the specificity of another while leaving intact the total specificity which as such reveals that it is but one of an immensely large number of conceivable specificities. Consequently, the cosmologist no longer addresses himself to physics when he defines, as does Prof. Hawking, the complete understanding of the universe as an answer to the questions: "Why it is as it is and why it exists at all?"[31] In raising such questions the cosmologist introduces a metaphysical question about the existence of a Creator who, by choosing one specific world, decides why the world becomes what it is, which is the reason it exists at all. If the cosmologist is ready to answer that metaphysical question, he forecloses any question about the Creator's creator unless he naively thinks that regress to infinity differs from endlessly postponing the answer.

Completeness with no laws

Hopeful assertions by cosmologists about a "complete" understanding of the universe almost invariably imply their belief that the universe is necessarily what it is and cannot be anything else. They should not take lightly such belief which, if taken consistently, would make good science impossible. Einstein hardly thought of this as he indulged in playing the role of scientific advisor to a Universe-God that had to obey his General Relativity and his Unified Field Theory.[32] Instead of profundity, naiveté blares forth from such utterances of his that what truly interested him was "whether God has any choice in the creation of the world,"[33] or if a physical theory contained something very simple "God [himself] could not have passed it up."[34]

Einstein's naiveté meant more than the superficiality of equating God with a universe that could not be created out of nothing. Had he reflected more on what physics can do, he would not have bogged down in the futile question about the understanding of the *how* of the creation of the universe. For if that *how* meant creation out of nothing, it could not be understood in terms of quantitative relations, the sole business of physics. And if that creation meant merely the tracing out of one specificity to another, let alone to an apriori set of simple equations, a mere play with the word "creation" was on hand. Most importantly, the "complete understanding of the universe" could imply a deadly threat to doing physics. For if the universe has to be what it is and cannot be any other than it appears on a patently apriori basis plausible to the theoretical physicist, then there remains no need for the physicist who experiments. Physicists still have to face up in full to this devastating consequence. Even an Einstein failed to realize fully the philosophical significance of his gut feeling for objective reality that made him give the last word to experiments and not to theory[35] whenever his avid pursuit of an ultimate theory ran up against plain facts.

That gut feeling was far weaker in Eddington who constructed philosophical reasons in support of his claim that the ultimate theory assures the existence of its object, the universe. His was an unabashed philosophical idealism, bordering on solipsism, with a tantalizing quantitative glamor. The latter shone through his derivation of the number of baryons (protons and neutrons) in the universe while he claimed to make no reference to physics and observations. The figure he gave as 2^{256} was remarkably close to 10^{70}, the figure estimated from the average density of matter in the universe in terms of General Relativity. With that figure on hand, he could, by correlating some basic physical constants, derive the ratio of the mass of proton and electron, and even the magnitude of the electron charge and other constants, such as the fine structure constant, or about 1/137, though not with complete exactness.[36]

Eddington could never convince others that his primary aim had been achieved on a truly a priori basis. The suspicion always remained strong that his was a lucky guess about 10^{70} being equal to 2^{256} where the exponent can be obtained by raising 2 to the 8th power. Even more debatable remained Eddington's claim that ten, the traditionally counted number of the mind's categories, demanded a repartition into 2 as base and 8 as exponent. To be sure, 2^8 had a mathematical form similar to the squaring of the fundamental numerical structure of quaternion algebra.[37] Such correspondence, however teasing, had no more to it than that surface glitter which numerical coincidences often carry with them. So much in a nutshell about the basic claim in Eddington's *Fundamental Theory* that the external world is isomorphous with the world of thought and that basic quantitative parameters of the latter determine the quantitative features of the former and indeed provide it with existence in a necessary way.

In the decades immediately following Eddington's death not a few physicists hoped to establish the necessary character of the existence of the universe with an eye on fundamental particle research. They looked for a system of those particles so simple as to provide assurance that no particles except those that would fit that system would ever be discovered. The success would have provided an end to the frustration which Oppenheimer once voiced in connection with the discovery of wholly unexpected particles: "These particles are not understood; they were not anticipated; no one had any idea that they would exist; they are not contained in any known theory . . . They go far beyond the framework of any speculation we had." Oppenheimer saw the wellspring of the physicist's efforts in the "faith that in this bewildering field of human experience, which is so new and so much more complicated than we thought even five years ago, there is a unique and necessary order." If however the order was not only unique, which it had to be if the universe was truly one, but also necessary, then a contradiction waited in the wings. It consisted in Oppenheimer's next remark that in the same order "the parts fit into a whole and that the whole requires the parts," though "we can [not] tell [it] a priori."[38] What this showed was the inconsistency of the physicist who, with an eye on experiments, renounced apriorism while as a theoretician he advocated cosmic necessitarianism.

More recently, hopes for a necessarily true ultimate scientific theory have been much strengthened by success along the unification of the various physical forces. The starting point, the Weinberg-Salam theory, is all the more noteworthy because Prof. Weinberg went on record with a telling statement about his ultimate motivation. He saw himself as a latter-day representative of "one of man's enduring hopes . . . to find a few simple general laws that would explain why nature, with all its seeming complexity and variety, is the way it is." Indeed, the hope has a very long history. A brief survey of that story — stretching from the Pythagoreans, through Plato, Aristotle, Plotinus, Descartes, Galileo, Newton, and Einstein to Eddington and beyond — would have revealed to Prof. Weinberg that the hope has more philosophical than scientific aspects. Philosophy was not, however, in sight as Prof. Weinberg gave his own special motivation. He found his research in fundamental particle physics, an enterprise very tedious in itself, a most rewarding activity because of the assurance that it is there that "we will find the ultimate laws of nature, the few simple general principles which determine why all nature is the way it is."[39]

When a physicist is so eager to find not only the way all things are, but also the reason why all things are the way they are, he is far more a philosopher, a metaphysician indeed, than a physicist. Moreover, he may trap himself in a pseudo-metaphysics most contrary to science, if he looks for an account of the universe that would show it to be a necessary or self-explaining entity, and not contingent on something beyond the realm of physics (*meta ta physika*) as its explanation. In vain would one argue with such a physicist about the pitfalls of his pursuit of a necessarily complete physical theory. From the pseudo-metaphysics of that pursuit he can easily slide into scepticism about the orderliness of the universe itself. The reason for this lies in the physicist's suspicion that his search for necessarily true laws may trap him in circularity. Then it becomes impossible for him to ascertain "where we are now," the title of a brief essay by Prof. Weinberg.

It is another matter whether the physicist will identify as the source of that impossibility the apriorism inherent in that pursuit. Apriorism is responsible for the intellectual confidence that sets the tone of the concluding paragraph of that essay: "In the last analysis, it seems to me that the best reason for believing in a deductive order of nature with its roots in particle physics is that it allows us to make sense in asking, not only *how* nature behaves, but *why* it behaves the way it does." But that confidence should seem unjustified not only in itself but especially in view of the scepticism that sets the tone of the preceding paragraph:

> I want to admit that the implicit background of what I have said here, a picture of the sciences branching out in logical order from particle physics, which itself has a few basic principles more or less like the principles of relativity and quantum mechanics, may be entirely wrong. Perhaps the logical tree isn't a tree at all, but something else, perhaps something with loops. For instance, according to a joke that went around when I was an undergraduate, the laws of nature are not fixed at all, but are revised from time to time by a committee of dead physicists in heaven. If so, then there is a logical circularity in nature, with particle physics following from defunct psychology, and vice versa. Who knows? More seriously, the laws of nature are discovered by human beings, and it may not be possible permanently to divorce the content of these laws from the psychology of their discoverers. Or perhaps there is no logical order to nature at all.[40]

When a physicist seriously entertains the possibility of a physical universe without order, he merely harvests the poisonous fruit of his avid pursuit of necessarily true laws. What he actually demonstrates is a glaring lack of philosophical sensitivity. Within that vacuum everything becomes senseless, that is, devoid of meaning and purpose. Not surprisingly, his survey of scientific cosmology made Prof. Weinberg conclude that the universe is meaningless and blinded him to the fact that no amount of science can justify such a conclusion.[41]

While the Greeks of old, attentive to the dictates of logic, branded such a conclusion as an elementary fallacy, a plain *metabasis eis allo genos*, few professors of logic have nowadays the same intellectual courage. They in fact seem to be unnerved when faced with prominent physicists who dress up in esoteric mathematics their unphilosophical claims about the exclusive validity of the scientific method in the quest for understanding. That method entitles no practitioner of it to make statements about meaning taken in an existential and ethical sense. Disregard for the strict limits of that method debases it to the level where a butterfly net is taken for a tool whereby angels may be caught. Deep as the net of physics is lowered, its catch consists only of the quantitative properties of things. Not physics but the physicist's common sense, a sort of basic philosophy, gives the assurance that those things have that marvelous property which is to *exist*.

Flying in the face of idealism

The mere fact that physicists shy away from philosophical or epistemological matters undercuts the promise of any discussion with them about the true merits of a necessarily true physical theory. Their solemn reference to the importance of philosophy turns into a hollow playing to the galleries as they fail to follow it up with at least a modest concern for basic philosophical questions about existence. The veneer of solemnity gives itself away when cavorting in paradoxes (that border on contradictoriness) goes hand in hand with invoking a vote on the crucial importance of philosophy. Not that

Prof. Wheeler made an error by quoting Thomas Mann's remark: "Science never makes an advance until philosophy authorizes and encourages it to do so."[42] Of course, the philosophy in question was not specified by Prof. Wheeler and one wonders whether Thomas Mann, a man of letters, ever cared to specify the one he had in mind. But the philosophy should appear very spurious if in the same breath there appears also Bohr's dictum that a "great truth is a truth whose opposite is also a great truth."[43] Does this mean that the great truth of democracy must be balanced with dictatorship as a great truth? Escape from dilemmas of this sort should seem rather easy when reality is sublimated into mere ideas. In fact such sublimation of the entire universe takes place when Prof. Wheeler declares that "some principle uniquely right and uniquely simple must, when one knows it, be so compelling that it is clear the universe is built, and must be built, in such and such way, and that it could not possibly be otherwise." Immediately preceding this statement, which is almost a direct contradiction of a famous dictum of Leibniz,[44] is another that could provide a firm basis for a fruitful philosophical discussion of the possible merits of that principle "uniquely right and uniquely simple." There Prof. Wheeler puts the enormous difference between mere equations and the real universe they describe, into an image which is classic in its simplicity as well as in its graphic character: "Not one of those equations will put on wings, take off, or fly. Yet the universe flies."[45]

In fact the universe does much more than "fly" and fly thereby in the face of idealism. Unlike those equations that are merely thoughts, the universe does exist, the very condition to do flying or anything else. This additional philosophical insight is not to be found in Prof. Wheeler's dicta so rich in daring conjectures and felicitous expressions, one of them being none other than the phrase, black holes. Worse, he urges us "to recognize that what we call existence consists of countably many iron

E

posts of observation between which we fill in by an elaborate papier-mâché construction of imagination and theory."[46] Actually he assigns no tangible reality even to those posts allegedly made of iron. For him they are but mere ideas because his real aim is to reduce all existence to the idea on which rests the ultimate self-explaining theory. The idea would make Planck's quantum appear as "an utterly simple— and when we see it — completely obvious idea." His next precept, "Explain existence by the same idea that explains the quantum,"[47] echoes the age-old presumption of idealist philosophers that physical reality and its quantitative specificity can be squeezed out of mere ideas.

If a physicist-cosmologist casts his lot with idealism, he rarely does so for a motivation that relates more to his work in physics than to his occasional encounter with philosophical authors. Such seems to be the case with Prof. Wheeler who offers as his last precept the fearful injunction: "Reduce time into subjugation to physics."[48] One wonders whether he pondered the lame retreat beaten by Einstein when faced with Bergson's remarks about the richness of time's reality.[49] It contains the reality of the *now*, the reality most universally and most crucially experienced by each and every man. That the *now* cannot be caught in the nets of physics deeply disturbed Einstein. As a result he should have had second thoughts about his agreement with Carnap that whatever the experienced richness of *now*, its being a mere "subjective experience" leaves intact the restriction of all truth to matters that can be reduced to physics, that is, to a set of quantities.[50]

This certainly shows that even a physicist of the stature of Einstein, and with his gut-feeling for reality, cannot really shake off the shackles of reductionism or physicalism or the infatuation with the quantitative method. It should therefore be futile to think that philosophical arguments would ever alert the physicist to a fateful prospect. His quest for an ultimate self-explaining theory can in fact destroy his grip on physical reality whether it is a mere iron post or that most metaphysical observational post which is the physical universe. The physicist could learn from a philosophy which is steeped in the real world, but such philosophy is incomprehensible to a physicist in search of that ultimate theory. For such a theory, if aimed at the elimination of the contingency of the universe, invariably leads to the sublimation of the real, so indispensable for the physicist, into mere ideas. One therefore has to turn to mathematics, for which such a physicist has an unbounded admiration. Needless to say, no recourse will be made to mathematics as if it could be a direct access to physical reality. Yet mathematics may be effective in cutting to size undue expectations about its ability to handle mere ideas.

Gödel's shadow

About that effectiveness an actual case relates to Prof. Murray Gell-Mann, a Nobel-laureate physicist. As one of a six-member panel on modern cosmology, he assured in October 1976 an audience over 2000 strong that within a few months, but certainly within a few years, he would come up with a theory of fundamental particles that would show why matter is what it is and cannot be something else.[51] As one of the panel I objected to his claim on the ground that it cannot be reconciled with Gödel's theorems of the incompleteness of mathematics. To my astonishment, and also to the astonishment of another member of the panel, a well known philosopher from Harvard,[52] Prof. Gell-Mann reacted as if he had never heard before of Gödel. Two months later I gave a lecture in Boston on cosmology and mentioned Gödel's theorems. After the lecture somebody from the audience walked up to me and said that he had just heard somewhere in the Midwest a lecture by Prof. Gell-Man who referred to Gödel's theorems as proof that an ultimate self-explaining theory of matter, or of the universe, for that matter, is unrealizable.

Of course, such an ultimate theory is unrealizable only if it is presented not merely as a factually true theory, but as a necessarily true theory. If the physical universe is truly a universe, that is, a totality of consistently interacting things, it embodies a specific set of mathematics which in principle can be found by the human mind. Such a possibility, justified by the foregoing philosophical definition of the universe and by the equally philosophical assumption that the human mind can know the real universe, is further strengthened for those who accept biblical revelation. There, in the Book of Wisdom, to be specific, it is stated that God arranged everything according to measure, number and weight,[53] or along mathematical parameters. Clearly the universe is the very opposite to being mysterious, the perhaps a million or so copies of Sir James Jeans' *The Mysterious Universe* notwithstanding. For, if according to him, modern physics shows God to be a mathematician,[54] why should not His handiwork, the universe, have all the clarity mathematics can provide? The only restriction on such a universe is that it cannot take from mathematics or from physics the clarity of the ultimate reason for being what it is.

For all the clarity mathematics can provide, it cannot provide all clarity conceivable. This is the very point of Gödel's incompleteness theorems. According to them no non-trivial set of arithmetic propositions can contain the proof of its consistency. Those aware of the fundamental role played by arithmetic in all mathematics will have no difficulty seeing the bearing of those theorems on mathematics in general. From almost the day when Gödel's paper appeared in 1931,[55] leading mathematicians, who had been working on an ultimate theory of mathematics, felt their fondest hopes were dashed.[56]

When such an emotion-filled reaction occurs, much more may be at stake than a mere love-affair with mathematics, and especially when the mathematics in question is supposed to be its ultimate form. For such a mathematics cannot be divested from its bearing on a physical universe that so readily yields its secrets to particular mathematical formalisms.[57] When therefore a mathematician addresses himself to the philosophy of his field, he will almost of necessity utter statements whose instructiveness bears watching. A case in point is H. Weyl's declaration that "the objective world simply *is*, it does not *happen*. Only to the gaze of my consciousness, crawling upward along the life line of my body, does a section of this world come to life as a fleeting image in space which continuously changes in time."[58]

As a champion of an essentially timeless, unchanging universe, Spinoza would have watched with approval. He would also have agreed that an apparently innocuous, yet utterly decisive difference can be carried by two such trivial verbs as *is* and *happens*. When emphatically used, *is* can serve as the most proper name of God, HE WHO IS. As to *happens*, if not used facetiously, it conveys most forcefully the very essence of contingence. Not only everyday things, that only a minute ago have not been on hand, *do happen*, but the entire universe too *had to happen* if it came into existence out of nothing at the command of Existence itself. Were Spinoza alive he would also note that taking the realm of ideas for the realm of genuine experience is the best way of securing for the universe the aura of uncreatedness. As one fond of idealist philosophy, Prof. Weyl could sense the blow delivered by Gödel's theorems to that realm. But precisely because of his fondness for that philosophy he was bound to miss its bearing on the limits of man's understanding of a universe which is more than a universe of ideas. In his *The Philosophy of Mathematics and of Natural Science*, none of his half a dozen references to Gödel are part of the chapter there on the *physical* picture of the world.

Pragmatists and empiricist philosophers of science were of necessity slow in taking stock of Gödel's theorems. Logical positivists positively resisted them. In vain did Carnap call again and again the attention of his colleagues in the Vienna Circle to the fact that their aim of achieving complete, that is, self-explaining systematization of all knowledge had no solid foundation.[59] Physicists and cosmologists dreaming about an ultimate theory still have to catch up. Long as Gödel's shadow may be, it is far from being long enough. It certainly has not yet penetrated the realm of best-selling high level popularizations of scientific cosmology. Absence of reference to Gödel in Prof. Hawking's book and in other similar books suggests that nothing, or practically nothing, is being said about Gödel's theorems in leading departments of astronomy and fundamental particle physics. No wonder. For as long as those places remain animated by Prof. Hawking's or others' pursuit of an ultimate cosmological theory, Gödel's theorems can only create an awful resentment. For as long as those theorems remain valid — and so far every effort aimed at showing their invalidity has conspicuously failed — ultimate cosmological theories may be true, but never necessarily true. A necessarily true theory that cannot contain the proof of its own consistency should seem a contradiction in terms. From this follows the chief bearing of Gödel's theorems on cosmology, namely, that the contingency of the cosmos cannot be contradicted. My repeated presentations of this aspect of Gödel's theorems, although offered repeatedly now over twenty years in books by prominent publishing houses,[60] have created hardly an echo.[61] Undoubtedly a future historian will be puzzled, may even look for reasons, and will be even more puzzled, if not indignant, on spotting some of these reasons.

One of these "reasons" may be a dark shadow cast on reason itself. Some philosophers have in fact created the fashion to see in those theorems a proof that truth has no better status than falsity. They received encouragement from prominent mathematicians. One of them, André Weil, said with an eye on Gödel's theorems that "God exists, since mathematics is consistent, and the Devil exists, since we cannot prove it."[62] The comment on this by a noted philosopher had that agnostic evasiveness which would have infuriated Mrs. Hawking. "It might therefore be said that he [Gödel] has clinched the case for Satan's existence. For surely, if mathematics *isn't* consistent we can hardly prove that it *is*. So Satan wins either way. God, on the other hand, may not fare so well; for should mathematics not be consistent, we would have to look to another aspect of His infinite bounty for proof of His existence." To this the same philosopher added: "These are heady matters, dark doings, and I do not propose to discourse on the present state of mathematical theology. I only raise them to give an indication of how far-reaching the philosophical consequences of Gödel's incompleteness theorems might be."[63]

The basic meaning of Gödel's theorems
Such is indeed a matter so serious as to raise the specter of an inevitable intellectual confusion about the ultimate fate of man's efforts to understand himself as well as the universe. It would therefore be imperative to seek whether that confusion comes from Gödel's incompleteness theorems, or from an initial misstep in reasoning that has nothing to do with those theorems. To search for that possible misstep is all the more appropriate because it is latent in all so-called ultimate and necessarily true cosmological theories.

The misstep is the illusion that the first step in reasoning need not necessarily be taken before taking all other steps. This will not be conceded by those who suffer under the illusion that reality can be understood in terms of mere ideas, including the idea of reality. No wonder they never get to reality, be it the object of their daily lives or of scientific cosmology itself. They at most wonder why they are caught in a posture not different from that of nervous animals trying to catch their own tails. Of course some tails are more attractive than others and the tales or stories of mathematics or mathematical physics can be attractive to the point of being plainly treacherous.

Gödel's theorems state the futility of the chasing of one's intellectual tail, although they do not forewarn about the treacherousness of that enterprise taken for the ultimate intellectual enterprise. Gödel himself thought that idealism is a good antidote to logical positivism or empiricism.[64] It was for that very reason that he entertained the possibility of deriving the true theory of the cosmos out of mere ideas.[65] This is why he failed to note that his theorems have nothing to say on the all important point whether in knowing reality consistency is the first step or whether it can be logically looked for only after one has made that very first step which is a real knowledge of reality. That knowledge of reality cannot be understood in terms of something else. It is that first step without which any other intellectual step will keep hanging in mid-air.

Further, if one does not explicitly accept one's knowledge of external reality as a primary datum, one will readily find in the glitter of mathematical physics a justification for taking mere ideas for the first step in reasoning about the real. The result will be the flippant ease with which leading cosmologists speak about reality as if it were primarily a matter of knowing co-ordinate systems. They care not for the enormous penalty to be paid for such facile games with reality. The price consists in losing hold of the co-ordination of data insofar as they relate to reality. For unless one takes one's certainty of the immediately perceived reality as the primary safe ground, no ground will be left for safely retaining any reality, let alone the reality of the universe. Then the universe will become one of those flashy tricks of which any number can be pulled at will from under very clever hats, a cosmic voodooism in scientific garb to be discussed in detail in the next chapter.

To keep with the thrust of these chapters, the parting shot at those ultimate and necessarily true theories of the universe should not be philosophical, let alone theological, but quantitative. Let it be assumed for the sake of argument that a theory does indeed explain everything in the physical world. Further let it also be assumed in an incredibly generous mood that no discovery will be made in the succeeding centuries or millennia that would conflict with that theory. Still that theory would have to include specific numerical data, such as the values of the basic constants of nature. Sweeping and utterly simple as that theory may appear, it would therefore still remain a specific theory. As such it would be just one out of a great many specific theories and therefore a pointer toward cosmic contingency. The specificity of that theory would not disappear even if those constants, that is, their numerical values, would be reducible to one another, say in terms of a number theory generating only those numerical values. For even in that case one still would have to reckon with the quantitative specificity of that theory or function. Of course, that reckoning would not be mathematical but philosophical.

To sum up, for those cosmologists who still think that Gödel's shadow is not long enough to touch them, for those cosmologists who do not want to recognize the fatal chinks in their search for the ultimate and necessarily true theory of the universe, for them there remains one ultimate and irremovable factor which will keep raising the question made famous by Leibniz: why this and not other? Nobel-laureates may hide their unphilosophical resistance to that factor in the glitter of their status but in doing so they offer not argument but glorified academic propaganda. As will be seen in the next chapter, that factor remains impervious to the most misplaced sophistications now making the rounds in scientific cosmology. In defiance of all sane thinking, spokesmen of that sophistication view the creation of the

real universe as a mere tunnelling out of specious speculations that rest on an elementary fallacy in interpreting
the bearing of the best available physics on basic physical processes.

Chapter Five

TURTLES AND TUNNELS

I have a bit of FIAT in my soul,
And can myself create my little world

T. L. Beddoes, *Death's Jest Book*

Notorious turtles and unnoticeable tunnels

Turtles entered cosmology several thousand years ago. According to ancient Hindu lore, the world is resting on the back of a tiger that stands on an elephant which in turn is supported by a turtle. In one way or another, the turtle is imagined to be self-supporting. This story must have been in the mind of that little old lady who went to hear a prominent cosmologist lecture on the stellar universe. She became legendary because her story, apparently true, has been retold many times and in the process has taken on some graphic details, such as that she wore shabby tennis shoes, perhaps a symbol of her resilience. What the cosmologist said is not recorded, but he obviously must have spoken of immense spaces, intangible nets of world-lines and the like that can easily create the impression that the universe hangs in mid-air. Something like this must have been in the mind of our legendary little lady and she was not pleased at all. When the scientist took some questions after the lecture, she walked up to him, wagged her finger and said with a shrill voice: "Excuse me, sir, but you've got it all wrong. The truth is that the universe is sitting on the back of a huge turtle." "Oh really?" the cosmologist asked. "Well, tell me, what is the turtle standing on?" The little lady was ready with the reply: "Oh, it's standing on another turtle." The cosmologist asked again: "And what is *that* turtle standing on?" Her reply came promptly: "Another turtle." The cosmologist began to repeat his former question, but she stopped him in mid-sentence: "Save your breath, sonny," she said. "It's turtles all the way down."[1]

Compared with turtles, tunnels are Johnny-come-latelies in cosmology. They entered cosmology through the expression alpha-tunnelling, a staple phrase in physics textbooks by the 1940s. There the phrase is often tied to the name of George Gamow, the first to give, in 1928, a quantitative treatment to the emission of alpha particles from atomic nuclei. In Gamow's letter to the editor of *Nature*, that brought to the English-speaking world his famous application of quantum mechanics to alpha radiation,[2] the word tunnelling does not occur. Instead, Gamow spoke of "the gradual leaking out" of alpha particles through the potential barrier which is formed by the very short-range force holding the nucleus together. Quantum mechanics provided the perspective, as Gamow put it, in which the alpha particle could be seen "to penetrate the potential barrier even if its energy is less than the maximum opposing potential."[3]

That Gamow did not speak of the alpha particle's climbing over the potential barrier but rather of penetrating it was a telltale sign that he had the idea of tunnelling in the back of his mind. Indeed, although the expression "tunnelling" was still to enter quantum mechanics, the idea was in the air. An indication of this is a letter that two Princeton physicists, Ronald W. Gurney and Edward U. Condon, communicated on alpha emission to *Nature* a few months earlier. Gurney and Condon described the area enclosed by the potential barrier as a valley, the barrier itself as a mountain, and the escape of the alpha particle as a "slipping through the mountain."[4]

Gurney and Condon, no less than Gamow, must have been groping for the word tunnelling. This word can indeed convey by itself the gist of the twist quantum mechanics gave to our understanding of the emission of alpha particles and of immensely much more. Gurney and Condon sufficiently adumbrated that gist in their final remark: "Much has been written of the explosive violence with which the alpha particle is hurled from its place in the nucleus. But from the process pictured above, one would rather say that the alpha particle slips away almost unnoticed."[5] Whatever one may read with the wisdom of hindsight into the phrase, "slips away almost unnoticed," it would have been rather difficult to picture as unnoticed, or almost unnoticed, the passing of an alpha particle *over* the potential barrier. Climbing over a fence or over a mountain carries with itself the idea of clear detectability.

As to the expression, "almost unnoticed," it should have struck by its studied vagueness. In the late 1920s reliance on a purportedly inexact expression could still be seen as a strategy more befitting philosophers than physicists. The latter, for the most part, loved to appear at that time as the cultivators of the most exact form of natural science.[6] Yet before long a leader of them, Niels Bohr, notorious for his obscure style, stated with no embarrassment that he could not speak more clearly than he thought.[7] In retrospect, nothing can be clearer than the crucial role Bohr played in laying the conceptual basis of the process whereby the studied vagueness connected with "alpha tunnelling" took on cosmic dimensions. One should look in this light at the innocuous looking expression "almost unnoticed." It anticipated much that has become the core of the physicists' use of the word "tunnelling." In addition, the phrase "almost unnoticed" was symbolic too. Its enormous philosophical instructiveness has remained largely unnoticed up to now, although it bears on no less an object of man's understanding than the universe itself.

Gurney and Condon would have been more correct, and also more in keeping with the latest in quantum mechanics, had they simply written that within the perspectives of quantum mechanics the alpha particle *may appear* to slip away almost unnoticed. For when a physicist simply says that something is almost unnoticed, he runs the risk of saying something equivalent to the facetious remark about a woman being "almost" pregnant.

Physicists have been willing to run even worse risks as demonstrated by the radical reversal of their appraisal of the status of the ether early this century. Throughout the two centuries of Newtonian physics, the ether stood for the most evident material entity although it could "almost" appear a mere inference. Maxwell merely echoed a long tradition when in 1872 he declared in the famous 9th edition of the Encyclopedia Britannica that the "ether was the largest and most evident body of which we have knowledge."[8] Yet nobody ever observed the ether. Indirect evidence of its existence failed to come through the continual improvements of the Michelson-Morley experiment which made the ether the *par excellence* "almost observable entity" one could think of. Still, physicists quickly turned their backs on the ether as if it did not and could not exist. They had some good reasons but the weakest of them was experimental, namely, the persistently null result of the Michelson-Morley experiment.

Quite different logic operated in their espousal of alpha-tunnelling with its non-existent tunnels and particles that were not almost but absolutely unobservable as they were tunnelling. The logic appeared in its full consequences when in the early winter of 1928, Gamow, already famous at 24, gave a lecture on alpha emission before the Royal Society of London. Following the lecture R. H. Fowler, a leading British expert on atomic spectra, put in a graphic manner the gist of Gamow's theory, namely, that in wave mechanics there are no impenetrable barriers: "Anyone present in this room has a finite chance of leaving it without opening the door, or, of course, without being thrown out through the window."[9] The condition not spelled out by Fowler was that as the physicist passed through the door, he was strictly unobservable and the big hole through which he passed or tunnelled was also unobservable, and therefore non-existent as far as physics was concerned. That no such mystery-mongering is part of the only story about passing through closed doors that has stubbornly maintained itself now for almost 2000 years may seem a chief factor in its favor.

As a physicist Fowler had no right to say that there were no impenetrable barriers. Quantum mechanics or not, this statement is ontological and as such beyond the reach of the methods of physics, classical or modern. Fowler should have rather said that quantum mechanics as a statistical operation accounts for alpha emission in the sense of giving average counts about it, the least philosophical form of accounting for anything. Moreover, there is a price to pay for that accounting. Taken in itself the price may seem enormous as it consists in a deliberate and methodical oversight of questions about the reality of the energy barrier. It should have appeared such even when measured against the successful calculation of the average number of alpha particles that appeared in a cloud chamber or on a scintillation screen within a given time. For an essential part of the new type of calculation was that individual events must be ignored. Once reality, which is always individual, however replete it may be with universal meaning, was allowed to be enveloped in the shiny nebulosity of probabilities, the philosophical conscience of the physicists could become almost completely pacified.

Laying of mines under the cosmic citadel
In an age when almost any play with truth is condoned until one is caught in the mischief, almost perfectly innocent could seem the game which the quantum mechanical explanation of alpha-tunnelling implied about reality. In that perspective the alpha particle is strictly

unobservable as it slips through the mountain or tunnels under it. Therefore if unobservability means non-existence, the existence of the alpha particle should be taken to be interrupted for the time of its tunnelling. This inference was not perhaps drawn in view of the extreme "smallness" of the mischief, namely, the very short time which the tunnelling takes. Yet the difference between "existing" and "non-existing" should seem strictly infinite, infinitesimally short as may be its duration. At any rate, no doubt arose about the reality of those tunnels that must exist if alpha particles pass along them, although no physicist ever thought those tunnels were observable. Yet, if the physicist claims the liberty of taking tunnels for mere metaphors, he should grant a similar measure of poetical liberty to his critics. As will be seen, there is more to the foregoing critical remarks about tunnels than slipping back into metaphors based on long-discredited mechanical models.

What should the physicist, respectful of logic, do when he has on hand a marvelous computational technique, quantum mechanics, which is also a technique that implies the impossibility of certain observations? He should simply say aloud that his use of probability functions bars him from making statements about reality as such. To admit this demands, however, a great deal of intellectual humility. The very last thing a human being would grant is that his method, spectacular as it may be, cannot be applied to concrete individual reality apart from which reality is a mere abstraction. Indeed, modern physicists have not been eager to recall Maxwell's words that "one of the severest tests of a scientific mind is to discern the legitimate application of the scientific method."[10] Maxwell would turn in his grave on hearing an Einstein (to say nothing of physicists of lesser stature), who owed him so much, take that method for the sole source of objective knowledge and reduce the noblest, most sacred and most indispensable principles of human life, individual and social, to the level of mere subjective experiences.[11] No wonder that most physicists took the easy way out when their method brought them face to face with reality as such. For over half a century they have been merrily falling back on innocent looking adverbs, such as "almost" and "slightly," whereby they pour soothing oil on conceptually troubled waters. Steady recourse to purely palliative methods is, however, bound to weaken sensitivity to a situation which, in the long run, would reveal an explosive character.

Tunnels, it is worth noting, have repeatedly served for placing explosives under the nerve center of the enemy's defenses. One such incident forms the high point of a historical novel by a Hungarian author about the siege laid by the Turks in 1552 on the fortress of Eger in north-central Hungary.[12] From a distance of over fifty years, I still feel something of the almost unbearable suspense as one waits for the answer to the big question: would or would not the defenders notice that a tunnel is being bored right under their citadel? They detected it but only by being exceedingly watchful. They shut out all noise from the citadel's deepest cellar where they held their ears against drums that would amplify the sound of digging and boring deep below.

The story matches the story to be unfolded in this lecture though not without a twist. Unlike in that Hungarian story, where the boring of the tunnel is done by enemies, in the story riveted on alpha-tunnelling the potentially destructive operation was started by insiders, that is, physicists themselves, and perfected by them as the years and decades went by. In fact, most physicist-cosmologists take it for a supreme achievement that the tunnelling has now reached under that citadel of physics which is the scientific understanding of the universe itself. They maintain their euphoria in spite of the fact that in the process the universe may appear to be blown into incoherent pieces, or may simply appear the mere by-product of the physicists' thinking, a blissful wallowing in incoherence such a thinking may be.

It would have, of course, been superhuman to foresee in 1928 such cosmic consequences for a misguided interpretation of alpha-tunnelling as accounted for by quantum mechanics. Even two decades or so later Einstein (and a very few other prominent physicists) still had suspected no such consequences as they deplored the "dangerous game" which the "Copenhagen people" were playing with reality.[13] Nor did those in Copenhagen, such as Bohr and Heisenberg, have cosmology in mind as they rejected in the name of quantum mechanics any concern about reality as such, that is, about ontology, as unscientific and unphilosophical, to be avoided at all cost in physics.[14] Yet if modern scientific cosmology has reached the point where it may be deprived of its very object, the universe, it is because the champions of the Copenhagen philosophy of quantum mechanics, hardly ever distinguished from the science of quantum mechanics, have succeeded in selling the idea that doing very good science justifies doing philosophy very badly.

About that Copenhagen philosophy it is still widely believed that its origins postdate the publication in April 1927 of Heisenberg's famous paper with the uncertainty relation in it.[15] According to that relation there is an inherent limitation to the accuracy that can be achieved in measurements. The limitation, of no consequence in everyday measurements, is noticeable on the atomic level and even more so as deeper and deeper levels of matter, that is, particles much smaller than atomic dimensions, are under investigation. From this Heisenberg immediately jumped to the conclusion that causality thereby had definitely been disproved.[16] Heisenberg should have rather warned that the principle of uncertainty had a permanent validity only on the suppositions that Planck's quantum would forever remain a quantum that cannot be divided, and that non-commutative algebra too would forever remain indispensable in dealing with atomic and subatomic phenomena.

This is not to suggest that even today there are any signs about a need to revise those suppositions. Yet had that potential revisability been pointed out by Heisenberg, he would have merely recalled a basic truth about physics which is the revisability of any of its theories, however successful. With that revisability in focus, physicists might have also been awakened to the all-important fact that physical theory is not about "being" as such, or ontology, but only about the quantitative aspects of things already existing. When a physicist does not see this, he puts himself on that intellectual skidrow that may land him in plain sorcery with words.

Heisenberg could hardly foresee sorcery being hatched as he wrote up his famous paper, although he relied there on a sleight-of-hand with philosophy as its victim. That very few objected[17] merely showed the widespread belief that in doing philosophy it was more important to satisfy the prevailing consensus, if not plain mood, rather than the dictates of elementary logic. Heisenberg's sleight-of-hand reflected the widely shared assumption that causality in a physical process depended on its exact measurability. The assumption was the fruit of the philosophical impoverishment that had been growing in the Western mind in the measure in which it had been overawed by the quantitative successes of physics.

Had Heisenberg sensed something about the inherent limitations of the method of physics, he would have refrained from stating that the inability of the physicists to measure nature exactly showed the inability of nature to act exactly. He would have needed only a modicum of philosophical sensitivity to note that the apparent truth of the foregoing statement depended on taking the same word, "exactly," in two different meanings: one operational, the other ontological. His confusion about those two different meanings meant an indulging in that elementary fallacy which the Greeks of old called *metabasis eis allo genos*. That fallacy was duly pointed out in courses in introductory logic that were part of exams in philosophy without which no doctor's degree in any subject could be granted in German universities when Heisenberg received his own in 1925.

Unscientific roots of the onslaught on causality

As a university student Heisenberg was far from being tuned to be impressed with elementary logic. According to his own recollections he was, during his first two years (1920-22) at the University of Munich, torn between two worlds. One was physics, the other was the Youth Movement (Jugendbewegung) about which Heisenberg mentions only its name. It drew its inspiration from such leaders of antiintellectualism as Ludwig Klages, Herman Keyserling, Rudolf Steiner, and Oswald Spengler, so many champions of the Lebensphilosophie of postwar years. There causality and exact science figured as the chief combination that produces cultural decay. Spengler could but strike responsive chords in the Movement whose leader had declared in November 1918 that some professions were "without value for a future community and its plans to conquer the world." At the head of the list was physics, followed by chemistry, engineering, and medicine,[18] all hard sciences where wishful thinking had little role to play. Young Heisenberg must have heard an earful about causality (physics) versus life in the Movement with which he fully identified. He comprises much in his admission that his participation in the Movement was no less complete than his dedication to physics: "Both worlds were so filled with intense activity that I was often in a state of great agitation, the more so as I found it difficult to shuttle between the two."[19]

Being so much part of the Movement, he could but lend willing ears to reports about how leading physicists were coming to some principal points advocated in Lebensphilosophie. Wilhelm Wien, who prior to and during World War I most intensely promoted the industrial utilization of physics-research, began to strike a very different note after it was over. Then in widely pub-licized lectures he described physics as a "craving for understanding," an expression with a clear touch of Lebensphilosophie.[20] In this turnabout exemplified by Wien sociological factors played a part. In the years immediately following Germany's defeat, German phys-icists, until then the toast of society, became the target of resentment. Military defeat was taken by many as the fruit of the cold Faustian attitude toward life, society, and nature, an attitude culminating in the work of physi-cists. To defend themselves and their profession, promi-nent German physicists began to speak about a better understanding of physics with room there for human values. Especially eager were they about restoring intel-lectual respectability to human freedom by softening up strict determinism in physical processes as demanded by the methods of physics.

Leading physicists and mathematicians, such as Sommerfeld (Heisenberg's mentor at the University of Munich) and von Mises, began to borrow from Spengler as they tried to present a more human form of physics. References to Spengler in increasing number by such physicists as Born, Einstein, Exner, Weyl, and Wien meant anything but an answer to the abuses that Spengler poured on mathematics and physics in the first and sixth chapters of his *Decline of the West*, first pub-lished in 1919 and reprinted over 30 times during the next five years.

The crisis mentality articulated by Spengler received a powerful boost when at the same time prominent Ger-man physicists sounded off about a crisis in physics. One can easily imagine the resonance in young Heisen-berg as he heard, still a member of the Movement, of Einstein's paper "On the Present Crisis in Theoretical Physics," dated August 1922.[21] In the storm center of the crisis of physics stood causality, a principle openly repu-diated by the summer of 1921 by Exner, Weyl, von Mises, Schottky, Nernst and several lesser figures. A year later

Schrödinger disavowed causality in his inaugural lecture at the University of Zurich. If not in the Movement, then certainly in the department of physics of the University of Munich, these developments could not fail to come to young Heisenberg's attention and receive his full sympathy.

Such details should create strong doubts about the "purely scientific" reasons that made Heisenberg and many other physicists part with causality. Of course, neither of the two forms of causality they parted with had a serious tie with reality. One of them, the Kantian notion of causality as an a priori category of the mind, represented a conceptual imposition on a reality that as a noumenon could not be known anyhow. Severed from reality, those categories (with causality among them) did not appear something precious to be kept when the construction of the first non-Euclidean geometries in the early 19th century challenged Kant's claims about the a priori truth of three-dimensional perception. The latter became a direct target when General Relativity showed the successful application of a four-dimensional manifold to the real cosmos. And so did the category of causality. Or, as Max Born put it as early as November 1919 and in the pages of the *Frankfurter Allgemeine Zeitung*: "No one who followed closely the development of relativity theory can dispose of doubts about the a priori character of the other categories of thought as well."[22]

Reality could be of no serious concern to those physicists who under the impact of Heisenberg's work parted with the notion of causality that Mach had by then made popular among them for over four decades. In his *The Analysis of Sensations and the Relation of the Physical to the Psychological* Mach noted that already in 1872 he had "proposed to replace the old traditional conception of causality as something perfectly rigid by the mathematical conception of function — that is to say, by the conception of the dependence of phenomena on one another, or, more accurately, the dependence of the characteristics of phenomena on one another." Not that Mach cared to unfold the full meaning of that "old traditional conception." He saw in it a simplistic reduction of all possible forms of mechanical causes to merely four, represented by the four elements, adding that "a sort of primitive, pharmaceutical conception of the universe is expressed in this view" insofar as "a dose of effect follows one dose of cause."[23]

Mach would have been the last to let that "old traditional conception" conjure up its true content, ontology, which he took for metaphysics identical to fetishism. In Mach's case too, science provided the rebuttal and much sooner than he could expect in 1906 when he saw through press the fifth edition of his book. By then Einstein had begun work on General Relativity that made untenable Mach's remark in the same context: "Though it may be possible to complete in detail the picture of the world in a scientifically determined manner when a sufficient part of the world is given, yet science cannot tell us what the total result of the world process will be."[24] For it is that total that had become the object of modern scientific cosmology which in turn was made possible by General Relativity.

Physicists who had entertained either the Kantian or the Machist notion of causality could have no compunction about Heisenberg's dismissal of causality in terms of the uncertainty relation even if Heisenberg had cared to refer to ontology. In particular, as a mere mathematical function, the Machist notion of causality readily lent itself to its statistical reformulation as demanded by quantum mechanics. In taking Heisenberg's principle for a final disproof of causality, no qualms could be felt by physicists in the Anglo-Saxon world where empiricism and pragmatism had for some time discredited questions about ontology. Leading physicists with a gut-feeling for reality failed to see the point at issue. While Planck quickly perceived that the Machist interpretation of science threatens confidence in the reality of a causally interconnected universe,[25] he invariably equated ontological causality with the possibility of perfectly accurate measurements. Again, whereas in his three-decade-long dispute with Max Born, Einstein often came to the defense of reality as such,[26] he never perceived what he really wanted to defend. Nor is it likely that he would have been told about it as bluntly by W. Pauli as the latter put the matter to Born in a letter written on March 31, 1954, in a room or two away from Einstein's own in the Institute for Advanced Study in Princeton.

Pauli's letter[27] began with his remark that he was "unable to recognize Einstein whenever you [Born] talked about him in either your letter or your manuscript." It seemed to Pauli that Born "erected and knocked down with great pomp a dummy Einstein." Then Pauli noted that Einstein in his conversations with him had often cautioned against taking "the concept of 'determined' to be as fundamental as it is frequently held to be." Einstein's point of departure, Pauli argued, is "realistic rather than 'deterministic' which means that his philosophical prejudice is a different one." Pauli's use of the word "prejudice" was more applicable to his own views on philosophy. He first gave about Einstein's train of thought a lengthy summary in which quantum mechanical technicalities dominated as if they had been decisive in a radically philosophical problem. This was, of course, partly justified by Einstein's own misjudgment of the real question. The latter was not the exact measurability of the really existing but the intellectual act of recognizing what exists really. Pauli himself failed to see this difference and therefore could not perceive the real reason why the notion of determinism, so readily identified by physicists with completely accurate measurability, should not be brought into the dispute between Born and Einstein. The crucial paragraph of Pauli's letter remains a priceless testimony about leading physicists' flippant way of thinking about ontology and of their instinctive confusion about knowing a thing with their ability to measure it exactly:

> As O. Stern [Nobel-laureate physicist] said recently, one should no more rack one's brain about the problem of whether something one cannot know anything about exists all the same, than about the ancient question of how many angels are able to sit on the point of a needle. But it seems to me that Einstein's questions are ultimately of this kind.[28]

Einstein's arguments on behalf of a reality existing even when not observed amounted to no more than graphic phrases and gestures.[29] He thought to the end that what he meant to be ontological causality, but which he never called such, could only be saved if perfectly accurate measurements were at least in principle possible. The chief failure of his famous thought-experiment with a clock on a spring scale was not that it did not work but that it granted a reduction of the ontologically exact to exact measurability. He could not, of course, expect from Bohr, who refuted that thought-experiment, to be reminded of that reduction since it was a principle with Bohr to avoid any reference to ontology as such.[30]

The uncertainty principle as burglar's tool

With the preconception of reducibility to accurate measurements being so much in the focus of attention, a most obvious pointer to ontology failed to be exploited. The failure should seem all the more tantalizing as the pointer was Heisenberg's own uncertainty principle, usually written as $\Delta x.\Delta p \gtreqless h$ (Planck's quantum divided by 2π). The pointer could have been spotted, though only with true sensitivity for real mass or matter. Written as m, real matter becomes a glaring part of the uncertainty principle if the latter is written in its equivalent form $\Delta E.\Delta t \gtreqless h$ or $\Delta mc^2.\Delta t \gtreqless h$. Since c or the speed of light is invariable, there will necessarily be on hand an uncertainty in measuring m or mass. That uncertainty will appear an ontological mass-defect if one is ready to see through the sophism on which rests the entire Copenhagen philosophy of quantum mechanics and the most recent phase of modern scientific cosmology. The sophism consists in the reduction of "exact" existence to "exact" measurability, while paying no attention to using, in the same breath, the word "exact" in two very different senses, the one ontological, the other operational.

Of course, only if one is agitated as Hamlet was about the difference between to be and not to be, will one be truly upset by not keeping the books of physics properly balanced. No such reaction can as a rule be expected in this modern culture of ours. There it has become a sign of sophistication to treat with a condescending smile the very source from which pre-Enlightenment Western culture derived its sensitivity for the real. The source is not Greek culture or philosophy, which found itself all too often oscillating between epistemological extremes. There the real was banished either to the realm of illusions or to that of disembodied ideas. Nor could the Greek mind prevent the Aristotelian realist middle ground from being misused for the purposes of aprioristic deductions about nature that cast doubt on man's ability to know the real world. The source of abiding concern for reality in pre-Enlightenment Western culture was that biblical revelation in which God revealed His name as He Who Is or ontology incarnate[31] and in which God's very Logos becomes a flesh and blood reality. Once that source was abandoned, reality became expendable whatever the endless lip-service, scientific or not, given to it.

As parts of that post-Enlightenment indifference to ontology, physicists felt no compelling reason to balance their books as they started working with Heisenberg's uncertainty principle. At first the imbalance could seem wholly negligible. The typical uncertainty in measuring the time and energy of an alpha particle did not involve more than a trillionth of its mass, in itself an exceedingly small quantity. While from the practical viewpoint such a quantity could readily be written off, there lay beneath that pragmatic attitude a logic of fearful consequences.

It is an old story that most of those getting into the habit of petty thefts will have the threshold of their moral sensitivity gradually lowered. With enough practice and time they can readily turn into professional thieves. Those responsible for the great train robbery were not newcomers to the art of taking liberties with alien property. If they had any anxiety, it was much less about the morality of the enterprise than about the physical risks involved in it. Moral anxiety can become practically extinguished when the art of theft is being handed down from generation to generation.

An illustration of all this is on hand in the claims of the proponents of the so-called inflationary theory of the universe as well as in the wide acclaim accorded to them, or inversely, in the almost complete absence of protest within and without the scientific community. The core of those claims is nothing less than the spontaneous tunnelling of the entire universe, nay of countless universes, through that infinitely high energy barrier that separates the "nothing" from what really exists. Compared with this robbery on a truly cosmic scale the great train robbery may seem the puniest of petty thefts.

The proponents of the inflationary theory are younger physicists. They did their undergraduate and graduate work in an intellectual milieu in which the Copenhagen interpretation of quantum mechanics had been for some time that very air which nobody asks about, let alone dares to question. About the true origin of that interpretation and the occasional qualms it prompted, they lacked that personal information which their teachers, educated in the late 1940s and early 1950s, could gain through direct reports about clashes between Einstein and Bohr, and the camps, very uneven numerically, led by those two. Moreover, whatever there was researched about that origin, it usually reflected the security of firmly established victorious troops. Mental perplexities were recalled to have tortured only those in the Einstein camp, advanced in years by the 1950s. At any rate, no clear picture was given about those perplexities because the ones, such as Einstein and Schrödinger, who most keenly felt them, had very confused philosophical notions on the subject. Just as unenlightening was the philosophy, usually a brand of pragmatism, of those who wrote the most widely read books about the philosophical roots of the Copenhagen interpretation.[32] Physicist defenders of the "realist" position have time and again failed at crucial junctures. A good illustration of this is a statement of A. Landé, best remembered as the discoverer of the Landé-factor in quantum mechanics:

> Neutrality toward the wave-particle paradox, elevated by Niels Bohr and Heisenberg to a 'fundamental principle' of duality inherent in all matter (and fields) is diametrically opposed to the realism of Einstein. . . . At heart all physicists are realists in Einstein's sense to whom there could only be *either* discrete particles *or* continuous waves of matter, rather than whole peas and pea soup at the same time, even if the two pictures might be complementary. Physical questions of the either-or type are not solved by tranquillizing pills dressed in philosophical language. Using the age-old scepticism of philosophers as to the reality of the external world to serve as a cover for our temporary ignorance and indecision, is the policy of if you can't explain it, call it a principle, then look down on those who still search for an explanation as unenlightened.[33]

Had Landé started with *philosophical* neutrality about the ontological substratum of the wave-particle paradox, he might not have missed out on the point at issue. It is not about *physical* questions of "the either-or-type" but about the *ontological* alternative of *to be* or *not to be*. Had he seen this, he might have written that such questions cannot be solved by falling back on a philosophical language alien to ontology. Most accurate was, however, his final remark that the attitude of those in the victorious camp toward their opponents was to take them for "unenlightened". Victory, however superficial, readily generates a condescending attitude.

Virtual versus real existence

Victors or not, physicists have been overawed by a technique which the Heisenberg uncertainty principle allows when written as $\Delta E.\Delta t \gtreqless h$. In that form it can be used to account for three forces — electromagnetic, nuclear, and electroweak — in terms of exchange particles, though only at a price which, tellingly enough, is to be paid in terms of reality. Just as the alpha particles are by definition unobservable as they tunnel through the potential barrier, those exchange particles too must be unobservable. That such "unobservability" bears on their reality is intimated by their name "virtual particles", though only for the philosophically lynx-eyed. They are very few in number among those proud to consider themselves the modern equivalents of the original members of the *Academia dei lincei* to which Galileo once belonged. They hardly sense that an expression like "virtual particles" suits metaphysics more than plain physics.

Insensitivity to this point is the clue to the process whereby fundamental particle physics has become cosmology in the most sinistrous sense conceivable. A quick look at the relation $\Delta E.\Delta t \gtreqless h$, with E being mc^2, makes it clear that the greater is the mass or energy of the virtual particle postulated, the shorter is its lifetime, a point of much relevance for experimental detectability when particles particularly heavy, such as magnetic monopoles, are being postulated and looked for. On the other hand when the energy in question is *almost* zero, the particle can have a "virtual" existence for an almost unlimited time. Suppose now that one is already in the habit of conveniently overlooking the difference between virtual and real existence when one notices a most interesting relation. It is the equality, within a not overly significant margin of error, of the rest-mass of the total mass of the universe with the gravitational energy of all its attractive forces. Since the former value is positive and the latter negative, the two seem to cancel out to a value close to zero. Putting that almost zero value for ΔE into the relation $\Delta E.\Delta t \gtrapprox h$, the universe, if it is a virtual particle, may appear to exist eternally. From this it follows for those who are ready to go all the way down the primrose path of the Copenhagen illusion, that the universe pulls itself out of nothing as if by a cosmic bootstrap.

It is in this light that one should read the reminiscences of E. P. Tyron, the one who spotted in 1973 that near-zero value. Although his views are not carefully distinguished from those of the reporter, the two obviously agree on the pivotal point that

> According to quantum mechanics, any small system with a very small net energy can appear from nothing, exist for a brief moment and vanish. These "virtual particles," or quantum fluctuations, are observed in the laboratory and appear spontaneously throughout space all the time. A quantum fluctuation as heavy as an electron-positron pair has a lifetime of only 10^{-21} second. One with 10^{21} times less energy could last for a full second. Any system with a net energy of exactly zero could appear from nothing in this manner and exist forever.
>
> Tyron realized that there is no limit to the size of the quantum fluctuations that are always occurring in empty space. Larger ones are merely less frequent than smaller ones. Given enough time even

the largest conceivable ones must inevitably occur, spontaneously and purely by chance. A very large system arising in this manner might be indisguishable from the Big Bang.

Tyron remembers vividly his feelings the moment it all fell into place. "The instant I saw the possibility I was so taken by it," he recalls. "I just felt, 'This is it!' That it was simple and beautiful and natural."[34]

That one feels elated, if not inflated, on thinking that he has found the "scientific" explanation of how the universe creates itself, is understandable. Hegelian metaphysicians and process theologians would rightly be jealous of him. Yet physics alone would call for a deflating of such euphoria. Contrary to the foregoing statement, no particles insofar as they are virtual have ever been observed in or out of laboratories, let alone that they emerge "spontaneously" and all the time. Philosophy or rather metaphysics is involved in the inevitable and spontaneous emergence *by chance,* the topic of the next chapter. Here let the expression "appear from nothing" be given a close look, or rather be judged by words taken from the mouth of a physicist most sympathetic to this kind of origin of the universe.

Such a physicist is J. S. Trefil, whose *The Moment of Creation* is possibly the best high-level popularization of what happened before the first millisecond. He explains the process as the replica on a cosmic scale of what takes place as pions appear out of nothing insofar as they are actual particles and as such act as the exchange particles between two nucleons and produce thereby the very strong though very short-range force binding them together. "We have said that the pion cannot appear out of nothing — a statement which is undoubtedly correct," writes Prof. Trefil, at present at George Mason University. Such a warning, so necessary from the viewpoint of good physics as well as sound metaphysics, appears only on occasion in the literature. When it does, it is forgotten right away. Prof. Trefil is a good example of this as he continues:

> Let us, however, put the question in a slightly differ-
> ent way. For how long could the uncertainty in our
> knowledge of the energy of the proton be so large
> that we could not, according to the uncertainty
> principle, tell if a pion had been created? In other
> words, what if the proton suddenly created a pion
> out of nothing but reabsorbed it too quickly for us
> to detect the pion's presence? Such a process would
> not violate the conservation of energy, since there
> would be no experiment that could be done, even in
> principle, that could show the energy of the proton
> to change spontaneously.[35]

The unintended instructiveness of this passage is inexhaustible. First, the proton is invested with the power of producing a pion out of nothing, although it had just been stated that the pion cannot appear out of nothing. Second, a process, impossible in itself, is hidden behind unobservability as if the magician's veil were a standard art of laboratory equipment. In other words, it is claimed that a process, in itself a violation of the conservation of matter principle, is not such a violation if it cannot be observed. This is, of course, but the reverse of the fallacy at the basis of the Copenhagen interpretation of quantum mechanics, namely, that an interaction that cannot be measured exactly cannot take place exactly. In both cases measurability by tools at our momentary disposal is set up as the condition for ontological reality. Third, a physical reality, nuclear force, is accounted for in terms of a zero energy-balance produced by the production ("creation") and absorption of the same particle. No attention is paid to the fact that one of those "creative" acts must *in reality* precede the other, and therefore relates to an ontological level. Questions about its ground are not answered by the assumption that it is immediately followed by its opposite, and therefore the two may appear to cancel out one another. Fourth, the entire performance is declared to be only "slightly different" from what has been stated to be a *true* creation out of nothing. To call "slightly different" that which is "infinitely different" is a punishment for loose thinking or, rather, a cover-up for it through artful play with words. That play has been a staple feature of talking away ontology in terms of the uncertainty principle and lurked in Gurney's and Condon's pleasing metaphor that the alpha particle "slips away almost unnoticed." It is that play with words that lies at the basis of any explanation of physical reality as a particle play.[36]

That such a play with words, equivalent to an unconscionable play with logic, may readily lead to a play with the entire universe can easily be seen if in Trefil's foregoing passage the proton is replaced with the quantum mechanical vacuum and the pion with the universe:

> We should say that a universe cannot appear out of nothing — a statement which is undoubtedly correct. Let us, however, put the question in a slightly different way. For how long a time could the uncertainty in our knowledge of the energy of the quantum mechanical vacuum be so large that we could not, according to the uncertainty principle, tell if a universe has been created? In other words, what if the quantum mechanical vacuum suddenly created a universe out of nothing but reabsorbed it before the time span or Δt assured by the uncertainty principle had run out? For in that case the change of energy, involving the entire rest mass of the universe, could not be detected and therefore the process would not violate the conservation of energy.[37]

It should be plain even to the plainest layman that what would be violated in this case, and in fact rendered impossible, would be plain good physics. For such a universe, being a virtual universe, could not contain actual observers doing physics or anything else, because they can exist only in a real universe.

What the plain layman may not suspect so readily is the readiness with which physicists may fall victim to the remorseless force of faulty logic once espoused by them. Less than a year after Tyron was seized by the cosmic applicability of Heisenberg's uncertainty principle, Hawking made the first quantitatively concrete step toward a quantum creation of the universe by the mechanism which showed that black holes would evaporate. The mechanism consists in the creation of new matter out of vacuum fluctuations near the black holes' event horizon.[38] A year or two later came A. H. Guth's proposal about an inflationary, that is, most rapidly expanding early phase of the universe. It quickly led, in Guth's hands, not only to the spontaneous emergence of a single universe from a vacuum-fluctuation governed by the uncertainty principle, but also to the statistically random emergence of any such universes, all with different sets of physical laws.[39] By the early 1980s many cosmologists took it for granted that the emergence of the universe duplicated on a cosmic scale the process whereby alpha particles tunnelled through the energy barrier posed by the force binding the nucleus together. In the summer of 1982 about half of the thirty-six papers presented at the Nuffield Workshop on cosmology in Cambridge were on the inflationary universe and most of the others were strongly influenced by it. Hawking's introduction to the Proceedings of the Workshop comes to a close with the remark that the "inflationary model gave grounds for hoping that we might be able to explain why the universe is the way it is."[40] F. Wilczek's survey of the papers contains the revealing remark: "The most dramatic qualitative prediction of the inflationary idea is that the universe should be essentially flat — with well-known consequences for the mass density ($\Omega = 1$), the deceleration parameter, and the age of the universe."[41]

The true bearing of all this was all too clear for the participants, all on the cutting edge of scientific cosmology with all its esoteric mathematics and strange semantics. Only for laymen should the last point made by Wilczek translated as it stands for the presumed eternity of the universe. Laymen also need further instruction about that flatness or zero space-time curvature, a favorite prophylactic against metaphysical forebodings for cosmologists who cannot bear their beckoning.

Inflationary universe or inflated egos?
The specter of metaphysics keeps pursuing cosmologists insofar as something numerically specific is involved in the idea of the creation of the universe by quantum tunnelling. Of course, inflationary theory or not, there remains the quantitative specificity of Planck's quantum and the apparent irreducibility to anything else of the electron with its specific charge. But since both specificities have been around for long, their ability to provoke minds to further reflections has diminished to the vanishing point, just as one would lose his palate's sensitivity if treated continually to the same candy, however special. What worries some cosmologists is the fact that "any universe arising spontaneously as a quantum tunnelling event (that is, by crossing a seemingly impenetrable barrier between emptiness and the existence of the Big Bang) must be closed,"[42] that is, must have a space-time curvature larger than zero. "We find this conclusion somewhat disappointing," wrote D. Atkatz and H. Pagels, of Rockefeller University, a remark that should appear an artful understatement in view of their admission: "We had hoped that the universe could have originated from flat empty space, a configuration that truly corresponds to nothing at all." Clearly, both were bothered by plain metaphysics. Otherwise they would not have added: "The question arises: where did *that* [non-zero curvature] come from? This is a question we

cannot answer."[43] It is ultimately not a question for physicists to answer. Physicists can merely postpone it by speculating about a four-dimensional subspace-manifold that would "tunnel" into a closed universe with a big bang.

Such physicist-cosmologists think, and this is the gist of Hawking's *Brief History of Time* which within a mere ten months has sold almost a million copies,[44] that if they can start with a zero space-time curvature no further questions need be asked about the universe. Yet, is not zero also a specific point on the scale connecting positive and negative quantities? More importantly, is zero as a mere numerical idea equivalent to that nothing which in ontology is the very opposite of real existence? Is science worth anything if it generates utter philosophical poverty that deprives one of appreciating one's own existence and that of the universe as well? Does the science of cosmology have for its object haphazard fluctuations between nothing and something? Is it the purpose of cosmology to dilute the meaning of its grasp of the cosmos by denying the reality of that grasp through reducing its object to a chance that defies definition?

As the 1980s approach their end, hardly a month goes by without the publication of another book on the latest in cosmology with fantastic details on ever wilder forms of the inflationary universe. There the reader is told that three major problems of cosmology can only be resolved if the universe expanded at an exponentially fast rate before shifting to its actual rate of expansion. One problem, known as the horizon problem, suggests that when the universe was about half a million years old and the formation of galaxies started, opposite parts of the universe were too far away from one another to interact and thereby come into that thermal equilibrium which is evidenced by the uniformity of the 2.7°K background radiation. (Little attention is given to the fact that if the ordinary Big-Bang model is considered in its much earlier phase, when the radius of the universe was very small, the problem might automatically resolve itself). The second, or flatness problem, derives from the closeness of the value of the average density of matter to the one which would turn the expansion into a contraction. (Here, too, in view of what has been said about the search for the missing mass, the problem may seem exaggerated). The third problem relates to the formation of galaxies which presupposes departures in many points in the universe from the average density of matter. It is argued that those points cannot arise in an ordinary Big-Bang model with a strong tendency toward thermal equilibrium. Whether the inflationary theory is really needed for solving this problem too should not seem so instructive to investigate as are some not-at-all scientific reflections that may arise in reference to that problem.

Thus in speaking about the galaxy problem, Trefil suddenly takes on the six-day creationists who found in it another argument against the time scale of billions of years as demanded by cosmic and biological evolution.[45] They seized here too, as in many other cases, on an unresolved scientific question to get further grist for their unenlightened mills. Obviously, if galaxies cannot form, there can be no stellar evolution which presupposes the formation of stars within galaxies. Six-day creationists can rightly be taken to task for their inability, if not stubborn refusal, to see that gaps in scientific knowledge have a regular way of being filled up. But to sit in judgment over six-day creationists may not seen very appropriate on the part of one who cultivates the same kind of primitivism in philosophy which creationists do vis-à-vis the Bible. For a cosmologist simply caters to primitivism in reasoning when he claims that the "creation" by quantum mechanics of virtual particles out of nothing is only "slightly different" from emergence out of literally nothing.

The same primitivism blares forth from another cosmologist's statement that "nothing means something a little different to quantum physicists than it does to the ordinary man in the street."[46] Actually, primitive man, or the man in the street with plain common sense, displays, by taking nothing for nothing, a far greater philosophical acumen than do some highly-educated physicist-cosmologists. The latter may debase themselves into unphilosophical street-walkers, prostituting sane reasoning, if they keep on with their claims that they have learned how to create universes literally out of nothing. For if it is true, to quote a favorite phrase of Guth, that "the universe could be the ultimate free lunch,"[47] there will be no limit to taking the layman, or the man in the street, for a free ride. He will then have to believe Guth that for all we know "our universe might have been created in the basement of a scientist in another universe."[48] The man in the street will be further bowled over on seeing Guth put another scientific coating on all this by noting that there may be insurmountable technological problems to the creation of universes in laboratories.[49]

For all that, creation remains a strictly philosophical as well as theological matter. It would, of course, be useless to argue a philosophical point with those utterly contemptuous of that basis of philosophy which is the definition of the meaning of basic words. When a physicist-cosmologist claims that "perhaps the reason that there is something instead of nothing is that [the] nothing is unstable,"[50] he plays an ugly game with words, man's greatest treasure. A result, unintended perhaps, of such a game is that it makes meaningless any debate. One can but throw up one's hands in despair when a graduate student at a most distinguished university turns to a guest-lecturer on cosmology, not with a question, but with the angry remark: "You have got it all wrong. Nothing is something." Poor victim of the Copenhagen brainwashing whose champions, famous and nondescript, continue in their perverse procedure of grafting on a splendid science a sinister philosophy. The latter received its most concise and most far-reaching formulation when Bohr abolished the ontological reality of the universe itself: "There is no quantum world. There is only an abstract quantum physical description. It is wrong to think that the task of physics is to find out how nature is. Physics concerns what we can say about nature."[51]

One should be grateful to Bohr for unfolding so much of the fateful logic of the anti-ontology of his complementarity which impales one on the horns of a fundamental dilemma while taking (or rather merely talking) away that very foundation which is the universe.[52] In fact he went so far as to give a glimpse of that next-to-last stage of mental perversion where human language becomes deprived of real objects and therefore of meaning. Not surprisingly, he did so, as many others nowadays do, by endorsing the possibility of a computer-generated artificial intelligence. He tried to allay fears that we might not be able to understand the diction of ultraintelligent machines with the remark: "Our problem is not that we do not have adequate concepts. What we may lack is a sufficient understanding of the unambiguous applicability of the concepts we have."[53] As countless others, Bohr too failed to see that, if this was so, he still had to proceed to the very last stage and throw there the principle of complementarity too, as he understood it, on the scrap-heap of irresolvable ambiguities.

Humpty-Dumpty cosmologists
Since such are strictly epistemological matters, that leave unfazed most victims of the Copenhagen brainwashing, it may be best to shift attention to a problem, purely quantitative or scientific, hatched by the inflationary theory. The problem evokes the predicament of Humpty Dumpty after he fell from a high wall. Inflationary cosmologists are now busy putting together the pieces of the great many random universes with randomly different laws generated by their brainchild. The last word

may evoke the idea of a self-reproducing universe, another proliferation of the inflationary theory. There, unlike in ordinary biological procreation, the offspring-universes detach themselves from their parent universes, never to be known to one another. Word about this wallowing in randomly generated universes has reached even the comic strips. A syndicated one, under the label Frank and Ernest, shows the Ancient of Days on the clouds, perplexed by a large box with the big label: CONTENTS: ONE UNIVERSE. SOME ASSEMBLY REQUIRED.[54] Perhaps, instead of a box a turtle would have served the purpose far better. Of course, it should have been drawn as a turned turtle which tries to do the impossible, namely, to regain its upright position through its own efforts.

If scientific cosmology has reached the stage of a turned turtle, the blame for this lies with the game, begun in the late 1920s. There one plays with tunnels that, although not existing, are imagined to be the condition for matter to come into existence. The real victim of that illusory game is not the universe. It will continue to exist in defiance of cosmologists with inflated egos who think they are its producers. The real victim is reason itself. The Copernican turn, that first marvelous step toward a true scientific grip on the universe, is now being turned against itself. Inflationary theorists note with feigned humility that not only the earth, the sun, the Milky Way galaxy, and ordinary or luminous matter have been dethroned from the center, but even our universe turns out to be an insignificant accident in a never-ending process whereby haphazard universes are being continually generated. Or, to quote Tyron, "our universe is simply one of those things that happens from time to time."[55]

To crown their farcical protestations of humility, some proponents of the inflationary universe see in it the only ground for hope and the only framework for endless wonders.[56] True to logic it never takes long for a turned turtle to show, by spreading a repulsive odor, that it has begun to decompose. David Hume's sarcastic smile was visible between the lines as he conjured up aborted, botched-up universes while delivering himself of his last drop of scorn for man's ability to infer from nature to nature's God.[57] An essential part of his argument was that science can show only such universes. Were he to see the inflationary theorists' theories about self-creating universes, he would gladly register the logic at work: To decompose God goes hand in hand with decomposing science too. Of course, the true God can be claimed dead only by filling His place with something else. The new god of the new cosmology has been known of old as Chance. Its alleged business in the cosmos forms the next chapter's subject.

Chapter Six

LOADED DICE

Chance is a word void of meaning, invented
by our ignorance
P. Janet

Chance or ignorance
For well over two millennia the chief spokesmen of
Western thought took the word chance for an ignorance
of true causes. They also noted, and from very early on, a
telling feature of the popularity of chance in some circles. Chance, Plato wrote in *The Laws*, enjoyed special
favor with those for whom man's right was co-extensive
with his skill to grab anything he could lay his hand on.
Plato observed in the same breath that young men often
saw paragons of wisdom in the champions of chance
whom he identified as the popular prosewriters of the
times.[1] He obviously meant those who eagerly lent their
pen to the message of the Sophists. A mere look at recent
celebrations of chance in high- and low-level science
popularizations can but increase one's admiration for
Plato's enduring perceptiveness.

For Plato chance was a problem only inasmuch as it
posed a threat to purposefulness in the cosmos at large
and especially on the human level. Plato owed his sensitivity to that threat to his having been the foremost disci-
ple of Socrates whose chief aim was to save purpose, cosmic and individual. Socrates hoped to implement that
aim by proposing a new physics. There, instead of looking for mechanistic or purely quantitative patterns, one

was to find the answer to the question whether it was *best* for things to move as they did, that is, whether their motion fulfilled a purpose.[2] This program about a new physics, to which Plato gave occasional attention,[3] was worked out systematically by Aristotle. Aristotelian physics, in which all motion is above all for a purpose and therefore can never be rigorously a chance happening, had two targets. One was the message of pre-Socratic *physikoi* for whom everything was matter and motion.[4] The other was the teaching of the Sophists who found the idea of chance very supportive of the tenet that might with sheer words makes right. For a cosmic foundation the Sophists reached back to the early atomists, but especially to Heraclitus. His dictum that "the fairest universe is but a dust heap piled up at random,"[5] could readily be used as a justification for any scheming, even for the promotion of plain anarchy.

These points are but indirectly in view in Aristotle's usually analytical discussion of chance. He granted to chance as much as he could. He recognized that things happened though their causes were unspecifiable and that things could happen through the confluence of causes that in all appearance had no previous connection.[6] The most interesting aspect of Aristotle's dicta on chance relates to the difference between conceptual and material reality. With respect to the former — which includes for him formal, efficient, and final causality — Aristotle allows some role to chance. In fact, on the few occasions when Aristotle faces up to the question of the freedom of the will, he finds some help in chance insofar as it can be assigned a purely conceptual reality. But when it comes to material causality, Aristotle allows no chance and quite logically. Chance as a material cause would imply for him the rise of something out of no antecedent material cause, that is, out of nothing. This is, however, inadmissible in the perspective of Aristotle who as a pantheist held the universe to be ungenerated and therefore eternal. As a matter of fact, on three different occasions he rejected the idea of something coming into being out of nothing.[7]

Even more emphatically, chance as a material cause is rejected by Aquinas. He, of course, admits the coming into being out of nothing, but in his Christian credal perspective this process can arise only through the creative power of God. About that power of creating something out of nothing, Aquinas most emphatically states that since it denotes absolute power over existence it can belong only to God and is in no way transferable to any creature, be it the highest among the angels.[8] For, as Aquinas rightly saw, creation touched not on this or that quality of things, but on their very being and presupposed therefore that full dominion over existence which could be had only by God, the only being which is existence itself. The lending of that dominion to any other being would have supposed the turning of a mere creature into a Creator, a doubling, so to speak, of the essentially one God. In the same context Aquinas also noted that such a process could but have resulted in a chain of ever more imperfect universes. But this is precisely the kind of cosmic chain of beings, Plotinus' antiscientific emanationism is a proof if one was needed, that cannot constitute a coherence and consistency that makes scientific cosmology possible. Such points may be profitably pondered by those Christian interpreters of modern scientific cosmology who think that Aquinas' arguments can be answered with a condescending "I don't see why this should be so,"[9] and take quantum mechanical chance for a proof that God handed over to the universe the work of creation.[10] Such Christians will be left with no reply when, with a reliance on the same chance, non-Christian leaders in scientific cosmology present themselves as masters of the universe or claim the know-how to create one.

Aquinas, who held in enormous esteem the consistency of the universe,[11] could but most zealously champion the tenet of the creation of all together as part of the

Christian creed.[12] Aquinas therefore felt at ease as he ascribed to the physical universe a degree of determinism even greater than the one advocated by Aristotle. For Aquinas strict determinism (which he never confused with perfectly accurate measurability) follows from the fact that there can be no hiatus along the line of material causality because any such hiatus would imply two contradictions. One is that matter can arise spontaneously, that is, by chance or without cause out of nothing; the other is that there would be new matter brought into existence by the Creator, although He had already created everything together. Of course, with his belief in a personal providential God as the cause of all, Aquinas, unlike Aristotle, experienced no perplexity about apparently purposeless events in reference to human lives. Those events could very well be purposeful in God's perspective.

Christian understanding of chance became less and less a part of Western intellectual consciousness as the latter moved from Renaissance through Enlightenment times toward the present, markedly post-Christian age. Bossuet had in mind non-Christian ideas on chance as he urged in the grand conclusion of his interpretation of universal history: "Let us stop talking of chance or luck, or at most speak of them as mere words that cover our ignorance."[13] The modern history of the notion of chance too shows that, like most returns, return to ancient paganism had to be gradual. Those in the vanguard of the de-Christianization of the Western world during the Enlightenment were yet most unwilling to tie their cause to chance. They would have taken it for a most unenlightened stance not to see in chance an absence of cause and therefore of reason as well as of reality. "Chance is only our ignorance of real causes," declared Hume,[14] who while among the *philosophes* in Paris must have heard the same on many occasions. "What we call chance," Voltaire declared in his *Dictionnaire philosophique*, "can only be the unknown cause of a known effect."[15] This is not to suggest that Voltaire meant to give to his emphatic dictum, "there is no accident,"[16] a thrust which a Christian apologist would give to it. Voltaire saw Christianity effectively undermined with a return to a materialistic determinism which he took to be incompatible with chance but very germane to his deism. Voltaire's God, a cosmic clockmaker, let things run on their predetermined course with no concern whether this left any room for human freedom and purpose, the only sources of conceivable "accidents" within a material universe.

Thus whether one was a materialist or a mere deist, a debunking of chance or accident could serve both an anti-Christian purpose and be also a claim to sheer rationality, usually identified in Voltaire's time with Newtonian physics. There action was strictly equal to reaction, meaning a strict equality between cause and effect in general. A good illustration of this view is a remark of Helvetius, an unabashedly materialist *philosophe*. In discussing the role of chance in the education and career of great men, Helvetius was most eager not to be taken for a debunker of strict causality: "I understand by chance the unknown chain of causes capable of producing such and such effect."[17] A hundred years later T. H. Huxley tried to turn the table on those who took Darwinism for a wholesale endorsement of chance: "Do they believe," he asked, "that anything in this universe happens without reason or without a cause?"[18] The question had a debating value because Huxley could claim that nothing was farther from Darwin's mind than a chance that meant the absence of cause.

Darwin was unable to accept even that "blind chance" that merely meant a cause operating within an ensemble where any outcome was equally possible. About the same time when Darwin published the *Descent*, where man was reduced to a merely material level, he wrote to J. Hooker. "I cannot look at the universe as a result of blind chance."[19] He must have thought that such a chance contradicted the enormously narrow range of specificities which living nature displayed everywhere in the present as well as in the past. Though Darwin would have been most reluctant to credit ultimately a Creator with the choice of those specificities, he would have undoubtedly endorsed the view that chance is merely a word for our ignorance about true causes.

Among the many contemporary proofs that such a view of chance represented a general conviction among men of science, one stands out for more than one reason. When Charles S. Peirce, son of the great Harvard mathematicisn Benjamin Peirce, published in 1877 his "Illustrations of the Logic of Science," he had already enjoyed international reputation as a physicist-astronomer. He was also emerging as a most incisive logician and philosopher of science. In that article Peirce set up a sharp contrast between chance and law as well as between chance and cosmos. In the latter connection the gist of his argument consisted in showing that non-probabilistic parameters lie at the basis of any evaluation made in terms of all methods of probability:

> The relative probability of this or that arrangement of Nature is something which we should have a right to talk about if universes were as plenty as blackberries, if we could put a quantity of them in a bag, shake them well up, draw out a sample, and examine them to see what proportion of them had one arrangement and what proportion another. But, even in that case, a higher universe would contain us, in regard to whose arrangements the conception of probability could have no applicability.[20]

Peirce also showed that chance, if taken rigorously, excludes the notion of law and he did so with a reference to the universe:

The chance world shown to be so different from that in which we live would be one in which there were no laws, the characters of different things being entirely independent; so that, should a sample of any kind of objects ever show a prevalent character, it could only be by accident, and no general proposition could ever be established. Whatever further conclusions we may come to in regard to the order of the universe, this much may be regarded as solidly established, that the world is not a mere chance-medley.[21]

The upshot of all this he put tersely: "A contradiction is involved in the very notion of chance world."[22]

Chance as a scientific pillow

In such logic that did not stop short of the universe itself one may be tempted to see a conviction difficult to abandon. Peirce not only developed doubts about it but with his bent on consistency he fully reversed his erstwhile position. About this development, well-known and often discussed,[23] that reached its peak around 1900, here only two points should be recalled. Although Peirce took pains to call his new philosophical system pragmaticism, so as to stand apart from William James' pragmatism, the two differed only in style. Both tried to break the stranglehold of a physicalist determinism by taking the sting out of a "lawless" chance. Both ended up by personalizing nature. The essence of Peirce's reasoning went as follows:

To undertake to account for anything by saying boldly that it is due to chance would, indeed, be futile. But this I do not do. I make use of chance chiefly to make room for a principle of generalisation, or tendency to form habits, which I hold has produced all regularities. The mechanical philosopher leaves the whole specification of the world utterly unaccounted for, which is pretty

nearly as bad as to boldly attribute it to chance. I
attribute it altogether to chance, it is true, but to
chance in the form of a spontaneity which is to
some degree regular.[24]

It could easily be seen, even if Peirce had not used the
word "habit," that in substance he offered but a rehash
of Hume's account of the laws of nature. But the
supreme irony consisted in Peirce's thinking that not the
pragmaticist but the determinist cut himself off the universe of specificities. With a little more effort in logic he
might have perceived that insofar as the determinist let
the mind itself be enveloped in physicalist determinism,
there remained no mind to think about anything, let
alone about the universe. Yet, the position he advocated
left no more room for thinking about the universe
because in it the universe was assumed to do all the
thinking in terms of a spontaneous trend to form habits
and regularities of which not the least was the bent of
mind on seeing orderly connections as the essence of
understanding.

As a pragmaticist, hardly different from the pragmatist
who rested all reason, as William James had done, "on
the will to believe,"[25] Peirce signalled a trend toward a
more "humanistic" science. Whether human nature
could be done more justice by sinking into spontaneity
the entire cosmos[26] is not the point at issue here. The
point to note is that the same kind of spurious
voluntarism was invoked as other men of science abandoned law for chance. Pierre Delbet, a biologist at the
Sorbonne, is a good illustration. In his book *La science et
la réalité*, published in 1913, the year Henri Poincaré
died, the latter's dictum, "chance is the measure of our
ignorance,"[27] was quoted as contrast to the new idea of
chance: "Chance appears today as a law, the most general of all laws. It has become for me a soft pillow like the
one which in Montaigne's words only ignorance and
disinterest can provide, but this is a scientific pillow."[28]

Delbet's words were all the more prophetic because he had finished writing his book some months and perhaps a full year before Bohr published his famous model of the hydrogen atom to account for its spectral lines. An invitation to dispense with some very hard thinking lurks between the lines of his famous paper. It became the starting point of a good deal in twentieth-century physics and also provided the softest "philosophical" pillow in all scientific history. Once more, as so often in that history, most successful mathematical formulas served as magic tools for making shabby philosophizing a most respectable attitude. Much of this was hinted at by Rutherford, an unshakable realist, who, on reading the draft of Bohr's paper, raised a prophetic point: "It seems to me that you would have to assume that the electron knows beforehand where it is going to stop."[29] A dozen or so years later the same troublesome specter of electrons knowingly choosing their paths in cloud-chamber tracks was conjured up by Dirac as a consequence of the philosophical interpretation which Bohr was giving to his atom model.[30] Still another sixty years later many physicists found it necessary to assume that photons do indeed "know" about one another.

This recent readiness to attribute "thinking" ability to particles of matter reveals something about that epistemological *cul de sac* in which physicists, fond of the Copenhagen philosophy of quantum mechanics, now find themselves. Their predicament has come to a head in the debates touched off by the experimental work on Bell's inequality. The latter is a casting into quantitative terms of a thought experiment proposed by David Bohm in 1951[31] which in turn was inspired by the famous paper published by Einstein, Podolsky, and Rosen in 1935.[32] The gist of that paper is that if the Copenhagen interpretation is correct, one must assume that two photons emitted simultaneously in opposite direction must communicate with one another, or, to recall a famous remark of Einstein, are involved "in spooky actions-at-a-distance" with one another.[33] In fact it was aptly said about those "spooky actions" that they represent not so much actions-at-a-distance as "passions-at-a-distance."[34] Such actions or "passions" are for physics the harbinger of a chaos compared with which statistical theorems involving the highest conceivable measure of randomness should seem to be so many tools of strict predictability.

As already argued in the preceding chapter, the Copenhagen interpretation implies the fallacious inference from a purely operational to a strictly ontological proposition, namely, that an interaction that cannot be measured exactly cannot take place exactly. This inference clearly states the primacy of a very special mental operation over a very special aspect of reality. The operation is the conceptual apparatus needed for making exact measurements, whereas the very special aspect of reality is its quantitative specificity. The subjection of the latter to the former is possible only if in a most general sense external objective reality is a function of subjective mental operations.

The development of the Copenhagen interpretation of quantum mechanics showed indeed the inexorable logic whereby a concession along a restricted area leads to yielding over the whole terrain. No sooner had the mind been granted priority over the quantitative aspect of reality than it claimed dictatorial powers over reality as a whole. Whenever in modern intellectual history, Hegel is the best known case, philosophers granted such powers to the mind, science as well as the universe could seem to be enveloped in utter chaos. Hegel's philosophy of nature is a chief evidence.[35] Those few physicists, who were not unfamiliar with some basic lessons which the history of philosophy provides, may have spotted chaos waiting in the wings. Possibly they took it for a bad dream, hoping that their skill with quantities would keep the specter of chaos at safe remove.

They were in for a rude awakening through experiments that strongly suggest the truth of Bell's inequality. They indeed had to face up to the vast implications of the question which Einstein addressed to Abraham Pais in the early 1950s. The question and the context is best given in Pais' own words: "We often discussed his [Einstein's] notions on objective reality. I recall that during one walk Einstein suddenly stopped, turned to me and asked whether I really believed that the moon exists only when I look at it."[36] Of course, Einstein could have simply asked Pais about the universe itself. Does it exist only insofar as we observe it and in particular when we do so with a scientific slant?

Pais made public Einstein's question long after his death, indeed at a time, in 1979, when experiments on Bell's inequality began in earnest and brought in focus once more the chaotic implications of the Copenhagen interpretation of quantum mechanics. No less tellingly, Pais, who since regaled the wider public with a big biography of Einstein, which begins with that question about the moon,[37] avoided giving to that question a plain answer. Most likely, he felt that no such answer can be had as long as one refused to part with the Copenhagen interpretation of quantum mechanics.

Indeed, as long as that interpretation is accepted, it will remain impossible to rescue the moon, or the universe for that matter, from being the dubious or chaotic product of observations. The latter are but accidentally connected insofar as they are carried out by countless individuals, all acting freely. All this can be gathered from a paper which Heisenberg contributed for Bohr's seventieth birthday.[38] The paper is a classic instance of the often observed fact that the philosophers' usual ignorance of physics is matched only by the physicists' ignorance of philosophy. With a reference to Einstein and others, Heisenberg stated that criticism of quantum theory starts "from the fear that quantum theory might deny the existence of an objectively real world, and so might cause the world to appear in some way (by a misunderstanding of the tenets of idealistic philosophy) as an illusion."[39] Heisenberg's instinctive defense of idealist philosophy reveals more than enough of his basic preference for it as well of his illusions about it.

Devotees of an illusory philosophy, be it idealism, readily yield to the necessity of making realist statements, a necessity often imposed on physicists by their very work.[40] Thus Heisenberg was quick to add: "The physicist must, however, postulate in his science that he is studying a world which he himself has not made, and which would be present, essentially unchanged, if he were not there." Such is the answer which Einstein expected from Pais but apparently in vain. Einstein, of course, would have remained sceptical about the promise Heisenberg held high as he specified the purpose of his paper, namely, to show "to what extent this basis of all physics has been maintained in the Copenhagen interpretation of quantum theory."[41] A stunning justification for Einstein' scepticism was indeed provided by Heisenberg a scant page later. There he stated that insofar as the world is not observed it is objective, nevertheless the quantum mechanical representation of that objectivity "is completely abstract and incomprehensible, since the various mathematical expressions $p(q)$, $p(p)$, etc., do not refer to a real space or a real property; it thus, so to speak, contains no physics at all."[42]

Heisenberg's use of the word "incomprehensible" is a hidden mine that explodes not only in the face of the physicist-philosopher preaching the Copenhagen Gospel but blows to pieces the entire physical universe as well. To see this one need only recall the statement of the British scientist, W. R. Thompson, who in the 1930s put most forcefully the identity between a "universe of chance" and "absolute disorder" or chaos with "no positive intelligible content."[43] On the basis of that identity, incomprehensibility may mean but absolute chaos. One need not be an expert in quantum mechanics, one needs only respect for logic, to suspect that something chaotic would be on hand when a physicist-champion of the Copenhagen interpretation of quantum mechanics writes that "observations not only disturb what has to be measured, they produce it. . . . We compel [the electron] to assume a definite position. . . . We ourselves produce the results of measurement."[44] At best such is a purely verbal game with reality, one of those many paradoxical expressions that modern physics inspired in large numbers. Dangerous as they may appear to the layman, he may find reassurance since they are often conveyed in the company of terms evoking esoteric mathematics. In connection with the manner in which the electron assumes its position, rather typical is the statement that "this nebulous, wavelike state of being collapses into definite form only when it is actually observed."[45] The idea of a "wave-like" state evokes enough mathematics to draw attention away from the magic whereby a "nebulous" being collapses into something so definite that it may be observed.

For his being misled, if not plainly deceived, the layman should blame not so much his inexpertise in mathematics as his philosophical myopia. For in the phrase just quoted only the "wavelike state" has a distinct connection with mathematics, the rest is unmistakably philosophical, or rather pseudo-ontological. To begin with, "the wavelike state of being" can only be a mere mathematical formalism, of a mere mental entity, since according to quantum mechanics it precedes those very measurements that create reality, a "creation" that deserves to be called "collapse". Further, quantum mechanics or not, a purely mathematical construct cannot be observed and therefore it cannot collapse into a kind of definite form which only tangibly real things do have. In other words, the phrase just analyzed is shere skullduggery and can be seen as such by a careful look that should not be beyond the reach of a layman sensitive to the plain meaning of words.

Specific information, though relatively easy to obtain, is, however, necessary if one is to see through the hollowness of Heisenberg's claim whereby he set up the quantum mechanical function of measurements as a ground for objective reality. He did so by invoking, of all things, the Aristotelian idea of transition from potency to actuality. The probability concept of quantum mechanics is, according to Heisenberg, "closely related to the 'potentia' of the natural philosophy of ancients, such as Aristotle; it is, to a certain extent, a transformation of the old 'potentia' concept from a qualitative to a quantitative idea."[46] In all likelihood, no so brief a statement has ever been packed with so much philosophical waffle as this one. As to the expression, "to a certain extent," a favorite with Bohr, its purpose is to smear out in uncertainty the true measure of the extent in question. The expression may suit genuinely Aristotelian philosophers with whom the doctrine of the analogy of being plays a pivotal role, but it should be avoided as much as possible by mathematical physicists. It amounts to a Trojan horse in the hands of those of the Copenhagen people who, like Heisenberg, try to create the illusion among realists that they too are realists. Whereas the realists have no fear of the doctrine of analogy, the latter, if equated with "to a certain extent" can act as a petard hoisted on the main gate of the Copenhagen fortress. As to Heisenberg's reference to Aristotle, it is doubly treacherous. First, the name of Aristotle evokes realist ontology and this may create the impression that Heisenberg too endorsed it. Second, his eminence as a physicist, a Nobel-laureate, can readily be taken for reliability in reporting about basic matters relating to the history of philosophy.

If there is anything clear in Aristotle's teaching about potency as opposed to act, it is that it always relates to real physical things insofar as they can take on new aspects, including substantially new aspects. But for Aristotle, who made many statements on mathematics, mathematical abstraction is not potency.[47] Unlike Plato,

Aristotle never held that the real world is a con-
cretization of a world of pure geometry or of a system of
integers as the Pythagoreans claimed. Nothing could be
farther from Aristotle's thinking than Heisenberg's claim
that "if we attempt to penetrate behind this [everyday]
reality into the details of atomic events, the contours of
this 'objectively real' world dissolve — not in the mist of
a new and yet unclear idea of reality, but in the transparent clarity of a mathematics whose laws govern the possible and not the actual."[48]

For all the Platonic flavor of this statement, Heisenberg was not a Platonist idealist. And just as is the case
with most champions of the Copenhagen interpretation
of quantum mechanics, he was not even a Kantian in his
advocacy of a priori ideas. He was merely a physicist
unable to see the extent to which his rightful preoccupation with quantitative measurements made him see everywhere quantitative contours alone and made him
blind to ontological factors antecedent to the possibility
of making measurements or anything else. Things must
exist before they have properties, quantitative or not, to
be operated upon. The chief penalty of that blindness is
anthropocentric subjectivism that quickly extends its
rule over the entire Nature or universe. "At this point,"
Heisenberg continues, "we realize the simple fact that
natural science is not Nature itself but a part of the relation between Man and Nature, and therefore is dependent on Man. The idealistic argument that certain ideas
are *a priori* ideas, i.e. in particular come before all natural
science, is here correct." The chief culprit for this
anthropocentrism is the obsessively overriding interest
in making exact measurements and is revealed by Heisenberg's final comment in which he mentions ontology
but only insofar as it is materialistic: "The ontology of
materialism rested upon the illusion that the kind of
existence, the direct 'actuality' of the world around us,
can be extrapolated into the atomic range."[49]

The key words are "the kind of existence." Undoubtedly, materialists and Marxists in particular objected to the Copenhagen interpretation of quantum mechanics precisely because their ontology was materialist. As such it was not a tool whereby one could penetrate beneath that surface of reality where quantities dominate and can be measured without any serious concern for the margin of inexactitutde. If Marxist or materialist ontologists feared losing reality through the Copenhagen interpretation of quantum mechanics, it was because the latter threatened in their eyes the reduction of human history to the tools of production. Consequently, their concern, however serious, for material reality did not in final analysis differ from the nonchalance which the champions of the Copenhagen interpretation of quantum mechanics show about physical reality. The identity of the two positions, apparently so different from one another, is another evidence about the often noted fact that Hegelian right and left make genuine bedfellows.

If these consequences of the physicists' preoccupation with the primacy of measurements are kept in mind, one will be spared much useless analysis of the unnecessary philosophical perplexity in which so many physicists found themselves because of the experiments about Bell's inequality. Of course, that perplexity teaches much about the truth of the remark that if a physicist "throws philosophy into the fire, his own subject will soon follow."[50] There is much to be learned philosophically from that schizophrenia which is displayed by the physics community. Some do quantum mechanics and ignore its Copenhagen interpretation. Others subscribe to that interpretation and avoid the question whether the moon, or the universe, is there only when observed.

The chaos of multiworlds

The answer is, of course, to be avoided for more than one reason, and in particular for the principal reason which is plain common sense. The five billion or so pairs of human eyes at present on earth can interact only with an infinitesimally small part of photons streaming through the universe. On that basis alone one can expect only an infinitesimally small part of the universe to "collapse into reality." Moreover, even that reality is but an occasional one inasmuch as individual observations are so many occasions. The Copenhagen interpretation of quantum mechanics can deliver but a heap of occasions, an indescribably puny heap of a universe in comparison with the true, but for that interpretation a purely potential universe. In addition to this partly quantitative problem to which a physicist must be sensitive, there is another, a strictly philosophical one, to which many philosophers have grown very insensitive. The problem relates to the ground of assurance that others' observations are not about something entirely other. Such problems have indeed surfaced, only to be swept quickly under the rug, in connection with the so-called multiworld theory, a logical unfolding of the Copenhagen interpretation of quantum mechanics, according to which there are as many universes as there are observers.

This consequence did not fail to appear as something bordering on the absurd even to its principal advocates. "I still recall vividly the shock," one of them reminisced,

> on first encountering this multiworld concept. The idea of 10^{100+} slightly imperfect copies of oneself all constantly splitting into further copies, which ultimately become unrecognizable, is not easy to reconcile with common sense. Here is schizophrenia with a vengeance. How pale in comparison is the mental state of the imaginary friend . . . who is hanging in suspended animation between only *two* possible outcomes of a quantum measurement.

Had this pathos not been somewhat misplaced, the resolution of it might have been less pathetic:

> To the extent that we can be regarded simply as automata and hence on a par with ordinary measuring apparatuses, the laws of quantum mechanics do not allow us to feel the splits . . . all the worlds are there, even those in which everything goes wrong and all the statistical laws break down. The situation is no different from that which we face in ordinary statistical mechanics. If the initial conditions were right, the universe-as-we-see-it could be a place in which heat flows from cold bodies to hot. We can perhaps argue that in those branches in which the universe makes a habit of misbehaving in this way, life fails to evolve; so no intelligent automata are around to be amazed by it.[51]

What this shows is that the perplexity of some physicists of the Copenhagen persuasion is so acute as to cease to be rational. This happens whenever a deliberate flight is taken from philosophy. Another illustration is the attitude of those physicists who claim that they are not troubled by the experiments on Bell's inequality, but refuse to tell why they are not troubled. Two other kinds of attitudes about those experiments have been registered. In addition to those who admit being troubled are those who claim they are not troubled and gave reasons for it.[52] It may be that some of their reasons are bad physics, although the search for hidden variable theories is a bad physics only as long as Planck's quantum remains truly a unit that cannot be divided.

The reasons so far given by those who claim not to be troubled do not include the only good reason. It consists in the recognition that measurements of quantities presuppose things with quantitative features and that exact measurements, always purely operational procedures, cannot be the guarantee and precondition of ontological exactness. Ontology will, however, remain a closed book for them as long as their philosophical readings, if they do any at all, remain limited to works of trend-setting philosophers of science. A leader among them, K. R.

Popper, is in fact proud of his studious avoidance of the term ontology. In his book, *The Open Universe*, of which more shortly, he states: "I avoided, or tried to avoid, the term 'ontology' in this book, and also in my other books; especially because of the fuss made by some philosophers over 'ontology'. Perhaps it would have been better to explain this term, and then to use it, rather than to avoid it. However that may be, questions of terminology are never important."[53]

The problems of philosophy are not solved by slighting the role of terminology, a procedure that can only open the door to imprecisions. Popper's endorsement of terminological inexactitude contradicts his professed aim to give scientific precision to philosophy. His lack of sympathy for ontology explains itself by his preference for "metaphysical determinism" as a substitute for the term ontology. Metaphysical determinism is hardly different in Popper's use from scientific determinism which is anyhow non-existent for most physicists, whatever their interest in precision in their own work. They may indeed gather from Popper's remark that sloppiness with terms may secure philosophical distinction. Also, a much touted philosopher's disdain for ontology may strengthen the physicist's readiness to think that quantities are everything and that looking beyond them is a yielding to a mystical urge to count angels on a pinhead.

These last remarks are part of W. Pauli's warning to Max Born that his three-decade long battle with Einstein was not about exact measurements, and not even about causality, but about reality.[54] Clearly, as long as physicists take concern for reality for a mystical urge, there is no point in wasting on them, or on anyone unduly impressed by their pseudophilosophical dicta, any reference to metaphysics, ontology, or even epistemology. For even if they claim to be concerned about epistemology, they offer a camouflaged excuse for reducing to quantitative formulas all that is objectively real. Were not this the case, they would not rush to the conclusion that since statistical methods alone are applicable to processes at the basic levels of matter, everything in existence is statistical. In fact, their view of the universe as a mere agglomerate of probability waves makes it appear as a chaos. For only that word is apt to convey that situation in which the overwhelming part of those waves fails to "collapse into a definite form" for not being the object of observation.

Yet what is true of classical statistical physics is also true of quantum mechanical statistics. Both are formalisms with factors, constants and postulates about which one is not at liberty to assume that they are chaotically variable if they indeed are variable at all. Otherwise those formalisms will collapse into something which is the exact opposite of a definite form, the very essence of any formalism properly so-called. Undoubtedly, within the framework of statistical gas theory things could be imagined to happen that were so fantastic as to conjure up a plain chaos. Boltzmann, one of the chief architects of that theory, spoke of tables that suddenly moved upward and of stars that reappeared where once they had burned out.[55] Only by giving credence to utmost improbabilities could one imagine that all the molecules in the table would at one strange moment move in the same upward direction or that atoms dissipated in empty spaces would suddenly reconcentrate. That they would do so at a sustained pace would, of course, have been a supposition whereby a miracle is supported by magic, or by something far more chaotic.

On the face of it, nothing may appear more rational than the expectation that, as the Nobel-laureate G. Wald put it, "one has only to wait; time itself performs the miracles". His argument, "given so much time, the 'impossible' becomes possible, the possible probable, and the probable virtually certain,"[56] implies *the* miracle that the time will be sufficiently long, but not too long, let alone "infinitely" long. For, certainly in that latter case, the great expectation will end in that utter disillusion which is prompted by the prospect of endless repetitions, the source of the worst nausea caused by a *déjà-vu* that keeps being served up. This happened in all those ancient cultures where, in the absence of a belief in creation out of nothing and *in* time, time appeared to be limitless. In all of them one very specific thing, science, failed to be served up, although imagination could cavort in the chaos of endless possibilities.[57]

In the chaotic world of imaginary gas theory where everything could become everything else, a number of things had to be imagined to remain strictly and unalterably the same in order to prevent probabilities from running amok. Gas molecules were assumed to be always perfectly elastic balls, they had to be invariably subject to the laws of motion, themselves invariable. Chaotic as could be the end points of the flights of fancy taken by imagination, the starting points were all most orderly states that remained operative even in the apparently chaotic outcome. In statistical gas theory the move was always from order to a chaos that was such only in appearance and never from chaos to order. Far from justifying the new-fangled shibboleth of "order out of chaos,"[58] statistical gas theory rested on the permanence of a most specific orderly state of things.

No different is the case with quantum mechanical statistics in spite of the fact that there the perfectly round and elastic molecules are replaced with diffuse wave packets. Yet the diffuseness of the latter serves its purpose only if subject to the control of sharp specificities. It should be enough to think of the various selection rules, among which atoms or electrons cannot select randomly. Nor is there anything variable, let alone randomly so, in the value of such universal constants as the electron's charge, the quantum of energy, and the speed of light, and the gravitational constant. No wonder that insightful handling of them allows the actual universe to be predicted.[59] Last but not least, all the mathematical tools needed by quantum mechanical statistics are very specific formalisms with very definite, and at times queer rules, such as the ones in non-commutative algebra and Hermite polynomials. One wonders whether Bohr thought of all this as he made one of his most revealing remarks: "I can't believe that. That's much too concrete to be real."[60]

Uncomplimenting complementarity
Apart from the specter of philosophical realism which he could not tolerate, Bohr should have been haunted by the specter of very specific formalisms, rules, and constants. They must be constantly used by quantum mechanical probability, if it is to produce the diffuse wave packets that are allegedly made concrete by the act of observation. To an extent far greater than one may suspect, the entire operational apparatus of quantum mechanics is a rebuttal of another famous remark of Bohr: "A great truth is a truth of which the contrary is also a truth."[61] To make the irony more complete he once illustrated that easily self-defeating idea with a juxtaposition of "there is a God" with "there is no God" as two equally insightful propositions.[62] He did not dare to be consistent to the point of declaring the validity of his atom model and its non-validity to be two equally great truths.

Much less was Bohr ready to grant that some philosophers might have had very good instinct in refusing to learn what he thought was most important to learn, namely, that the complementary description of nature "was an objective description — and that it was the only possible objective description."[63] Bohr was not ready because beneath the apparent liberality of his complementarity there lay hidden a rigid dogmatism which forced him to keep ontology out of view. This is why he failed to see that the shoe was on the other foot as he took A. H. Compton, whom he greatly respected as a man and a physicist, for an advocate of a "primitive" philosophy. Not that Compton had been enough of a philosopher to see the specter of ontology as he kept claiming that for God there was no uncertainty principle. "That's nonsense," was Bohr's dismissal of Compton's view. "In physics we do not talk about God, but about what we can know. If we are to speak of God we must do so in an entirely different manner."[64] With ontology being barred from the court of reason, not only God had to be "entirely different," but also that reason whose role was not merely to know (an impossibility) but to know something, that is, things or existents in their immense variety and concreteness.

Whatever truth there may be in the motto of Bohr's coat-of-arms, "contraria sunt complementaria," its truth content even in physics is specifically limited. Constants are forever constants, or at most they change at a regular rate; selection rules are rules and not conveniences complementary to other conveniences. In fact, one may take any aspect — experimental or theoretical, observational or mainly interpretative, macroscopic or microscopic — of the vast picture of modern physics about the universe, and one comes up against the same lesson: the last word belongs to specificities. Even the highest form of simplicity must be specific to be useful in physics. Those specificities may be used statistically as so many dice, but they remain nonetheless very similar to real dice. The latter serve their purpose only if they have invariable specific characteristics: equal sides, center of weight, straight edges etc. There is indeed some subtle misunderstanding of the nature of dice in Einstein's remark that God does not play dice.[65] For in any throwing of dice it must be assumed that they cannot come to stop in mid-air or on their corners and edges, but only on their sides. This should seem an extremely specific limitation in itself, in view of the fact that between 1 and 90 degrees there are an infinite number of possible angles.

An implied acknowledgment of such limitations is Einstein's famous remark that the good Lord is subtle but not malicious. For the Lord's subtlety is revealed by the fact that nature is understandable and that it is natural for man to understand things. Of course, if man is taken for a chance product of blind evolutionary forces, the battle, be it waged by Einstein against the rule of chance, cannot be fought convincingly. A dark lining lies hidden in Einstein's musing that "the most incomprehensible thing about the world is that it is comprehensible,"[66] precisely because it carries with it a touch of scepticism about what a physicist cannot be sceptical. For if anyone then a physicist should know that the comprehensibility of the world depends on the fact that nature is limited to a very narrow and coherent set of specificities, the very object of the physicist's work, and that therefore the universe cannot constitute a chaos.

Those reluctant to draw the proper lesson about the contradictory character of randomness or chaos would do well to look at themselves for a moment in the mirror of John von Neumann's words that strike at the very root of mathematically conceived randomness: "Anyone who considers arithmetical methods of producing random digits is, of course, in a state of sin."[67] On a not so subtle level as the one on which von Neumann's genius worked, a similar mirror is on hand in the recent scientific studies of "chaotic" state. For insofar as those active in those studies "are looking for the whole,"[68] they renounce the notion of chaos. A chaos can never be a whole, that is a co-ordination of parts, without ceasing to be a chaos, properly so-called. Highly significant should seem the fact that none of those studies yielded a satisfactory definition of chaos. Circumlocutions about it, especially if loaded with esoteric mathematics, may impress even those who should know better. When a science reporter states about a major conference on chaos that it "had attained the status of buzz word, but few of the physicists attending the conference knew what it meant,"[69] he merely reveals his inability to pick up the truly valuable information. Rather he should have said that none of those physicists really knew what they were talking about. And on having heard them state that "chaos is an agent of order" or that there is a "sensitive chaos,"[70] he should have warned them about the dangers of linguistic confusion.

Loaded dice and undefined chance

The shadow of confusion lingers in the statement that "God plays dice with the universe. But they're loaded dice. And the main objective of physics now is to find out by what rules were they *loaded* and how can we use them for our own ends."[71] (Italics added.) Physicists have never done anything but ascertain such rules, selection rules, that is, rules which drastically limit what can happen in the physical universe. When physicist-philosophers forget this, they run the risk of settling with resignation in ultimate ignorance about the physical universe although their method rests on the assurance that the universe is fully investigable in its quantitative properties. Such physicist-philosophers may be tempted to read their own resignation into God's very mind. Heisenberg was one of those physicist-philosophers about whom the story is told that on his deathbed he specified the question he would pose in meeting his Maker, "Why relativity, and why randomness? I really think," Heisenberg continued, "that God may have an answer to the first question."[72]

Relativity theory, being the most absolutist theory ever proposed by physics, should seem to pose no problem to God, the Absolute. But even He cannot make sense of what is a contradiction in terms, namely, to comprehend that chaos which by definition cannot have specifiable, and therefore comprehensible features. When seen in this light, the atheist Monod's condescending concession that "the a priori (beforehand) probability that the inorganic and organic structure of the universe arose by chance is next to zero,"[73] will appear a hollow play with "chance," the most hollow of all words.

Hollowness does not become less hollow when its volume is made to grow to cosmic dimensions as done by advocates of a universe *open* to *all* possibilities such as Prigogine and Popper. What they actually look for is not so much a universe open to intellectual inquiry as a universe lost in diffuseness where one cannot be sure of any specific rule and certainly not of the rule of chance. Indeed the very same physicist, Alvin Toffler, who wrote the introduction to *Order out of Chaos* of Prigogine and Stengers, admitted that the book does not have an answer to the question, What is chance?[74] In the absence of a clear definition of chance, even as a mathematical formalism, the ultimate result will be a universe that continually tries to come up with its real identity but does not succeed. Radical uncertainty envelops everything in that book, even the Creator. Tellingly, it is not the biblical Creator but the one in the Talmud that Prigogine and Stengers find congenial to their train of thought. That "creator" does not say that all was very good but merely: "Let's hope it works." Worse, he does say this only after he had made two dozen trial-and-error moves to create a universe.[75]

The intellectual twilight of Cabbala, as a mere game with numbers,[76] will reveal its sheer darkness when exposed to beacons that come from two opposite corners about the ultimate or ultracosmic significance of chance. In one corner, one finds a high Communist official declared guilty for having cavorted with objective truth transcending the fiats of the Party. To defend the wilful and therefore ultimately capricious or chancy character of Party dictatorship, the agent of the KGB remains the victim of an age-old connection: specific, objective truth ushers in God, whereas "as long as chance rules God is an anachronism."[77] In the other corner one finds John Henry Newman, one of the very few great intellects who could claim without boasting of not having sinned against the light. As Darwin's *Origin of Species* filled many Christians with dark forebodings, Newman, the great logician, kept his cool. He knew that since ultimately logic prevails, those with logic on their side can be patient. No touch of drama weakens the devastating force of his remark made in 1868 that "at first sight I do not [see] that the *accidental* evolution of organic beings is inconsistent with divine design — It is accidental to *us* not to *God*."[78] Had he been asked a few years later, after the publication of the *Descent of Man*, he would have settled the issue with a similar distinction resting on plain logic. No more and no less is deserved by such latter-day sequels to the Darwinist descent of man as Monod's pontification: "Man at last knows that he is alone in the unfeeling immensity of the universe, out of which he emerged by chance."[79] The origin of chance in a universe which, according to Monod, could not be the result of chance, remains a question of logic not of science, a question never confronted either by him or any of his allies.

Propensity as pseudo-mysticism
No answer to a similar question of logic is offered by Popper who in order to explain man's creative freedom invests the universe with creativity. His *Open Universe* should have been entitled "the diffuseness of an animated agglomerate." One can hardly speak of uni-verse if it is, as Popper would have it, partly causal, partly probabilistic, and partly emergent. That such a universe is a contradiction in terms transpires from Popper's claim that the universe is open because it contains man with a creative freedom and yet the universe had been possessed of freedom before it produced man.[80] It is not logic that supports Popper's claim, made also very recently at the World Congress of Philosophy in Brighton this past August, that the universe is ruled by propensities.[81] To be sure, Popper did his best to couch this Bergsonian rehash of Darwinism in the scientific

metaphor of dice-throwing. That he offered mere rhetoric should be clear from his rather low esteem for scientific cosmology and cosmogony which, in his very words, are "still almost borderline cases for physical science."[82]

Propensity is not a factor that can be subjected to falsification, the Popperian criterion of truth. Propensities are like tastes, unarguable. The free propensity of a nature which, in all evidence, is without freedom to produce free man capable of doing cosmology, that is, to have genuine science about the cosmos, is a quasi-mystical idea that may warm one's heart but only by closing one's mind. Quite open to cold scientific considerations is, however, the very basis, this earth of ours and its immediate cosmic neighborhood, from which alone can man do cosmology. As it has been argued in the first six chapters, 20th-century man's efforts to unveil the features of the universe show one common result: the universe everywhere appears exceedingly specific and all efforts aimed at diluting those specificities run up against inexorable specificities, observational and theoretical. As will be shown in the next chapter, this is no less true when a close look is taken at the very physical basis of cosmology, the earth and its immediate cosmic neighbourhood.

Chapter Seven

EARTH'S LUCK

> This spaceship earth, and the luckiest in all
> space
>
> S. L. Jaki

Eratosthenes' luck
Physicist-cosmologists time and again have waxed philosophical to the point of wondering, the very point where philosophy begins. Insofar as their chief object of research is the universe, they have been given to wonderment in two ways. Either the mind that grasps the universe appeared to them wondrous, or they were amazed by the extent of that grasp as being co-terminous with the universe itself. The first is instanced by Einstein's calling it a most incomprehensible thing that the mind could comprehend the universe.[1] The second is often sparked by reflecting on the fact that a mere earthling can carry his thoughts into the farthest spaces in a way which is not a flight of fancy but solid science.

This fact reminded Prof. Murray Gell-Mann of an ant discoursing confidently about the skyscraper towering above it. An ant as related to a skyscraper is much too large to convey man's proportion to the universe. By his size man stands somewhere in the middle between atoms and a typical galaxy of which there are billions in the universe. Yet for all his puniness man is now reaching out towards the very boundaries of the universe. His eventual success will be, to continue with Prof. Gell-Mann, a marvel far more impressive than all the techno-

logical wonders that have come along with scientific cosmology and are still to come: "Most remarkable will be
that a handful of beings on a small planet circling an
insignificant star will have traced their origin back to the
very beginning — a small speck of the universe comprehending the whole."[2]

The last words, "comprehending the whole," are philosophical to such a degree as to make it almost irresistible
not to seize on them. Yet, as has been noted repeatedly in
the previous chapters, it is most unlikely that physicist-
cosmologists would be seized by philosophical vistas
with horizons far deeper than the ones afforded by idealism, empiricism, and pragmatism, the kinds of
philosophies they know at least by hearsay. It is more
promising to press physicist-cosmologists on some scientific points with specific exactness as possible openings
for perspectives that are genuinely philosophical. In the
foregoing quotation such a point is the reference to a
small planet, that is, our earth. For the science of cosmology is more profoundly earth-based than generally
assumed, if this fact is paid attention at all. Indeed, no
useful start could be made in a scientific understanding
of the universe until the earth had been literally sized up
more than two thousand years ago and in Greece, of
course. But there too, the feat, simplicity itself as it may
appear in retrospect, had been preceded by a series of
gropings in the dark.

The speculations of the Ionians about the universe
may seem tantalizing in retrospect, but they offered no
scientific hold on it. No tangible advance toward science
was implied in their general cosmological dicta, such as
Thales' reduction of all kinds of matter to one, water, or
Anaximander's speaking of the earth's stability "on
account of its similar distance from all things."[3] The specific data they offered about those things — the earth, the
planets and the stars — may seem, in retrospect, to block
rather than promote that advance. Suffice it to recall
Anaximander's account of the earth as a flat cylinder

whose height is a third of its width, or his cosmology dotted with quaint specifics:

> The heavenly bodies come into being as a circle of fire separated off from the fire in the world, and enclosed by air. There are breathing-holes, certain pipe-like passages, at which the heavenly bodies show themselves; accordingly eclipses occur when the breathing-holes are blocked up. The moon is seen now waxing, now aging according to the blocking or opening of the channels. The circle of the sun is 27 times the size of the earth, that of the moon 18 times; the sun's circle is the largest, the circles of the fixed stars are the smallest.[4]

Very wrong quantitative data about the cosmos posed only slightly less of an obstacle to its being grasped scientifically than did utterances which smeared out the specifics by allowing an infinite variety of them. "The circular cloak or membrane," which according to Democritus enveloped the cosmos through the entanglement of atoms hooked with one another, could not appear very real in the context of his often quoted declaration:

> There are innumerable worlds which differ in size. In some worlds there is no sun and moon, in others they are larger than in our world, and in others more numerous. The intervals between the worlds are unequal; in some parts there are more worlds, in others fewer; some are increasing, some at their height, some decreasing; in some part they are arising, in others failing. They are destroyed by collision one with another. There are some worlds devoid of living creatures or plants or any moisture.[5]

Clearly then, that all-encompassing membrane too had to be subject to being varied in a great many ways, in size as well as endurance. Such an implication could but cast pallor on the notion of the universe as a strict totality.

The early atomists' carefree cavorting with all possible sizes, so different from interest in an always narrowly specific actual size, is reflected in Anaxagoras' thinking about the universe. Whether he had taken other worlds to be endowed, like ours, with a sun and a moon, was a point of debate in Late Antiquity.[6] No doubts seemed to exist about the genuineness of his view that

> the sun, the moon and all the stars are red-hot stones which the rotation of the ether carries round with it. Beneath the stars are certain bodies, invisible to us, that are carried round with the sun and moon. We do not feel the heat of stars because they are so far from the earth; moreover, they are not as hot as the sun because they occupy a colder region. The moon is beneath the sun and nearer to us. The sun exceeds the Peloponnese in size. The moon has not any light of its own but derives it from the sun. The stars in their revolution pass beneath the earth.[7]

For taking the celestial bodies for mere stones, however fiery, and the sun to be not much larger a stone than the stone-strewn Peloponnese, Anaxagoras became guilty of impiety and was banished from Athens. More serious should seem the crime of his reductionism. It provoked a most fateful turn in Western thought. From the extreme of his youthful enthusiasm for Anaxagoras' mechanical explanation of everything, physical as well as mental, Socrates moved to the other extreme and, through his extraordinary influence, he carried with him much of the rest of Greek intellectual history. Through the Socratic influence pre-modern Western man became overly preoccupied with search for goals, that is, whether everything happened for its good.[8] The injection of value-judgments into mere physical processes could but slight questions about their quantitative aspects.

This is not to suggest that Plato and Aristotle, who articulated in full the implications of the Socratic turn, succeeded in turning every intellect away from the quantitative study of nature. Such studies did not, however, create a sufficiently broad interest. Had the opposite been true, less mysterious would be that development which, during the era of Plato and Aristotle, led to Euclid's astonishing systematization of a vast geometrical lore on hand. The same lack of broad interest may explain why so little has been preserved about the quantitative speculations concerning the earth's size that must have preceded its exact determination by Eratosthenes about a hundred years after Euclid, or in the latter half of the 3rd century B.C. To be sure, the sphericity of the earth, as well as of the sun, moon, and stars, had been for generations before Eratosthenes a widely accepted view among the learned. But just as spheres with no specific size are of little use, the earth's sphericity too remained, through its lack of being measured, useless for a concrete grasp of the size of the universe enclosed within the sphere of the fixed stars. The sphericity of all celestial bodies could at most inspire, from Plato on, guesses about harmonies, ratios, octaves, and the like about the relative distances of the planets.[9]

When seen in this light, Eratosthenes' method, by which the size of the earth could be computed to within 95 per cent of its modern value, will appear much more than a pointer to large distances on the earth than previously imagined. Eratosthenes himself did not perceive the implications of his method for a first step toward a reliable size-up of the cosmos as it appeared to him and to the learned of classical times. Though called the "all-around" scholar in his time and the "beta," that is, the second only to the best specialist in any field,[10] Eratosthenes remained mainly a geographer. He did not earn for himself the respect of Strabo, *the* geographer of classical Antiquity, who himself lacked interest in cosmology. Otherwise Strabo would have been puzzled by the fail-

ure of the learned in the court of Pharaoh Necho to ponder a curious report of some Egyptian sailors who started
their voyage southward along Africa's east coast. A year
or so later, as they turned around what is now called the
Cape of Good Hope, they found the noon-day sun shin-
ing on them from starboard. This was a proof of the
sphericity of the earth, but for reasons that will be clear
shortly, it could not make a dent on the ancient Egyp-
tians' view of the cosmos.

Taken in itself, Eratosthenes' method should seem
simplicity itself, though not without a generous ingredient of luck of which even a modern geographer should
be appreciative. Of all long rivers on the earth, there is
only one, the Nile, whose course is not only south to
north, but also connects a point directly under the eclip-
tic with a point in the relatively temperate zone in which
a great center of learning, such as the Museum of Alexandria, could develop. From there Eratosthenes could
sail up to Syene, a city at about 5000 stades to the south,
to verify the fact that there at noon the sun is directly
overhead and casts therefore no shadow. Eratosthenes
had, of course, countless occasions to note that at equi-
noctial noon in Alexandria an angle of seven and a half
degrees was formed by a pole and the sun's rays. From
this he could easily calculate the circumference of the
earth to be about 250,000 stades which is about 5 per cent
less than the actual value or about 24,890 miles.

The moon's lucky place

Luck on earth was not enough to lift cosmology into its
first phase of soaring from that launching pad which
Eratosthenes' method constituted. A real start in scientific cosmology would not have come about if the earth
had not had for companion the moon, deserving to be
called the earth's greatest luck. This luck has usually
been ignored in the context of the recent upsurge of
studies of the history of science as they replace more and

more the study of classics as the main framework of cultural formation.[11] Little attention is paid to that "greatest luck" as references are made in those studies to Aristarchus[12] who around 150 B.C. provided man with his first genuine opportunity to soar in mind, but in a quantitatively reliable way, above the earth to the moon and beyond it to the sun. Yet paying close attention to that "luck" was an essential ingredient to Aristarchus' success in devising his method of measuring the size of the moon and the sun and their relative and absolute distances from the earth. His method will readily appear the first truly scientific step in the study of the cosmos through a quick look at Ptolemy's system of the planets. The latter would have remained a bizarre complex of paths generated by a superimposition of circles had it not contained, with a reliance on Aristarchus' work, an intimation of the vastness of a geocentric system of the world.

Actually, that intepretation would have remained on the level of Plato's *Timaeus* and Aristotle's *On the Heavens*. That level may seem very advanced compared with the grossly animistic views prevailing in all ancient cultures about the cosmos. While Aristotle speaks of the universe as a living being,[13] he, though a biologist, brings in no biological metaphors. His cosmos is worlds removed from the crude biologism of the Egyptian myth in which the arching body of a female deity, Nut, represents the sky, the body of another deity Geb, the earth, and the two are kept apart by the body of the god Shu. Aristotle's cosmos contains no traces of that Hindu myth which presents the universe as the perspiring body of Brahman or of the ancient Chinese explanation of the cosmos in terms of part of the human body. But Aristotle's cosmos should seem an unlucky construct compared with the modern view which ultimately rests on Aristarchus' sagacious use of the fortunate equality between the apparent sizes of the sun and the moon. Because of that equality it takes exactly as much time for the moon, at a full lunar eclipse, to disappear completely in the shadow of the earth as it takes for its leading edge to reappear from the shadow. As a result, a very simple set of interconnected triangles could be drawn by Aristarchus to illustrate the absolute sizes of the sun and the moon as well as their absolute distances from the earth.

Neither Ptolemy, nor Proclus who carried such distance calculations to the sphere of the fixed stars,[14] nor Aristarchus himself (to say nothing of modern narrators of his most ingenious method) expressed wonderment over the fact that both the night sky and the day sky were dominated by a large body of the same apparent size. Possibly they found in this a nice, that is, "natural" symmetry. Aristarchus' most ingenuous method depended, of course, also on the close coincidence of the planes of the sun and the moon without which there could be no full lunar eclipse. Whatever the probability of that coincidence, the improbability of that equality must appear rather obvious to modern man in possession of data about the distances from the sun of Mars, Jupiter, Saturn, and Uranus and about the size of their systems of moons.

To be specific, while from Mars the sun's apparent diameter is only one half of what it appears from the earth, no one at Mars can see with the naked eye its two very small moons. Only one moon of Jupiter, Io, would appear from its planet roughly equal in size to our moon. Galileo, Ganymede, and Callisto, Jupiter's three other large moons, would appear from there as having, respectively, one-half, one-third, and one-fifth of the moon's apparent diameter. From Jupiter the sun would appear a small disk, hardly larger than a bright star. Seen from Saturn the sun would be just another bright star. Titan, Saturn's largest moon, would have one half of our moon's apparent diameter. Only one of Uranus' moons, Titania, would have one half as large an apparent diameter as does our moon. Aristarchus was indeed lucky not to live on any of those planets, and not to live even on the moon. From there the earth's apparent diameter would appear three times as large as the moon appears from the earth.

That the moon just covers the sun in a full solar eclipse was not necessary for the purposes of Aristarchus, but has been most helpful for modern astronomers. That coincidence made possible the study of solar proturberances. Of course, astronomers needed spectroscopes before they could definitely decide that those protuberances belonged to the sun and not to the moon, but their spectroscopes would have been useless without the moon's providing the appropriate shield from the light coming from the sun's disk. It was in this connection that W. McCrea remarked: "Man's interpretation of the heavens might have been significantly different had the two bodies [the sun and the moon] been seen to have manifestly different [apparent] sizes."[15]

Aristarchus had no reason to assume that the moon could have been bigger or smaller, let alone that it was far from necessary for it to move in its actual plane. At this point one might be tempted to say that, of course, now we know better. Actually, few people do. In the broader cultural consciousness, scientific and lay, it is widely assumed that the moon has to be where it is. The reason for this is that myths die hard even in science. Ever since Laplace formulated his nebular hypothesis about the formation of the solar system, most questionable features of that hypothesis have remained part and parcel of the scientific outlook.[16] The fact is that if there is one feature of the solar system which is unexplainable on the basis of Laplace's theory, or of its subsequent rehashes, that feature is the earth-moon system.

The moon as the earth's luck
Laplace's hypothesis begins with a roughly spherical and slowly rotating large gaseous mass. As it contracts under its gravitational attraction, its rate of rotation

increases and its shape flattens. The next step, largely
hypothetical, is that the outer edge of that further flatten-
ing spheroid separates itself in the form of a ring from
the main body. After this process repeats itself several
times, one has on hand a main central body surrounded
by concentric rings. These rings are then supposed to
coalesce into single bodies, or protoplanets. It is further
assumed that the protoplanets too can by the same
mechanism produce satellites or moons around them. In
sum, in the Laplacean theory a planetary system, fairly
similar to ours, is a typical outcome around each and
every star. What is, however, typical, is not a product of
luck, if luck can produce anything at all.

Wishful thinking is the only explanation for the great
popularity which the nebular hypothesis enjoyed for a
long time. Laplace himself should have known that his
theory could not cope with the fact that whereas 98 per
cent of the solar system's mass is in the sun, the sun has
only two per cent of the total angular momentum.
Laplace could also have found out that a ring of small
particles of matter does not coalesce into a single body.[17]
At any rate, Laplace was not perplexed at all by the fact
that among the 30 or so moons in the solar system one
moon, our own moon, is enormously large with respect
to its planet, the earth. Jupiter's diameter is over 20 times
that of its largest moon, Callisto, and Saturn's diameter
is over 30 times that of its largest moon, Titan. Phobos
and Demos have diameters that are 200 and 400 times
smaller than that of Mars. Compared with the fractions
1/20, 1/30, 1/200, and 1/400, the ratio 1/4 of the diameters
of the earth and the moon should seem enormously
large. Even more striking will the largeness of the moon's
mass appear with respect to the earth when one considers the total mass of any other moon-system and relates
that value to the mass of the particular planet that keeps
them together. While the figure is 0.012 for the moon-
earth mass ratio, the corresponding figure is about a
hundred times smaller for Jupiter, Saturn, and Uranus,

and ten times smaller for Neptune, although all these planets have moons in large numbers.[18]

Such disparities, available for the most part during the second half of the nineteenth century, did not play a serious role when during the same time specific objections began to be raised about the general validity of Laplace's theory. One could not, of course, expect a Herbert Spencer, who took that theory for the highest form of science, to pay heed to detailed demonstrations of its basic faults as they culminated around 1900 in the studies of Chamberlin and Moulton.[19] Herbert Spencer's autobiography, published in 1904, concluded with a reference to 30 million or so planetary systems similar to ours in the Milky Way.[20] But even those with less dogmatic attachment to Laplace's theory failed to notice the deadly blow which the earth-moon system implies for the explanation of our solar system as a typical fact present in every nook-and-cranny of the universe. It may, of course, be such a fact but all evidence, theoretical and observational, gathered during the last hundred years, indicates the contrary.

A hundred or so years ago George Darwin offered his explanation of the origin of the moon that could appear to be compatible with Laplace's theory.[21] No new mathematics or physics were relied upon by Jeffreys when half a century later he showed that, contrary to Darwin, the moon's origin cannot be looked for in a body fissioned from the earth owing to the latter's fast rotation.[22] Jeffreys' work dealt a further blow to the view, already in some disrepute in the 1920s, that the solar system developed through a typical, that is, most probable mechanism. By then it had become abundantly clear that the planetesimal theory, proposed around 1900 by Chamberlin and Moulton, could not assure the coalescence of small bits of matter, called planetesimals, into single planets, and much less into such planets with a dynamical equilibrium with one another and with their central sun. No help in this respect came when in the 1940s O.Y. Schmidt showed that if one assumed a finely-tuned collision between two stars and a gaseous mass, the angular momentum problem of the resulting "solar system" could be solved.[23]

The wealth of new data that has accrued since the onset of the space-age about the planetary system, only increased the complexity of its origin. Those data strongly support the blunt words that "the solar system is a horrible scientific experiment. It's a bunch of odd balls — but we're stuck with it."[24] If in that bewildering situation there appeared a clear delimitation of the avenue to be followed up, it related to the origin of the moon. The fact that among all planetary bodies only the moon and the earth had identical oxygen isotope ratios served one more evidence against seeking the moon's origin in the capture of a body from an independent heliocentric orbit. The same ratios also posed added difficulty to the theory of a co-accretion from a swarm of planetesimals in a geocentric orbit.

Had not problems of this type been very much in the back of the minds of those forming the subcommittee of the Lunar and Planetary Sample Team, they would not have found most congenial the suggestion of one of their members: "Why not expand the focus to the origin and early evolution of the lunar crust?"[25] The result was the three dozen or so papers presented at the Conference on the origin of the moon, held in Kona, Hawai. October 13-16, 1984, papers issued in an impressive volume two years later.[26] Although at the Conference the capture, fission, and coaccretion theories still had some advocates, the majority tended in the direction of various forms of the giant impact theory. Enough is revealed about the strength of that shift by the words of a somewhat wary observer: the Conference saw "a megaimpact hypothesis of lunar origin emerge as a strong contender, not because of any dramatic new development or infusion of data, but because the hypothesis was given a serious and sustained attention for the first time. The resulting bandwagon has picked up speed (and some hastened to jump aboard)."[27]

In a simplified form the megaimpact scenario, first outlined in papers published in 1975 and 1976,[28] begins with a very finely tuned impact against the earth by a body with about one-tenth of the earth's mass. The impact must, of course, occur in the right plane, at the right time, at the right angle, in the right direction, and with a very specific speed. With all these conditions satisfied, computer simulation of the results indicate that six minutes after the collision of that body with the earth, their surfaces are crushed together; another six minutes later two gaseous jets, one larger and one smaller, erupt; still another six minutes later the large jet, with a temperature of 12,000°C, begins to cool and expand; ten hours later its material begins to coalesce and 23 hours after the collision it appears in the earth's sky as a large disk with a slowly outward spiralling orbit around the earth. The chief advantage of the theory, also called the Big Whack hypothesis, is that it explains why such heavy metals as platinum and gold are found close to the earth's surface and why the moon is very deficient in iron and siderophile materials. They are the remnants of the crushed body of the moon's predecessor. There is, however, no need to subscribe to H. J. Melosh's glowing appraisal of the process: "The giant impact scenario seems to have cut the Gordian knot of the three classic theories. It requires no magic, no special pleading, and no deus ex machina. It just works."[29]

The probability of the entire process, be it simulated by a giant computer,[30] should seem very low. This seems to be implied in R. H. Durisen's remark: "Before there was a tendency to think that if you appealed to a random event, that was sort of a cop-out, not an explanation. Now you actually expect there to be a few oddball events."[31] The opposite is conveyed by the figure submitted by W. K. Hartmann and D. R. Davies in 1975,[32] and defended by Hartmann at the Kona Conference: "This model can thus account . . . at the same time for the moon's uniqueness; the moon may have originated by a process that was likely to happen to one out of nine planets."[33]

Behind this exceedingly generous estimate, there may lie at work an assumption that throughout the entire modern history of theories of the origin of planetary systems distracted from obvious and very serious problems. The assumption derives from the essentially a priori belief that planetary systems ought to be an ubiquitous feature throughout the universe.[34] While that belief can be found clearly voiced in the vast literature, all too often one finds there but indirect expression of a still more influential belief supporting the former. According to that belief, more metaphysical (or rather counter-metaphysical) than scientific, man is a necessary product of purely physical evolutionary processes. Advocates of that belief have always found an uneasy reminder to the contrary in evidences in the light of which the planetary system appears a most improbable event. It should seem rather revealing that advocates of an evolution based on "chance" cannot live with "chance" insofar as it means truly a chance, that is, a very low probability.

The idea that it is very lucky for the earth to have not only a moon but our very moon, goes far beyond the opportunity offered thereby to Aristarchus and the subsequent development of cosmology. Without the moon there would be no cosmologists because cosmologists had to be preceded by cavemen and cavemen by a long sequence of humans and hominids, who in turn are but the latest ripple in a long evolutionary wave of life. In the production of that wave the role of the moon, and its coming to the stage at a most specific time when the earth's crust was not yet fully solidified, was paramount.

In the role played by the moon in biological evolution on earth, the most obvious is the moon's tidal pull as the cause of tidewater zones which are known to have been indispensable for the passing of life from the ocean to the dry land. But the moon's role is far deeper in the literal sense too. Its tidal pull caused the gradual deceleration of the earth's rotation from about 4 to the present 24 hours. A gradually slower alternation of daylight and darkness was very beneficial to the evolution of life which also benefited from an ever slower decrease in the earth's rotation. But the rotation of the earth's metallic molten core did not decelerate to the same extent and this is why the earth still has a very strong magnetic field. The latter deflects much of the cosmic radiation from the all-important ozone layer in the upper atmosphere, and therefore indirectly maintains the high amount of oxygen in the lower atmosphere.

This is not to suggest that a double planet, such as the earth-moon system (a unique feature even in the solar system), has much time during which the conditions on the main or active member (the earth) are favorable for the development of life. But on a single planet the chances should seem practically nil for the same to happen. Were our earth without its moon, its mass should be far greater and its rotation much faster in order to have a molten core with a strong magnetic field, but then the earth would have lacked other characteristics necessary for the development of life. Leaving aside the hypothetical status of the origin of organic life on earth (let alone that of intelligent life), a proper magnetic core not only promotes biological evolution but also gives it strange twists. The behaviour of the earth's molten core is subject to turbulences with the result that its axis of rotation can completely reverse itself. Consequent to this reversal of the earth's magnetic field are major climatic changes that bring about the extinction of many species.[35] The surviving species, including us humans, can once more thank the earth's luck in having the moon for a companion.

The earth as the cosmologists' luck
Earthlings interested in doing cosmology have in the

earth a lucky platform for other reasons as well. One is
the fact, hardly a necessary outcome in geological evolution, that much of the dry land is located in the northern
hemisphere. There the chances were not too low for an
eventual guessing of the slow variation in the position of
the apparent celestial pole. The reason for this is that
Polaris is one of the sixty brightest stars in the entire sky.
Moreover, Polaris is visually connected with two such
notable constellations as the Big Bear and the Small
Bear. No sufficiently bright star is visible around the
southern celestial pole, an area conspicuously void also
of any significant constellation of stars. Hipparchus, the
first to speak of the precession of the equinoxes, could
have hardly made that discovery, so portentous for the
eventual recognition of the rotation of the earth, if he
and the Babylonians, from whom he inherited many
data, had lived in the southern hemisphere.

Modern astronomers too should consider themselves
lucky for having the earth for their observation post.
First, Sirius, the brightest star in our sky, happens to
have a white dwarf for its companion from which enormously much has been learned about stellar structure
and evolution. From our earth, or the vicinity of the sun,
there is an excellent view of the Crab nebula, which is
one of the extremely rare supernova remnants. It is the
basis of so much information in astrophysics that an
astronomer was prompted to say that astrophysics consists of the astrophysics of the Crab nebula and the rest.[36]
Then there is the famous quasar 3C 273 which is 100
times brighter than the 100 million or so quasars within
the reach of existing optical telescopes. It is also an X ray
source, it contains two compact radio sources, gives
strong emission in the infrared too, and has a visible jet.
In addition, its component features can be studied with
great accuracy because its position is frequently occulted
by the moon. The chances for this are 1/2000, a figure
which, however expressive, is an insignificant addition

to the incredibly high improbability that the moon is a companion of the earth at all.

Of course, the chief luck of the earth, with or without the moon, is that it is still where it is. If the earth is a spaceship, it is the luckiest in all space for its course could not have been charted in a more perilous way. At every 25 million years or so the earth is exposed to an unusually heavy bombardment by comets and meteorites of all size. The most likely reason for this is our sun's still hypothetical dark companion, called Nemesis,[37] whose orbit periodically goes through the very "dusty" main plane of the Milky Way and by its gravitational pull unleashes from there a horde of meteors and comets toward the solar system. Their impacts on the earth can produce craters with diameters of 30 miles, such as the one in Arizona. Similar craters were found even in ocean beds through photographs taken by artificial satellites. Such craters are the remnants of impacts that stir up enormous amounts of dust. The result is in each case a sudden greenhouse effect on earth with the consequent extinction of many forms of life.

This is not the place to survey the impact which all this made on students of evolution. One wonders what today would be the reaction of Darwin who staked the success of his theory on a slow, non-catastrophic geological evolution of the earth's surface and atmosphere. The answer to the question is not too difficult to guess. Darwin would stick to his theory, just as he did when Wallace, the co-discoverer of natural selection, argued that man's need for verbal communication as a tool of survival, presupposed the existence of a larger brain which that need was supposed to generate in very slow steps. Presented with a cart-before-the-horse problem Darwin denied its existence with an imperious No![38]

This attitude can be noticed on many occasions in the writings of present-day evolutionists. The great generalization of evolution makes its champions time and again insensitive to countless difficulties and unsolved prob-

lems in it. They are wont to take the enormously hazard-
ous, wobbling, reversing course of evolution with its
thousands upon thousands of dead-ends for a straightforward course, necessarily issuing in intelligent beings.
Hence the widespread belief, almost a cultural dogma,
that it is most reasonable to spend large sums of money
on equipments whereby one can tune in to radio-mes-
sages from extraterrestrial civilizations.

The six million dollars recently appropriated by the
US Congress to be spent in Fiscal 1989 on an improved
MCSA (multichannel spectrum analyzer) is a first step
in an estimated 90 million-dollar program which is to
take ten years to implement.[39] Actual listening is to start
on Columbus Day 1992, the 500th anniversary of the discovery of the New World and a symbolic anticipation of
detecting signals from worlds far beyond the solar system. Listening will be done simultaneously on millions
of wavelengths, but especially on wavelengths emitted by
natural masers, that is, free floating hydroxil molecules
which are abundant in regions, such as the Orion nebula, where stars are born, or in the atmosphere of red
giants. Such natural masers emit waves in unison and
therefore can conceivably be used as natural amplifiers
of artificially generated signals.

"An advanced civilization might use such natural
masers as an amplifier," so stated the acting director
of the project sponsored by NASA.[40] What is hidden in
that statement, apparently purely technical, is a philosophical assumption, or rather a very selective view on
evolution. Only a few in the SETI (Search for Extra-Ter-
restrial Intelligence) program would admit that, in view
of evolution's most haphazard history on earth, life
would not produce human-like beings elsewhere in the
universe, as even on earth evolution would not take
again the same course. Yet even these relatively few
hardy souls take it for granted that intelligent life will
necessarily arise, strange as its bodily form may be. A
classic in this respect is a passage of Loren Eiseley who

tried to balance his description of man's utter loneliness in the universe by evoking the presence everywhere of intellectual power. Yet that power was embodied "in great instruments handled by strange manipulative organs" whose owners could but "stare vainly at our floating cloud wrack." They could not therefore be taken for our cousins, however distant: "In the nature of life and in the principles of evolution we have had our answer. Of men elsewhere, and beyond, there will be none forever."[41]

But can an evolutionary theory, in which all is matter, provide logical ground for the emergence of mind as a form of living matter which is not subject to the law of speciation? That law means the inexorable rise of barriers among the different species. A chief of those barriers means the breakdown of biological altruism. While more often than not members of the same species do not feed on one another, members of one species all too often constitute the basic food for members of another species. There is a profound biological wisdom in the remark, now three decades old, by the Nobel-laureate physicist, C. N. Yang, that we should not try to answer an eventual radio message from another planetary system.[42] Unwisdom, indeed a rank misunderstanding of what alone can be derived from the premises of Darwinian evolution, blares forth from Carl Sagan's protest against a *New York Times* editorial, a protest aimed at taking the sting out of a possible "extraterrestrial cannibalism":

> It is implicit in the evolutionary process that extra-terrestrial carnivores are unlikely to find the sequences of amino acids in human proteins especially tasty. Even if human beings were a famous interstellar delicacy, the freightage would be prohibitively high; it would be much cheaper to synthesize proteins in the amino acid sequences favored by extraterrestrial gastronomes than to muster a luncheon expedition to Earth.[43]

Sagan's rebuttal, with a reference to radiosignals, of the objection that "we are unlikely to understand a message from another civilization," is also gravely at fault from the viewpoint of Darwinism which he so spiritedly advocates. The law of speciation means also that communication breaks down among animals that have earlier been members of the same family in active communication with one another. The incredibly crafty steps that constitute the skill of the European female cuckoo, whereby it makes a large variety of other birds hatch its eggs, failed to be imitated by them, advantageous as it could be for at least some of them. The reason for this is that no skill can be communicated across species barriers. Language, which is man's foremost skill, is a tool for communication only with those with whom he can interbreed, exaggerated claims about successful teaching human words to gorillas notwithstanding.[44] Within the genuinely Darwinist perspective there is no ground for assuming that extraterrestrial beings, as described by Eiseley, could communicate except with their own kin. Indeed, within that Darwinist perspective there is no ground for supposing that they would develop scientific instruments which, as far as we know them, are intrinsically connected with *our* way of conceptualizing and verbalizing our perceptions of the external world. Every human word in any human language is the intellectual registering of a universal, a demonstration of the intellect's universality and of the universal intelligibility of the material world. But this is precisely what cannot be assumed within the strict materialism of the Darwinist evolution (or of artificial intelligence programs) without begging the question about the meaning of the intellect.[45]

Utmost caution should therefore be exercised in reference to the so-called anthropic principle. Its reliable part is the recognition, largely connected with the consequences of the 2.7°K radiation, that the universe is so constituted from its earliest phases as to issue in the formation of the Mendeleev-table of elements. There carbon is the element that offers by far the largest variety of chemical combinations. It is therefore no accident that the enormous complexity of life substances is carbon based. But does it follow from this that the universal presence of carbon guarantees the universal presence of life, let alone of intelligent life? The distance from simple carbon to large organic molecules is in itself very long, and the road from there to self-reproducing units is even longer and not yet fully charted. Beyond that is the even vaster course of evolution properly so called with all its hazards, detours, dead-ends, and, what is even worse, regularly recurring come-uppances.

The latter take place whenever the mind forgets its true status vis-à-vis physical reality. Science was born in the midst of endless references, it is enough to think of Francis Bacon, to the docility which man must show toward the physical world if its structure and workings are ever to be deciphered. Here too success went quickly to the head and great accumulation of success literally turned some heads. Not a few utterances of 20th-century cosmologists are shocking examples of that hubris whereby man's mind tries to understand the universe so thoroughly as to cast doubt on understanding insofar as it means the comprehension of something distinct from the mind. No wonder that some prominent cosmologists readily gave self-defeating interpretations to the anthropic principle. Science writers and plain journalists, always ready to seize on intoxicating views, do the rest. A telling case of this is the caption, " I think therefore the universe exists," that graced in *The New York Times Book Review* the account of *The Anthropic Cosmological Principle* by J. Barrow and F. Tipler.[46]

That there is some connection between that caption and the thrust of that book may be gathered from two facets in it. One is that the entire first part, about 200 pages, of a book written by an astronomer and a mathematical physicist, is a survey of a more than two-thousand-year-old history of the design argument, and of the no less philosophical topic of modern reformulations of teleology. As one would expect, the result is heavy on dilettantism, though with one saving grace. The authors' very selective reading of the literature, old and new, could not make them realize that in doing philosophy (even as a historical survey) the first and most elementary precept is to take proper stock of one's own philosophy. For even with a clear consciousness of one's philosophical convictions, one's appraisal of the views of others can be subject to distortion. Without it distortion becomes the rule. That Barrow and Tipler are victims of a most serious distortion can readily be gathered from the other facet, namely, that they asked Prof. Wheeler, well known for his preferences for the philosophical apriorism of an idealism that borders on solipsism, to write a foreword to their book.[47]

The book has been best remembered by its argument, recalled even in an editorial of the *New York Times*, that if there had been advanced extraterrestrial civilizations, visitors from there would have long ago landed on our earth.[48] Of course the point was made half a century ago by Enrico Fermi who dismissed speculations about extraterrestrials with the questions: "Where are the extraterrestrials? Why haven't they landed in their flying saucers on the White House lawn to welcome humanity to the Galactic Club?"[49] These questions imply much more than Fermi suspected, or Barrow and Tipler for that matter. Fermi may have thought of the technical difficulties of space travel which two decades later, shortly after Sputnik ushered in the Space Age, prompted another Nobel-laureate, E. Purcell, to settle the matter with words that demand no familiarity whatever with physics in order to be understood. Travel from one planetary system to another, he said in a lecture given at Brookhaven Laboratories in 1961, belongs to where it has been most prominently featured, the sides of cereal boxes.[50]

There is far more to the problems involved in interstellar travel than educated guesses as to what are the potentialities of the latest and best in science and what are the "scientific" merits of this or that technical proposition for detecting evidences about extraterrestrial civillizations. To limit attention, as Barrow and Tipler do, to such propositions that in spite of their scientific garb should rather to be called fancy guesses,[51] may, of course, earn "scholarly" reputation in an age in which only quantities, however irrelevant at times, seem to count. For all that the procedure is a mere battling of castles in the air, targets worthy of Sancho Panzas but not of rigorous thinkers. As to those castles, they are as unreal as would be any baseball game that started not from the pitcher's mound and from the batter's box, not even from first, second, or third base, but from the very last step which it takes the runner to touch home plate.

For the crucial question is not whether the potentialities of modern science can or cannot be stretched to the point of making the idea of interstellar travel or interstellar communication even remotely plausible. The crucial point is the philosophical answer given to the questions: what it means to know and what organ it takes to know? And since such philosophical perspectives, if they are really philosophical in the sense of a realist metaphysics, strike no chord with the typical cosmologist, in reference to extraterrestrials too a not so immediately philosophical area may be first explored with the hope of some meeting of minds. The area is the study of the manner in which science has reached its actual stage. Advocates of extraterrestrial civilizations assume that the rise of science on our earth, the place of the only known scientific civilization, is a foregone conclusion. To have such a view one needs to be trapped in a most superficial knowledge of the history of science, a view not much better than the one in which science begins when an apple falls right on the nose of Newton.

The lucky course of science on earth
The story about Newton and the apple may be unlikely,[52]

but it was not at all unlikely that young Newton might have become a victim of the plague that ravaged Cambridge in 1673. Historians of science still have to ponder the consequences if the duelist's sword, that cut off Tycho Brahe's nose, had also ruined his eyesight. A difference of a mere inch in the path of the sword of Brahe's antagonist would have deprived the world of those many and unusually accurate observations on which Brahe's assistant, Kepler, based his epoch-making work in astronomy. And what if young Horrocks, who served as the bridge between Kepler and Newton, had died not at the age of twenty-one but nineteen, just before putting in print a perspicacious account of Kepler's achievements, an account crucial for Newton? Any mortuary statistician, familiar with Horrocks' poor health, would be entitled to take the alternative for a tossup, although the alternatives meant drastically different consequences for science.

One may also ponder some outstanding chance discoveries. What if Roentgen had not placed a key on his stack of photographic paper in a room in which he worked with cathode rays? Of course, sooner or later someone else might have done it, but soon enough? For the exploitation of X-rays for the study of the structure of the atom came hard and fast following Roentgen's announcement of his discovery. Indeed, had that work been delayed, young Niels Bohr would have arrived to the scene much too soon. Had Bohr not devised his famed model of the hydrogen atom in 1913, Compton, de Broglie, Schrödinger, and Heisenberg, all young men in the 1920s, would not have had at their disposal data and ideas at a time when their genius was at its creative peak. The result, quantum mechanics, was indispensable for young Gamow to work out, in 1928, his theory of alpha-tunnelling, and was even more indispensable for him twenty or so years later, when he suggested the existence of a cosmic background radiation, characteristic of the very early universe. Without a fully developed quantum mechanics, not even a first step could have been made in the investigation of that universe which constitutes a major part of modern scientific cosmology. Quantum mechanics made possible the arrival in the early 1950s of semiconductor devices, of lasers and masers, and of high-speed computers — all of which are indispensable for experiments aimed at detecting signals from extraterrestrial civilizations. The long and precarious chain of all these developments could have been aborted right at its very start and interrupted time and again.

Cosmologists would do well to recall and ponder another scenario. What if Oersted had not made an inadvertent move with the compass in his hand? For the original aim of his classic experiment was to show that electric currents do *not* produce magnetic fields.[53] One may, of course, argue that in view of the ever larger number of current-carrying wires, Oersted's discovery would have been made sooner or later. But would it have been made soon enough to inspire that Faraday who himself was a most unlikely comer to the scientific scene? Was it blind chance or a Hand from above that led the poor apprentice through most improbable steps, first to Humphry Davy's laboratory and later into the directorship of the Royal Institution? From the purely sociological perspective the odds were astronomical against Faraday's success whatever his most methodical approach to the problem of electromagnetic induction. Nor was it necessary that Faraday be an Englishman, although this fact greatly facilitated Maxwell's exposure to the idea of lines of force which then led him to the theoretical derivation of electromagnetic waves, the very basis of any speculation about radio-communication with extraterrestrials. Those speculations still have to be extended to the estimating of chances that such and many other improbable modern scientific developments would be readily duplicated elsewhere in the cosmos.

For historians of science Maxwell is the great stepping stone to Einstein. Had the industrial bankruptcy of Ein-

stein's father occurred not in 1902 but in 1896, young
Albert Einstein could not have gone to a Swiss gymna-
sium to qualify for entrance at the Zurich Polytechnic
and might not have entered any university at all. About
his special relativity he readily admitted that it would
have been quickly formulated by someone else. He was
emphatic in attributing general relativity to his own
genius.[54] But he did not claim that without him it would
have never been formulated. In view of the logical connection between special and general relativity, the latter
too would have been formulated eventually, though perhaps with half a century delay. In that case twentieth-
century scientific cosmology would still have to be developed.

Of course, science is not made by geniuses alone, but
their role is as indispensable as it is unfathomable. Only
diehard Marxists and Dewey-type empiricists still entertain the illusion that geniuses are the inevitable products
of their socio-economic milieux. If there is a branch of
cultural history which lacks inevitability, it is science. To
see this one can safely ignore the role of a chance fall of
an apple in Newton's life. What cannot be ignored
relates to the chances that Newton should connect the
fall of anything, be it an apple, with the fall of the moon.
The special position and apparent size of the moon
haunt science at its major steps. In addition to its special
eclipses, the moon is also that celestial body whose
course can be measured with far greater accuracy than is
the case with any of the planets. Without that precision
no identity would have been discovered between the
acceleration of a freely falling body on the earth and of
another body in the heavens.

No problem in all this is seen within those easy gener-
alizations that make historiography, and the historiography of science too, a most reassuring and, by the same
stroke, a most misleading affair. It was, of course, fairly
straightforward for Newton to bring together the fall of
the apple and the fall of the moon, once he had decom-

posed the motion of the moon into an inertial and an accelerated motion. But what consideration gave him the courage to make that decomposition which would have been inconceivable, indeed, a sacrilegious procedure for Ptolemy, for Aristotle, for Plato, and for countless others who took the heaven for something divine, that is, totally different from the terrestrial realms?

Before facing up to that question loaded with theology, it may be useful to follow up the purely scientific problem behind Newton's decomposition of the moon's motion into an inertial and an accelerated motion. Although Newton did not invent the idea of either of those two motions, it may be assumed that once they were formulated, they would be further developed to the point where he could make ready use of them. In fact, for three centuries prior to Newton both kinds of motion had been discussed in ever wider circles and with ever greater precision. While there was some inevitability in that, the same cannot be said about the starting point, or Buridan's break with Aristotle's interpretation of the motion of celestial bodies. That break, in the form of Buridan's impetus theory,[55] made it possible for Copernicus to cope with the physical objections to the heliocentric theory.

It is the myth of the inevitability of the rise and development of science that generates insensitivity about the failure of the Greeks of old to formulate the idea of inertial motion, so pivotal for Newtonian physics. Endless celebrations of the Greek genius make it even less likely that the same problem should be considered in regard to other great ancient cultures — Egyptian, Hindu, Chinese, and Babylonian. Yet they all were rich in talent and most resourceful in practical inventions and technical achievements, some of them monumental. Once their failure with respect to the idea of inertial motion is considered, one may begin to sense that the rise of science was far from inevitable. Otherwise science would not have suffered repeated and monumental stillbirths[56] in cultures which included an India where the invention of the decimal system did not lead to a science of mathematics, and a China where the invention of gunpowder did not lead to a science of ballistics, and an Egypt where the greatest perhaps of all inventions, phonetic writing, did not dispel most irrational ways of thinking about the workings of nature.

Compared with ideographic writing, phonetic writing represents the kind of advance whose enormous measure suggests the very opposite to inevitability. Again, while inevitability may not be intrinsically absent in the still hypothetical transition from cave drawings to ideographic writing, the opposite is suggested by the fact that the tens of thousands of years of cave drawings show no trace of ideographic writing. The great number of wholly unsatisfactory theories of the "natural" origin of language, so indispensable to do either magic or science, does not make the appearance of talking animals an inevitable process. Invocation, if not plain incantation, of the word "evolution" is a sugar-coated nostrum to allay nagging doubts about the inevitability of cultural and ultimately scientific developments. Nothing has remained more timely than the remark made by the anthropologist, H. S. Harrison, before the British Association in 1930: "Man did very well before he was man at all, and no one has given any reason why he ceased to be an ape."[57] And if one dares to face up to the fact that on a strictly Darwinian basis the emergence of apes or of any earlier species, was anything but inevitable, one will open up a Pandora-box of questions that ultimately conjure up the greatest of the earth's lucks even from the perspective of science alone.

The greatest luck of science
For if one looks for reasons that operated in Buridan's mind as he formulated the idea of inertial motion, one stands out by the mere fact that Buridan explicitly refers

H

to it. The reason is that for him the universe is not only created out of nothing, but also created in time. It is the createdness of the universe that allowed those who believe in it to consider the celestial regions of being on equal footing with the rest and therefore governed by the same laws. Unlike Greek and other paganisms that drew the dividing line between the heavenly and terrestrial regions, Christianity drew that line between the supernatural and the natural.

There are, however, scientifically specific matters connected with that line as drawn by Christianity. Jacques Monod did not let those details transpire for a reason because any of those would have cast doubt on his chief contention that ethical considerations are "in essence *nonobjective*" and therefore "forever barred from the sphere of knowledge." Clearly then he could only admit no more about that radical distinction, to which he assigned the creation of science, than that "if this unprecedented event in the history of culture took place in the Christian West rather than in some other civilization, it was perhaps thanks, in part, to the fundamental distinction drawn by the Church between the domains of the sacred and the profane."[58] Monod shied away from the obvious question of how such a fundamentally ethical distinction, with no objective content, could help, however slightly, the eventual rise of science, allegedly the sole depositor of objective truths.

In particular as a Frenchman, Monod had no intellectual excuse for creating the impression that the help in question was merely possible. The militantly rationalistic French academia he represented can but have nightmares wherever reference is made to the name of Pierre Duhem, the most universal French genius around the turn of the century. For the whole rationalist interpretation of modern culture loses its credibility if serious attention is given to Duhem's monumental demonstration of the medieval Christian origin of science.[59] In that demonstration Buridan and his most prominent student,

Oresme, the future bishop of Lisieux, are the kingpins, a fact that does not appeal to many *gloire*-hungry Frenchmen and women because it is above all a Christian glory.

For Buridan's belief in a Creator was not simply a monotheistic belief. Its origin is, of course, that Jewish monotheism which, owing to Abraham's roots in Babylon, a land of rampant polytheism, cannot be taken for an inevitable development. But Buridan's monotheism was not Jewish, nor Muslim, for that matter. The Christian monotheism of Buridan has very special features because belief in Christ, as the only begotten Son in whom the Father created all, is a most special belief. A belief tied to a most obscure birth in an obscure corner of the globe may appear a mark of irrationality. The matter will look very different if one recalls the proverbial proclivity of Jewish and Muslim intellectuals towards pantheism and eternalism.[60] Belief in creation out of nothing and in time, on which rests Buridan's reasoning about the inertial character of the motion of celestial bodies, remained intact and robust only within Christian monotheism. The latter is, of course, anchored in an event which certainly qualifies as the very opposite to inevitability.

About the doctrine of Incarnation a most unhistorical claim has been made in a recent survey of the history of idea of the plurality of worlds and extraterrestrial civilizations. Contrary to that claim no Christian of any stature worried in the 17th century that the sighting of new worlds (planets and stars) by telescope would force a rethinking of Christ as a planet-hopping savior.[61] On the contrary, genuine Christian thinking during that century was still heavily indebted to a long-standing tradition. Within that tradition, a very dogmatic one, extra intellectual strength was given to the testimony which, according to the Psalms and other Old Testament writings, nature brought about its Creator.[62]

Part of that testimony related to the moon as the "faithful witness in the sky," to quote the words of Psalm

89. The moon was considered faithful, that is, fully reliable in its course, because its origin was not placed in
blind inevitability, the sole ground for assuming that
countless stars are surrounded by a planetary system
with bodies similar to our earth and moon. The moon
served as a lucky spark for science on earth only because
the moon, with countless other factors, is part of a development which is the very opposite to inevitability not
only on the physical and biological but also, and even
more so, on the intellectual level. As a result the earth
could become the abode of that most unpredictable outcome whereby an allegedly accidental byproduct of
blind material forces has a mind that gives him intellectual mastery over the cosmos. The mastery means much
more than a genuinely scientific exploration of immense
spans of time and space. It means above all the fact that
the cosmos need not be the object of even a scientifically
blinding cult but can serve as the ground for a cult whose
object transcends the cosmos and makes thereby possible the cultivation of a genuinely scientific cosmology.

Chapter Eight

COSMOS AND CULT

This world's no blot for us,
Nor blank; it means intensely, and means
   good:
To find its meaning is my meat and drink.

                                    R. Browning

The cultic guarantee of cosmic unity
The close link between cosmos and cult should seem
obvious to anyone affiliated with a religion that has God,
the Creator of all, as its object of worship. That the recognition of a strict and coherent totality of all things, or the
universe, logically propels one toward such a worship is
a story with many tell-tale pages. The most revealing of
such pages were in fact written by thinkers most anxious
not to be drawn into the vortex of religion. Henry Adams
gave a generous glimpse of that anxiety in *The Education
of Henry Adams*,[1] his autobiography written in the third
person, which culminates in his bemoaning that his education did not include a thorough training in the sciences, and especially in mathematics.

Even if he had not been the great-grandson and
grandson of two American Presidents, as an elder states-
man of American historians Henry Adams would have
had no problem in meeting the best minds in America.
He was consulting leading physicists as he turned sixty
around 1898 and, with his great work on the administra-
tions of Madison and Jefferson behind him, started
thinking about the laws of history. The laws had to be
scientific and, in view of the great complexity of human

history, much more complex than the laws of Newtonian physics, yet not so complex as to imply that there could be no unitary trend. At that point Henry Adams still hoped to steer clear of molecular gas theory that meant universal dissipation.

Before long Henry Adams settled with universal dissipation in history too, by subjecting it to the second law of thermodynamics. The result was *The Degradation of the Democratic Dogma*[2] which he, a New England aristocrat, must have written with perverse satisfaction. Long before that he went through a short period of deep perplexity. It was triggered by his humanity's revulsion against the philosophical proof, which he got from Karl Pearson's *The Grammar of Science*,[3] of the view that science is a set of formulas convenient for us to classify our sense data, but wholly impotent to reveal any regularity in the universe, let alone to reveal the universe itself. Logically enough, Pearson's book contained no chapter on cosmology. Indeed Pearson barred the universe from his discourse as he wrote:

> Geometrical surface, atom, ether, exist only in the human mind, and they are "shorthand" methods of distinguishing, classifying, and resuming phases of sense-impression. They do not exist in or beyond the world of sense-impression, but are the pure product of our reasoning faculty. The universe is not to be thought of as a real complex of atoms floating in ether, both atom and ether being to us unknowable "things-in-themselves," producing or enforcing upon us the world of sense-impressions. . . . The scientist postulates nothing of the world beyond sense; . . . The ghostly world of "things-in-themselves" behind sense he leaves as a playground for the metaphysician and the materialist. There these gymnasts, released from the dreary bondage of space and time, can play all sorts of tricks with the unknowable, and explain to the few who can comprehend them how the universe is

"created" out of will, or out of atom and ether. . . .
The scientist bravely asserts that it is impossible to
know what there is behind sense-impressions, if
indeed there can "be" anything.[4]

That Pearson put the verb *be* between quotation marks
reveals both his radical positivism and his blissful oversight of the disastrous bargain he struck. It was not a
Kantian pseudometaphysics or its Fichtean voluntarist
form that he parted with, but a real universe.

Unlike Pearson, Henry Adams clearly perceived that
radical positivism was a road to nihilism and, as he put
it, "nihilism had no bottom"[5] because only some
glimpses of unity could secure any firm ground. As one
not blind to the deeper than purely esthetic message of
medieval cathedrals, of Mont St Michel and Chartres in
particular, Henry Adams obtained some education from
it, whatever his putting Spinoza and Thomas Aquinas
into one pantheistic boat: "Mind and Unity flourished or
perished together." By unity he meant the universe. Otherwise he would not have continued: "This education
startled even a man who had dabbled in fifty educations
all over the world; for, if he were obliged to insist on a
Universe, he seemed driven to the Church. Modern science guaranteed no unity."[6]

More than he suspected, Henry Adams was right.
Newtonian science could not guarantee a universe which
had become a lost item in it. Nor could Henry Adams
suspect, in fact no scientist did around 1900, that the universe was soon to be regained by science. In a sense
Henry Adams could not have cared less. Still he was
anxious lest he, like so many of his predecessors faced
with a similar dilemma, be "caught, trapped, meshed in
this eternal drag-net of religion."[7] For the net, as Henry
Adams accurately saw it, was not merely a religious net
but the net of a very specific religion, the one professed
and proclaimed by the Roman Catholic Church. For a
former Unitarian from New England that Church was as

much the ultimate in obscurantism, if not in something far worse, as it was for one of his great heroes, Thomas Jefferson. Yet, there was no denying, as Henry Adams put it, that the "Church alone had asserted unity with any conviction and the historian alone knew what oceans of blood and treasure the assertion had cost." What then had to be done by the would-be-scientist-philosopher of human history? "The only honest alternative," Henry Adams answered, "to affirming unity was to deny it; and the denial would require a new education. At sixty-five years old a new education promised hardly more than the old."[8]

A few years earlier, as he read a book by J. B. Stallo, a Cincinnati lawyer doing philosophy of science for avocation,[9] Henry Adams noted ruefully that it was too late for him to learn mathematics without which one could not really grasp what went on in modern science. Of course, from Stallo, Pearson, Mach, or other positivists, Henry Adams could not learn that no amount of mathematics would teach physicists sound philosophy, on which rested any and all broader application of their work to the real world and in particular to that world which is a universe. Much less could he have learned from them that no mathematics, or any experimentation for that matter, entitles scientists to discourse on the legitimacy of making those steps whereby one goes beyond the universe and posits a true Creator as its ground of existence.

Had Henry Adams lived to the 1920s or even to the 1930s, he would not have fared any better in any of those respects by reading works of leading philosophers of science. Then logical positivists were building their conceptual world systems in which no justice could be given to the concept of the universe, let alone to its reality. Henry Adams could not have easily learned from leading physicist-cosmologists that through Einstein's work the universe had been regained for science. As to that gain's metaphysical bearing, a few, like E. T.

Whittaker, might have given him the wrong lead as if science has ascertained the temporal origin of the universe. Most of them, if pressed, would have snorted as Einstein did: "Let the devil take care of priests who make a capital out of this [cosmology of mine]. There is no remedy for that."[10]

The cosmological argument: its cultic place
Such was the reaction of one very much in the grip of pantheism, one of the two cults that can be inspired by the universe. The other cult, the worship of the Creator of the universe, forms the basis of all monotheistic religions, but with considerable differences. They all profess to be the recipients of special revelation about God's direct involvement in human history. They all have their special history of salvation from which they derive their main strength as well as their occasional and, in some cases, systematic delusion. They differ considerably in specifying the measure in which a purely rational view of the universe can be a source for the recognition of the Creator's existence and therefore an integral part of a monotheistic cult.

The Old Testament contains emphatic references to the witness of nature about the Creator and even implies the logical priority of that witness to the historic *magnalia Dei* aimed at establishing God's covenant with man. From the Koran too, whatever its emphasis on the inscrutable will of Allah, one can gather brief dicta on the witness of an orderly nature about its Creator.[11] The Jewish philosophical tradition can boast of a Maimonides, most intent on strengthening rational assurance about the existence of God. The Kalam cosmological argument shows ample interest among Muslim scholars in natural theology. But in both traditions the chief trends were either the observance of a specific set of rules of conduct or, especially among the intelligentsia, a cavorting with pantheism. Spinoza and

Einstein were not accidents within Judaism and the same is true about Avicenna, Averroes, and their modern Muslim counterparts espousing various forms of idealism.

As to Christianity, natural theology could not be attractive within Eastern orthodoxy, steeped in its devotion to sacramental and monastic mysticism. Within Protestantism, its erstwhile orthodoxy and present-day neo-orthodoxy had, owing to their overemphasis on the fallenness of human nature, no choice but to reject the cosmological argument and frown on natural theology. Protestant Scholasticism, whose champions tried to reconcile respect for reason's metaphysical ability with the Reformers' uneasiness about it, could not establish itself on an enduring basis. As to liberal Protestantism, it usually produces, in respect to the cosmological argument, comments similar to T. H. Huxley's remark: "We are all Gallios who care for none of those things."[12] If among Evangelical Protestants there is a serious interest in the cosmological argument, it is only because they try to be Protestants without taking on the obligation to carry in its integrity the intellectual cargo of the Reformation. Sooner than they expect, Evangelicals will have to face up to the burden of logic in the stance they try to maintain. As to Anglicans, most of their varieties call for comments already given in connection with Protestants. Bishop Butler's "analogy" merely represents a higher form of Anglo-Saxon pragmatism that admits "pointers" but no strictly valid demonstrations.

The only place within Christianity where the cult of the Creator based on the cosmological argument had been systematically emphasized is the Roman Catholic Church. This is not to suggest that many Roman Catholic theologians and philosophers had not been swayed by ever recurring waves of "intuitionism" or something worse. But Catholic ranks were fairly free of such unstable thinkers when around 1950 Einstein left it to the devil to deal with priests, very few to be sure, bent on promoting the Creator's cult with reliable references to scientific cosmology. Furthermore, then, as before and now, there was an official Roman Catholic teaching about the certainty whereby reason can recognize the existence of the Creator from the evidence of the cosmos. The certainty, insofar as the solemn declaration of Vatican I goes,[13] refers not to that concrete psychological matrix which is always an integral part of any human reasoning. The certainty in question refers to the intrinsic validity of the argument itself, which, since it starts from the consideration of the visible world, may best be called the cosmological argument.

Vatican I supported that declaration with a famous passage from Paul's Letter to the Romans[14] as if to underline the fact that the rationality of Christian revelation depends on the ability of rational man (irrationally as he may behave) to recognize from the physical realm its Creator. That Paul stressed the rationality of Christian worship (*logiké latreia*) in that very letter of his to the Romans (12: 1), in spite of his dramatic portrayal there of man's depravity, intellectual and moral, should seem especially significant. But precisely because of this, a dogmatic declaration, supported with a quote from that Letter about the demonstrability of God's existence, had to be accompanied with explanatory notes on the moral help needed by fallen man if he was to recognize with psychological effectiveness the validity of the argument. This proviso will appear even more timely after a survey, to be given shortly, about the various and sinister failings of the 20th-century mind as it approaches the reality of the universe.

As has been emphasized in chapters 1 and 2, the cosmological argument can derive much support from modern scientific cosmology insofar as it implies the reality of the cosmos as the true object of science and reveals it as a most specific entity. But the cosmological argument does not begin at the point where one's mind encompasses the universe as such, with or without the help of modern scientific cosmology. The argument begins in that immediate cosmic neighbourhood which is one's own backyard, indeed one's own study, living room, or desk for that matter. One will never look at the specific universe as contingent, that is, something that might have been otherwise, unless one looks at the pencil in one's hand, or at any object within one's reach as something contingent in that very sense, and be thoroughly impressed by this profoundly basic philosophical truth.

Of course, most such objects are artifacts. The craftsmen that produced them had in each case their free choices among a large number of possible forms. Natural objects — raindrops, snowflakes, pebbles — while they show a great variety of forms, do not immediately reveal their contingency. Indeed, it is the chief business of science to show in each and every case that the actual form or structure is the necessary outcome of the interaction of other similarly specific forms. Modern scientific cosmology has in fact shown that (leaving the question of the origin of life aside) all natural objects actually existing, from chemical elements to galaxies, are the necessary unfolding of some provisionally initial conditions, very specific in themselves. Modern scientific cosmology has not reached the point, nor can it ever reach it, where it can remove that provisionality from the "initial conditions," no matter how "initial" they may appear. As has been argued in chapter 3, there is no observable state, however primordial, about which physics could establish that it had to be preceded by that very nothing which, unlike the "nothing" of the Copenhagen people, has really nothing to it.

Insofar as that chain of provisionally initial conditions stands for an ontological sequence, its *raison d'être* cannot be looked for in forever postponing the definitive answer. The tactic of infinite regress will appear promising only to regressive minds that at the critical point want to get a tranquilizer against the metaphysical dynamics which is fueled by attention to the contingency revealed by specificities. Not that they would not try avenues of escape left for them while they blissfully ignore that several of those avenues have been made impassable by modern science. Thus two generations after Gödel published his famed theorems, some still dream about a cosmological theory that would show the universe to be necessarily what it is. The avenue of escape offered by Kant, namely, that the notion of the universe is not a reliable notion, hardly seems an intellectually decent alley to be followed up in this age of scientific cosmology. The latter, by emphasizing the comprehensive character of the universe may, however, have lent some intellectual respectability to another possible escape route. Can the universe appear as the result of a transcendental choice if there are no other universes to compare the actual universe with?

Undoubtedly, telling analogies can be formulated abou the impossibility of observing one universe from another with an eye on the self-contained space-time manifold that is incorporated in scientific cosmology. Already around 1920 Einstein called attention to the restriction placed, for instance, on two-dimensional surface creatures living on a plane of indefinite extent:

> Suppose that they have organs, instruments, and mental attitude adapted strictly to this two-dimensional existence. Then at most, they would be able to find out all the phenomena and relationships that objectify themselves in this plane. . . . Independent of this, there might be another cosmic plane with other phenomena and relationships, that is, a second analogous universe. There would be no means of constructing a connexion between these two worlds, or even of suspecting such a connexion. . . . Thus we must reckon with the finitude of our universe, and the question of regions beyond it can be discussed no further, for it leads only to imaginary

possibilities for which science has not the slightest use.[15]

Such was Einstein's elaboration of the possibility "that other universes exist independently of our own".[16] In his analogy, if applied to the four-dimensional space-time manifold of his cosmology, three-dimensional human beings would appear as extremely thin coins that are free to slide unimpeded on the surface of an immense sphere but never able to send a signal away from that surface in the direction of other universes.

Yet, the self-contained character of the actual cosmic manifold will turn into an epistemological boomerang if used as a factor that excludes the empirical testability of the universe.[17] First, it may hit the meaning of all particular measurements of specificities before undermining the meaning of scientific inferences about the measure of the universe. That measure is on hand in estimates of the total mass of the universe and of its radius, the latter being the inverse of the minimum curvature of paths that can be followed by any material body. Second, too much emphasis on empirical testability may lead even the unwary to the point where the question would impose itself whether empirical testability is empirically testable. The proper answer may then readily lead to the recognition that all mental operations, that must be embodied in words, are a rebuttal of an empiricism which presupposes the existence of strictly individual things.

Empiricism is a linguistic impossibility. Every word stands for what is universal in things and processes. Through every word the intellect grasps a range of intelligibility which represents a whole, let it be called a class or a group. Such is the essence of the age-old doctrine about universals, the indispensable justification of the meaningfulness of all human discourse. Whenever the reality of that whole, which is the universe, is made the target of a scepticism parading in the garb of empiricism, it is the whole range of human words, each standing for a whole, that becomes the ultimate target of the sceptic's blow. Universals and universe form a seamless garment.

Idealists of the Platonic kind have always understood this, only the ideas which they imposed on physical reality could not lead them to the real physical universe. No idealist articulated that impossibility more unwittingly as well as revealingly than did B. Bosanquet. He was as close as any philosopher could be to the universe already at the very starting point, the "concrete universal," of his idealist system. For him every "concrete universal," that is, every idea relating to a thing, was a world, a subclass member of *the* logical universal or the world itself: "A world or cosmos is a system of members, such that every member, being *ex hypothesi* distinct, nevertheless contributes to the unity of the whole in virtue of the peculiarities which constitute its distinctness." Beyond concrete universals he saw the "logical universal" which "takes the shape of the world whose members are worlds. "Their diversity is recognised as a unity, a macrocosm constituted by microcosms."[18]

While for Bosanquet "truth could be defined as the whole,"[19] the physical whole or universe had no appeal to him. He did not lay the blame for this on mechanistic science. Yet, although he saw in it an essentially dissecting factor, he, unlike some critics of science, did not deny its ability to contribute "to the construction and apprehension of the whole."[20] Bosanquet's real stumbling block on the mental road toward the universe was that idealist mind that could not surrender to reality as the very source of ideas.

So much in a way of rebuttal of arguments that aim at discrediting the universe or aim at weakening the mind's confidence in grasping it in a reliable manner. Their impact illustrates that general truth which C. S. Lewis pointed out in reference to what can happen in literary criticism if instead of the universe the individual's world is taken for the standard of meaning:

> Either there is significance in the whole process of things as well as in human activity, or there is no significance in human activity itself. It is an idle dream, at once cowardly and arrogant, that we can withdraw the human soul, as a mere epiphenomenon, from a universe of idiotic force, and yet hope, after that, to find for her some *faubourg* where she can keep a mock court in exile. You cannot have it both ways. If the world is meaningless, then so are we; if we mean something, we do not mean alone. Embrace either alternative, and you are free of the personal heresy.[21]

Indeed, if man is to have meaning, he must not withdraw into a "faubourg" (false town) because, looked at from there, the surrounding universe will appear utterly meaningless. For if man is to have meaning, he cannot have it in isolation from the universe. Only by looking for meaning in the context of the whole, or the universe, in all his particular actions and thoughts will man find a firm ground and, indeed, a ground which is not inert.

The argument as mental training

Such a universe will serve him as a jumping board that through its inner dynamism gives to the one standing on it the sense of upward mobility. Of course, such a mental sensation will be had only by one who steps on that board with mental legs that have already been trained to feel the metaphysical dynamism that any thing exudes by its contingency contained in its specificity. When in front of a thing, those legs must be impressed with no less intensity by its contingency than the one Sartre demanded for his own brand of existentialism: "Existence . . . must invade you suddenly, master you, weigh heavily on your heart like a great motionless beast — or else there is nothing more at all."[22] Of course, for Sartre the source of that intensity was the isolated ego that could not be sure even of its own continuity from one moment to another, and not the *things* external to, and existing independently of the ego. At safe remove from that existentialist self-aggrandizement, the mind will readily recognize the universal in each and every thing and the universe in their consistently interacting totality. No philosophical sophistication, only robust common sense is needed if one is to be electrified by the plain realization that, as put by Chesterton with his customary incisiveness, "nothing can be more universal than the universe."[23]

With such mental conditioning on hand, man will naturally feel, as he consciously takes his stand on that board, that he is set in an upward motion toward God, the only being beyond the universe of specific, that is, contingent beings. Man will then experience something very different from that leap in the dark which those try to perform agonizingly who never have really felt the universe, and at times not even plain ordinary things, under their very feet. The move toward God, if it is to be a safe one, must not be a separation from the universe. The move rather consists in sensing the pulse of cosmic contingency, the relentless pointing of the universe beyond itself. A mental experience of this type animates St Augustine's celebrated passage:

> I spoke to all the things that are about me, all that can be admitted by the door of the senses, and I said, 'Since you are not my God, tell me about him. Tell me something of my God.' Clear and loud they answered, 'God is he who made us.' I asked these questions simply by gazing at these things . . . I asked the whole mass of the universe about my God, and it replied, 'I am not God. God is he who made me.'[24]

That this passage is from Book X of the *Confessions* is not accidental. Book X begins with Augustine's asking his readers to thank God for his conversion described in

Book IX. His conversion meant among other things the opening of his eyes to the mind's fascination with glittering half-truths and specious fallacies. The cosmological argument will appear a delusion unless those fallacies and half-truths, which the modern world mass-produces about the universe, are seen for what they truly are. It is precisely because the modern intellectual atmosphere is polluted to suffocation with disastrous ideas about the universe that any vote cast on behalf of the cosmological argument may appear a sheer defiance of all accepted standards of intellectual respectability.

Hostile atmosphere: some humanists
One source of that pollution is the belief that all of man's conclusions, however well tested, are but myths on a level with the myths of aborigines. Not all anthropologists would, of course, voice so outspokenly as did James George Frazer, their contempt for objective truth, but few of them feel real unease on reading his remarks about the picture science affords about the universe:

> We must remember that at bottom the generalisations of science or, in common parlance, the laws of nature are merely hypotheses devised to explain that ever-shifting phantasmagoria of thought which we dignify with the high-sounding names of the world and the universe.[25]

And, as if to prevent his being misunderstood, Frazer defined magic, religion, and science (though perhaps not his own science of cultural anthropology) as so many means of "registering the shadows on the screen." Again, as if to reinforce his point, he dismissed scientific predictions about the eventual collapse of the solar system with the assertion that

> these gloomy apprehensions, like the earth and the sun themselves, are only parts of that unsubstantial

world which thought has conjured up out of the
void, and that the phantoms which the subtle
enchantress has evoked to-day she may ban too,
like so much that to common eyes seem solid, may
melt into air, into thin air.[26]

Those many, who delight (at least in the privacy of their
musings) in this kind of sublimation of the universe, can
hardly be expected to respond, however vaguely, to the
cosmological argument. The same is true of those who in
their comfortable hours cozy up to ideas about the universe akin to Taine's reasons for his denying that there
might be anything real beneath the phenomena. They
culminated in Taine's definition of the universe as "an
immense aurora borealis,"[27] a sight certainly capable of
sidetracking all but the strong-minded. Perhaps in this
age of avid pursuit, through the use of costly and dangerous hallucigens, of rose-colored dreamworlds, Taine's
intellectual experience about the cosmos would
recommend itself for its inexpensiveness. One can give it
by taking more than one step away from the soberingly
real world toward a subjective heaven behind which
lurks the realm of the absurd.

A literary critic may not be expected to portray in
detail the cosmological bearing of his subject. But there
is more than what meets the eye in the appearance of the
word 'universe' in M. Esslin's account of the absurd in
modern drama as a reflection of an experience shared by
"many intelligent and sensitive human beings" of mid-
twentieth century: "Suddenly man sees himself faced
with a universe that is both frightening and illogical —
in a word, absurd. All assurances of hope, all explana-
tions of ultimate meaning have suddenly been
unmasked as nonsensical illusions, empty chatter, whis-
tling in the dark."[28] To cure that condition by acting it
out on the stage may not necessarily act as a means of
catharsis. What Esslin calls "liberating laughter" may be
on hand only if beneath foibles, however cruel and dis-
ruptive, normalcy still can be assumed. But will not the

laughter have a shrill tone to it if it must be touched off by "the recognition of the fundamental absurdity of the universe"?[29] Physicist-cosmologists who cavort in producing absurd twists to scientific models of the universe may well note that the theater of the absurd includes a play that has "pataphysics" for its target. In B. Jarry's *Faustroll* "pataphysics" (a physics worse than pathological) is defined in words that are eery anticipations of some expressions that have become standard in recent cosmological literature: Pataphysics is "the science of imaginary solutions, which symbolically attributes the properties of objects, described by their virtuality, to their lineaments."[30] Advocates of "virtual worlds" and of worlds made of line-like strings, may not be as original as they appear to be to the uninformed.

The relevance of the absurd to some aspects of modern scientific cosmology implies more than stunning verbal similarities between the two. Long before the 'nothing' had undergone a semantic facelift in the scientific trickery whereby universes are made to appear to produce themselves out of the oscillations of a not entirely vacuous quantum mechanical vacuum, the reification of the nothing had been the logical product of a fashionable surrender to the absurd. Samuel Beckett, a principal playwright of the absurd, did not take by accident for his favorite motto Democritus' dictum that "nothing is more real than the nothing."[31] The dictum could indeed serve as an appropriate vignette for a major trend in modern scientific cosmology and as a capsule diagnosis for its eager reception by the public.

Here too playwrights merely registered a social symptom without probing into its genesis. By repeating that "what is not is the only thing that is beautiful,"[32] Rousseau reflected a malaise that was to take over Western culture in the measure in which it distanced itself from its Christian moorings. In declaring that "the real is never beautiful,"[33] Sartre proved himself an epigone, however influential and representative. This celebration

of the nothing and the accompanying scorn for the real
had for its natural soil an enervating estheticism to
which even a poet like Paul Valéry could give a philosophical gloss as he claimed that "the universe is but a
flaw in the purity of non-being."[34] Professional philosophers did not, of course, reveal the extent to which they
took fundamental concepts for subtle hallucigens. Yet it
is difficult not to feel the difference between the clear
atmosphere of Leibniz's question, "Why is there something rather than nothing?"[35] and the faint murkiness of
Heidegger's query, "why is there existent at all, and not
much rather plain nothing?"[36]

Heidegger's popularity is but a symptom of the long-
ing of modern man for a sort of nirvana. The same long-
ing still may be gratified when the reality of the real is
undermined by a denial of that nothing against which
alone does the contingent real reveal its true reality.
Bergson's characterization of the nothing as a pseudo-
idea[37] should be seen in this perspective. Then one
understands the quaint irreality of Bergson's apotheosis
of a creative evolution and the hollowness of his description of the universe "as a machine for the making of
God."[38] For just as the word "God" becomes a deception
if the "nothing" means nothing, creation too becomes an
impossibility and therefore the universe can but be
described with Bergson as something "which is being
made continually."[39]

Between this kind of thinking, or rather state of mind,
and the thinking implicit in the cosmological argument
there can be no substantive meeting point. Any spokesman for the cosmological argument must realize that
Santayana's phrase, "the Universe is the true Adam, the
Creation the true Fall,"[40] is not a mere proposition but
the tip of an epistemological and ideological iceberg. In
fact, the same spokesmen are less exposed to illusions
when that tip appears without the seriousness of philosophical parlance. The customary grin of Anatole
France immediately reveals that one faces not so much

an argument as a carefully nurtured scorn (enjoyed by so many) as he delivered his parting shot at efforts aimed at demonstrating the existence of God:

> A being infinite in space and time had, after an eternity of solitude, the impudence to create the world. What prompted him? Love, they say, that love which inspires so much foolishness. His creation caused him obvious damages and inextricable difficulties. His relation with an imperfect world exposed him to endless frictions. Man's creation caused him the most painful miscalculations. . . . In order to govern man, He proposed himself to be moral, without being prepared for it. Living alone for eternity and savoring the pleasure of solitude, He had no manners and could not have them. With respect to man He took on, as one would expect, the manners of a savage tribal chief. Thick volumes have been written about His cruelties and extravaganzas.[41]

A large variety of factors made possible the apparent ease with which Anatole France regaled his world-wide readership with that sarcastic grin. One of them was his contempt for the information science had disclosed about the physical universe. While science had by the late 1800s reached the point of ascertaining new elements in the sun, and photographing tens of thousands of galaxies, Anatole France maintained that "the universe which science reveals to us is a dispiriting monotony. All the suns are drops of fire and all the planets drops of mud."[42] Familiarity with the scientific universe might have spared Margaret Fuller, a pioneer champion of higher education for women and a rather fearsome conversationalist, from committing a howler of cosmic dimensions. It happened as she attended a party with Carlyle present. She easily succeeded in making everybody listen to her sententious acceptance or dismissal of a wide variety of ideas. She hoped to carry on after she

had incidentally remarked: "I accept the universe." But
Carlyle broke in, "Gad, you'd better," which silenced
Margaret Fuller for the rest of the evening.[43] Not that
Carlyle had any right to expect others to read genuine
modesty into his remark, "I don't pretend to understand
the universe — it's a great deal bigger than I am — People expect to be modester."[44] Familiarity with genuine
science he certainly lacked.

Hostile atmosphere: some cosmologists

Yet, studies, even professional, of the scientific universe
do not necessarily impart an awe for it. Were it otherwise, cosmologists would not be sparing with statements
such as that the "universe, by definition, includes everything."[45] For, if the cosmologist really meant that "the
universe is the largest possible object in existence," he
would hardly have stated in a tone smacking of indifference that "the next step brings us to the ultimate, the
Universe."[46] Actually, the feverish increase in the attention given during the last two decades to cosmology produced one more illustration of the saying that familiarity
breeds contempt. Trendsetting cosmologists talk of their
subject as if they formed an Intergalactic Club of Flippancy. Their diction echoes at times the one decried by
the Psalmist; "Our tongue is our strength. Who is our
master?"[47] By treating their subject with "the detailed,
critical, and dispassionate methods of the scientist,"
authors of papers presented at big conferences on cosmology comply only with one part of Tolman's memorable injunction. Lip service, if not something less, is given
to the other part: "it is appropriate to approach the problems of cosmology with feelings of respect for their
importance, of awe for their vastness, and of exultation
for the temerity of the human mind in attempting to
solve them."[48]

Physicist-cosmologists can do even worse vis-à-vis the
universe. In a distinctly tragic sense, they exemplify

those inhabitants of a remote island in the Pacific that during World War II served as a refueling base for cargo planes. With the war over, the planes were no longer coming — which the natives refused to accept. They put on wooden earphones, erected bamboo antennas, and waited for the sound of planes. Such was Feynman's favorite simile about those whom he charged with "cargo science." Psychology was a chief target of his, but only second to metaphysics, as he remarked about the meaninglessness of the universe.[49] He failed to see that in doing so he wore wooden earphones of his own making. The many sophisticated instruments which register a large variety of waves coming from cosmic depths are so many wooden earphones with respect to the wavelengths that carry the meaning of the universe. To say this may amount to a *lèse majesté* in view of the prodigious qualities of those instruments. But it is in this quality of theirs that lies the greatest obstacle to the convincingness of the cosmological argument.

A sickly mental and cultural atmosphere, fomenting the cult of the absurd may easily reveal its repulsive nature and encourage thereby a fresh look at old arguments or proofs. But infatuation with the "proofs" of the scientific method may blind one to a wider meaning of proofs. For the narrowest sense of proof is precisely what assures science its effectiveness. Its proofs are for the most part identity relations, plain tautologies, to recall a remark of Bertrand Russell.[50] Those proofs work as long as one remains within the limits of mathematical formalisms, but are of no help when a physicist wants to demonstrate the reality of the telescope he uses. Statements about the reality of this or that object, however trivial, cannot be cast into the moulds of mathematics. Should one therefore give up confidence in the possibility of proving the reality of any object in the laboratory or in the world around us?

One indeed reveals a grave myopia for very broad consequences when one declares that instead of the cosmological argument or proof, one should talk about pointers the universe affords about the existence of God. For if pointers do not point unambiguously, that is, with certainty, what is the point of using them? But if the difference between proofs and pointers is merely verbal, why the reluctance to speak of proofs? Or is it perhaps one's particular cult, in which certainties are not welcome, that recommends the abolition of proofs along a broad front so that a particularly sorry predicament might not appear for what it truly is?

A chief reason about doubts concerning the demonstrative value of the cosmological argument may lie in a pathetic surrender to a cultural cliché which Niels Bohr wanted to see elevated, as if he had been a magus and not a scientist, into a secular cult. In one of those "unforgettable strolls" during which Bohr "would so candidly disclose his innermost thoughts," he commented on the "guidance and consolation" which many people sought in religion and not in science." Then he added "with intense animation that he saw the day when [his principle and understanding of] complementarity would be taught in the schools and become part of general education: and better than any religion . . . a sense of complementarity would afford people the guidance they needed."[51] Steeped in the ambiguity of all knowledge, as claimed by Bohr, his complementarity could only provide a guidance with no certainty whatsoever. Such is the ultimate clue to certain aspects of modern scientific cosmology and to the widespread vacillation about the cosmological argument in circles that should rather inspire firmness about it.

The need for firmness and its benefits
The effectiveness of the cosmological argument depends on whether one can take for certain elementary everyday realities. To take for certain something is not an act of faith, an agonizing leap in the dark, but an act of plain intellectual recognition of its reality. Any proof relating

to reality depends on one's confidence that one knows things, but the intellectual act does not thereby become a matter of emotions with a resulting loss of its objective certainty. About the latter it is important to keep in mind that man's connection with external reality is not a beatific vision in which the knower and the known are in a permanent, indissoluble unity. This is why knock-down arguments are impossible, unless they merely state the identity between two definitions, a purely conceptual matter. But whatever the discontinuous, and therefore precarious character of human knowledge of reality, it lacks no certainty. This is why truth is given its greatest service when its certainty is held high unconditionally. Only then does truth perform its very role which is to liberate man. The cosmological argument too will demonstrate with certainty only if no hesitation is allowed about the fact that man can truly know and whenever he knows he perceives the universal, the whole, in the particular.

The spokesman of the cosmological argument will therefore know that only by intellectual firmness will he serve the purpose of that argument and those who want to profit by it. The very last thing he should do is to give the kind of concession which is giving away the game, however subtly and at times crudely. An example of this is contained in A. Toynbee's reflections on his vast studies of history. He noted the elementary truth that we "cannot think about the universe without assuming that it is articulated" . . . and that "without mentally articulating the universe we ourselves cannot be articulate — cannot, that is, either think or will." At the same time he also stated "that we cannot defend the articulations that we find, or make, in it [the universe] against the charge that these are artificial and arbitrary, that they do not correspond to anything in the structure of reality, or that, even if they do, they are irrelevant to the particular mental purpose for which we have resorted to them." Toynbee might have perceived something of the gratuitousness of his concession had he reflected on the justification he gave for it: "It can always be shown that they [those articulations] break up something that is indivisible and let slip something that is essential."[52]

What this proved was merely the inevitable limitedof any conceptualization. But limitedness applies also to any and all criticism of those articulations. The grasp of wholeness cannot be opposed except by a "wholesale" criticism which precisely by claiming to be of universal relevance testifies to the reliability of man's grasp of reality as a whole. It is not accidental that a word, *grasp*, that denotes a hold on some totality, can be so synonymous with the word *understanding*. As to the word *dissect*, it makes sense only if there is something that can be decomposed into its constituent parts.

Had Toynbee been something of a philosopher he might have noticed that the real dissecting or fragmentation is perpetrated by those who make that charge described above. Their typical ultimate resort is the claim that no absolute proof is possible. They never specify what they mean by that impossibility. Were they to entertain the notion of pure spirits of angels, they might notice that minds not dependent on the welter of physical change can alone zero in on a given truth and remain consciously and uninterruptedly attached to it. This is not given to a being like man whose intellect can operate only through the body and therefore his grasp of truth becomes of necessity discontinous. But that grasp does not thereby become uncertain in the sense of never being truly in possession of its object. Discontinuities are an inevitable feature even of one's grasp of one's identity. Does it thereby follow that one's evidence of one's own existence is not certain? This patently self-defeating inference becomes, however, inevitable once one takes with consistency the position that external reality, or the universe for that matter, cannot be known with certainty. H. Reichenbach, once a leading logical positivist and philosopher of science, who specialized in the art of dissecting, deserves credit for spelling out this connection: "We have no absolutely conclusive evidence that there is a physical world, and we have no absolutely conclusive evidence either that we exist."[53]

For all its expressiveness Reichenbach's admission lacks depth. He and many other logical positivists failed to follow up logic to the edge of the chasm where the full consequences of bartering certainty for absolutely conclusive evidence show up. Existentialists may have caught a glimpse of that bottomless chasm but they did their literary best to gloss it over. In that sleight-of-hand a tell-tale mishandling of the universe plays a pivotal role. "A world that can be explained even with bad reasons," stated Camus in *The Myth of Sisyphus*, "is a familiar world," but, "in a universe suddenly divested of illusions and lights, man feels an alien, a stranger."[54] Once more a great literary man argued in a partial vacuum and he had no excuse insofar as he wanted to do justice to the *full* range of human experience and inquiry.

The sole mitigating factor in Camus' blunder is that in the early 1930s cosmologists failed to shout their heads off about their fast growing grasp of the universe. Had they kept shouting, their voice might have penetrated the universities and even such a distant one as the University of Algiers where Camus studied. Thus he might have quite innocently brought in the universe as a backdrop to his portrayal of Sisyphus as being happy with his existence in a Sisyphean universe "without a master." For if that universe, or rather the stone and mountain of Sisyphus, did not appear sterile and futile to him, it was because "each atom of that stone, each mineral-flake of that night-filled mountain, in itself forms a world."[55] Such was a clever way, unjustified though in terms of *The Myth of Sisyphus*, of letting normalcy support the abnormal. A world, be it that of an atom or of a mountain, casts that light in which the entire universe is bound to loom large. Most philosophers around 1940, when Camus wrote *The Myth of Sisyphus*, could be of no help to him, whereas cosmologists did not see their opportunity to be universally helpful with the very universe in their grasp.

The fruits of intellectual trust

If, however, one sees the inconsistency of falling back on reason while celebrating incoherence, one will not paint a Sisyphus for whom, unlike to his mythical archetype, "all is well," to recall Camus' words. One wonders whether Camus perceived the irony in writing that "one must *imagine* Sisyphus happy"[56] (italics added). The question is whether he can consistently be known to be happy. Attention to consistency could indeed lead one face to face with crushing unhappiness of which the universe is an integral victim. In C. S. Lewis' loss of faith and in his recovery of it, the universe too is lost and regained. In his *Surprised by Joy* he tells us how he concluded, after losing his faith, that "the universe was a rather regrettable institution." There he also noted the truly liberating role which the universe can have for man. To be sure, when, through his first reading of Bergson, C. S. Lewis perceived the idea of necessary existence, he saw it embodied in the universe. But he also realized that the universe conceived as "the Whole" could be neither praised nor blamed for anything and therefore pointed beyond itself.[57]

The same liberating role of an intellectual trust in the universe was recounted even more dramatically by C. S. Lewis' chief master, G. K. Chesterton.[58] As G. K. C. turned twenty, he had a bout with rationalist logic-chopping that can logically trap one in that mental straitjacket which is solipsism. Chesterton escaped from its grip because he perceived the deadly dangers of being cut off from the universe. His first major book, *Heretics*, written while he was still in his twenties, was a wholesale attack on all those gurus of the times who were heretics, that is, practiced in one way or another the art of making the crucial cut at the wrong place: between man and the universe, instead of between the universe and God. They did so in order to escape the necessity of recognizing God as distinct from the universe.

Once the *Heretics* is seen in this cosmic perspective, Chesterton's discovery of "orthodoxy" will appear a foregone conclusion. And so will, in view of Chesterton's relentless exploration of what is implied in any basic truth, his lifelong celebration of the universe that included stunning anticipations of the gist of modern scientific cosmology.[59] They were generated by his siding resolutely with those "who think that the most practical and important thing about a man is still his view of the universe. . . . We think the question is not whether the theory of the cosmos affects matters, but whether in the long run anything else affects them."[60] Later, in a tone harking back to the Gospel words, "only one thing is necessary," Chesterton wrote: "There is one thing that is needful — everything. The rest is vanity of vanities."[61]

Chesterton's case illustrates that to discover the universe means a journey beyond the universe. It proves that there is no stable point between belief and unbelief. They both, not only belief as customarily understood, are inseparable from some form of cult. Unbelief, which all too often sinks to the level of that lawlessness where might makes right and selfish interests are supported by hollow sophistication, can rise no higher than the cult of the universe. Yet even there that cult will remain, as John Henry Newman put it in 1836, a "religion of beauty, imagination, and philosophy, without constraint, moral and intellectual, a religion speculative and self-indulgent." To that "Pantheistic spirit" or cult, which he identified as "the great deceit which awaits the Age to come," any other cult was acceptable only as a contributor to culture but not as a "separate and definite something, whether doctrine or association, existing objectively, integral, and with an identity, and forever, and with a claim upon our homage and obedience."[62]

Cosmos and Christian cult

The only other cult that exemplified that specific cult was, of course, Christianity. In this age of scientific cosmology no small credential to it should seem its holding high the reality of the universe. It did so against the Gnostics who anticipated some modern cosmologists in sublimating the universe into their fleeting thoughts, the very next thing to irreality. The resolve with which an Irenaeus defended the truth of the real universe as one that grounds the truths of faith, may serve well some modern cosmologists who think that galaxies and stars exist only on their retinas. The resolve with which Athanasius dwelt on the full rationality of the universe as something that follows from the divinity of the Logos in whom the Father created all, may still be an indispensable antidote to many cosmologists' flirtation with irrational randomness. The resolve with which Aquinas asserted man's capability of grasping the universe may still be a chief bulwark against empiricist scientists who, like Bridgman, debunked cosmology.[63] The resolve with which John Henry Newman spoke of the universe as the highest thought next only to that of its Maker, [64] may still be the only remedy against debasing the universe by raising it too high.

In view of the threats, mental and moral, that envelop man's understanding of his true relation to the universe, a recourse to every-day reasoning about its true provenance may have more merit than one would dare to assume. I mean such rebuttals of unbelief that may not stand up in the courts of logic-chopping but reveal an unerring grasp of some basic logic. One such rebuttal I witnessed when in late September 1947 I was on a train on my way to a town near the Hungarian-Austrian border. My preoccupations about my eventual crossing that border through fields loaded with mines were momentarily dissipated when a fellow traveler, a newly blossomed Communist, needled me (traveling in cassock) with objections to the existence of God. A gracious woman in

the same compartment chimed in on seeing the ineffectiveness of my replies. "Why don't you ask him," she
turned to me, "whether he had ever seen boots that made
themselves?" Another rebuttal of the same sort took
place some time ago in this University. The president of
one of the colleges was having an evening discussion
with one of the undergraduates about theological matters. At the end of the discussion the student said, "Well,
I am sorry, Sir, but I still don't believe in God and as it is
dinner time I must now go to my dinner." As he rose the
president said to him, "I hope you enjoy your dinner —
by the way, do you believe in cooks?"[65]

To speak of cooks and cosmology in the same breath
is far less incongruous than it may appear. Modern scientific cosmology has in fact discovered in the early
stages of the universe a situation that may be best compared to a cosmic soup into which a very specific number of ingredients were placed with utmost attention to
their respective proportions. That cosmic soup is indeed
of such great refinement as to provide sustenance to the
immense chain of living forms. They all rise and perish.
This picture of universal death, often going together with
an apparently senseless waste of life, appeared to Darwin as irreconcilable with the reality of a Creator. In his
case too, the argument was a cover-up for an earlier loss
of faith and for apparently different reasons. At any rate,
human suffering seems to be the only serious argument
against God's existence. Yet all that suffering, insofar as
it is a purely physical process, takes place in terms of
laws that also govern the entire universe. Those laws are
a powerful beacon in a mental landscape which, whatever its dark areas, is lit up by not a few beacons. They all
reinforce one another and give enormous justification to
that trust in the Creator which is more than an intellectual recognition of his existence. This is why a deep and
broad resonance is found in human hearts and minds by
the chorale in Bach's St Matthew Passion:

Commit your way,
And whatever troubles your heart,
to the trustiest care
of Him who controls the skies;
He who gives clouds, air, and winds
their paths, courses, and tracks
He will also find ways
where your feet can safely pass.

The cult that inspired that chorale reaches to points
where, if taken for a mere esthetic item, it can be of no
use. Such points are those of excruciating pain, of disas-
ters, and last but not least the point where one sees the
moment of one's death approaching. In itself a most
esthetic description of that moment is a favorite saying
of Francis of Assisi that one should wait the last hour as
if an invisible sister were to come to close one's eyes. Had
Francis been a mere esthete, however extraordinary, he
could not have inspired followers such as Claire who
said as she died: "Blessed be Thou, Lord, who hast created me."[66] Of course, both Francis and Claire took their
inspiration from a cult of which the daily recitation of
the Psalms was an integral part. They both, and countless others, repeated at least once a week the Psalmist's
words: "I thank you for the wonder of my being, for the
wonders of all your creation."[67]

J

NOTES

CHAPTER ONE

1. This and the subsequent quotations from Donne are from his "Anatomie of the World. First Anniversary," in *John Donne. Complete Poetry and Prose*, ed. J. Hayward (London: Nonesuch Press, 1946), pp. 202-03.

2. Galileo conveniently ignored that by explaining the haziness of the Milky Way as the optical effect of the fusion of the light of many stars there, he repeated the ideas of many medievals. See on this my work, *The Milky Way: An Elusive Road for Science* (New York: Science History Publications, 1972; reprinted 1976), ch. 2.

3. *The Complete Poetry and Prose of John Milton* (New York: Random House, 1950), p. 253.

4. For this and subsequent quotations, see ibid., pp. 266-70.

5. This is also an echo of Luther and Calvin who in their commentaries on Genesis 1 see in the various physical impossibilities of the six-day creation story so many opportunities for man to cultivate unconditional faith in God's written word.

6. Milton here echoes the purely formalistic interpretation of astronomy that Cardinal Bellarmin had earlier endorsed against the realist interpretation advocated by Galileo. The pre-17th-century story of those interpretations is P. Duhem's *To Save the Phenomena: An Essay on the Idea of Physical Theory from Plato to Galileo*, tr. E. Doland and C. Maschler, with an introduction by Stanley L. Jaki (Chicago: University of Chicago Press, 1969; reprinted 1985).

7. In that respect too, Newton differed from Descartes who counted the Incarnation, together with the creation of the world out of nothing and human free will, as one of the three great marvels made by God. See Descartes' "Cogitationes privatae," *Oeuvres de Descartes*, ed., C. Adam and P. Tannery (Paris: L. Cerf, 1897-1913), vol. 10, p. 218.

8. First published together as *Eight Sermons Preached at the Honourable Robert Boyle Lectures in the First Year MDCXCII* in London in 1693. For further details, see my *The Paradox of Olbers' Paradox* (New York: Herder & Herder, 1969), pp. 60-66.

9. Newton's manuscript, "De gravitatione et aequipondio fluidorum" (1672), is printed *in Unpublished Scientific Papers of Isaac Newton*, ed. A. R. Hall and M. B. Hall (Cambridge: University Press, 1962), pp. 89-156; see especially pp. 139 and 142-43.

10. Addison did so in the July 9, 1714 issue of *The Spectator*.

11. See *Oeuvres complètes de Voltaire* (Paris: Garnier Frères, 1877-82), vol. 22, p. 403.

12. First published in 1957 and widely available in Harper Torchbook edition.

13. A. Koyré, "Galileo and Plato," *Journal of the History of Ideas* 4 (1943), p. 404.

14. *Pascal's Pensées*, tr. W. F. Trotter, with an introduction by T. S. Eliot (New York; E. P. Dutton, 1958), #72.

15. Ibid., #67.

16. Such is the grand conclusion of Koyré's *From the Closed World to the Infinite Universe*.

17. Novalis (F. P. von Hardenberg), *Hymns to the Night and Other Selected Writings*, tr. C. E. Passage (Indianapolis: Bobbs-Merrill, 1960), p. 71.

18. See "Infini," vol. VIII (1765), p. 702. There is no article on the universe in the *Encyclopédie*. Its very brief article "Monde" deals with geography.

19. The article in question was written by Olbers, the book by O. Struve. Both are discussed in detail in my *The Paradox of Olbers' Paradox*.

20. See *Immanuel Kant's Critique of Pure Reason*, tr. N. K. Smith (London: Macmillan, 1929), p. 449.

21. Ibid.

22. Kant's only reference to scientists throughout the 25 pages (pp. 396-421) of his discussion of the four antinomies is a quasi-anecdotal detail, quoted on the authority of a French astronomer, J. J. d'Ortous de Mairan (p. 419), about two astronomers who disagreed whether the moon rotated on its axis as it moved around the earth.

23. For details, see my translation, with introduction and notes, of *J. H. Lambert: Cosmological Letters on the Arrangement of the World Edifice* (New York: Science History Publications, 1976), pp. 23-24.

24. Ibid., pp. 47 and 216. At the same time Kant offered hollow rhetoric on mathematics to suggest his expertise on it. See *Critique of Pure Reason*, p. 423.

25. N. K. Smith, *A Commentary to Kant's Critique of Pure Reason*, (2nd ed.; London: The Macmillan Press, 1923), p. 519.

26. *Dialogues concerning Natural Religion*, ed. with an introduction and notes by N. K. Smith (Edinburgh: Thomas Nelson and Sons, 1947), pp. 167-69.

27. See my translation with introduction and notes, *Immanuel Kant: Universal Natural History and Theory of the Heavens* (Edinburgh: Scottish Academic Press, 1981), pp. 106-08.

28. See sections 9-10 in Part I of his first major publication, an appraisal of Leibniz's doctrine of force (1747) in *Kant's Gesammelte Schriften: Kant's Werke* (Berlin: G. Reimer, 1902-55), vol. 1, pp. 23-24.

29. *Kant's Opus postumum*, ed. A. Buchenau (Berlin: Walter de Gruyter, 1936-38), vol. 1, p. 25.

30. For text and discussion see my *The Paradox of Olbers' Paradox*, pp. 131-43 and 256-64.

31. See my article, "New Light on Olbers' Dependence on Chéseaux," *Journal for the History of Astronomy* 1 (1970), pp. 53-55. The problem mainly arises from the fact that Olbers, who as a rule was most careful in giving credit to others, owned a copy of Chéseaux's book and even made notes of a part of it about 20 years before writing that article.

32. Kant's distinction, Gauss wrote on November 1, 1844, to the astronomer, H. C. Schumacher, "between analytic and synthetic propositions is one of those things that either run out on triviality or are false". *Gauss Gesammelte Werke* (Göttingen: K. Gesellschaft der Wissenschaften, 1870-1933), vol. 12, p. 63.

33. In a lecture given in Heidelberg as well as in Köln, Helmholtz praised Kant's view on the evolution of the planetary system "as one of the happiest insights of science". See my translation of Kant's *Universal Natural History and Theory of the Heavens*, p. 56.

34. Quoted from Kelvin's lecture, "The Wave Theory of Light," delivered in 1884 at the Franklin Institute in Philadelphia and inserted later into his *Popular Lectures and Addresses* (London: Macmillan, 1889-94), vol. I, pp. 314-15.

35. "On Ether and Gravitational Matter through Infinite Space," *Philosophical Magazine* 2 (1901), pp. 161-77.

36. A. M. Clerke, *The System of Stars* (2nd. ed.; London: Adam and Charles Black, 1905), p. 349.

37. *Bulletin de la Société française de philosophie* 6 (1906), pp. 108-09.

38. J. F. K. Zöllner, *Uber die Natur der Cometen: Beiträge zur Geschichte und Theorie der Erkenntniss* (Leipzig: W. Engelmann, 1872), pp. 299-312, in a chapter dealing with the finiteness of matter in endless space.

39. Quoted from his lecture, "The Philosophy of the Pure Sciences," delivered at the Royal Institution in March 1873. See *W. K. Clifford: Lectures and Essays*, ed. L. Stephen and F. Pollock (London: Macmillan, 1901), vol. 1, p. 387. Clifford's failure to refer to Kant is all the more noteworthy because earlier in that lecture he noted the devastating consequences of evolutionary theory for Kant's doctrine of a priori truths.

40. For details see my *The Milky Way: An Elusive Road for Science*, p. 276.

41. A Einstein, *Uber die spezielle und die allgemeine Relativitätstheorie (Gemeinverständlich)* (5th ed.; Braunschweig: F. Vieweg & Sohn, 1917), p. 71. The same argument had already been used, in a somewhat different notation, by Kelvin in 1901. See note 35 above.

42. A Moszkowski, *Conversations with Einstein*, tr. H. L. Brose (New York: Horizon Press, 1971), p. 127. The German original was published in 1921.

43. A. N. Whitehead, *Science and the Modern World* (New York: Macmillan, 1926), p. 12.

44. Of those books only the one by M. von Laue is not available in English. Eddington published two books on General Relativity, one a technical report, sponsored by the Physical Society of London (1920), and the non-technical *Space, Time and Gravitation*, also published in 1920. In the latter, Ch. X, "Towards Infinity," begins with a long quotation from the same essay of Clifford in which the latter emphasized that non-Euclidean geometry had restored the validity of the notion of the universe, a point that failed to arouse Eddington's interest.

45. Einstein thoroughly disagreed with Brunschvicg on the latter's endorsement of the Kantian antinomies. See the *procès-verbaux* of the discussions in *Bulletin de la Société française de philosophie* 17 (1922), pp. 91-113, especially p. 101. As to Bergson's query concerning the status of time Einstein denied that

there was a philosophical time. He admitted only a psychological time as different from the time of the physicist (ibid., p. 107).

46. Bertrand Russell did so in his famous radio-debate with Fr. F. Copleston, S.J. For the text of their debate, see H. J. Hick, *The Existence of God* (New York: Macmillan, 1964), pp. 174-75.

47. The gist of Whitehead's *Process and Reality: An Essay in Cosmology* (London: Macmillan, 1929). See especially Part V. "Final Interpretation".

48. *Dialogues of Alfred North Whitehead*, as recorded by L. Price (Boston: Little Brown & Co., 1954), pp. 133-34.

49. Ibid., pp. 367-68.

50. *Process and Reality*, pp. 529-30.

51. *Dialogues of Alfred North Whitehead*, p. 297.

52. New York: John Wiley, 1972. Its index contains no entry on the universe, a fact perhaps expressive of the scepticism which Weinberg conveys through his citing a dictum of Xenophanes: "And as for certain truth, no man has seen it. . . . Opinion is fixed by fate upon all things" (p. 611).

53. New York: Interscience Publishers, 1965. Lanczos' few statements on the comprehensibility of the universe in terms of Einstein's work (pp. 12 and 112) reveal their weakness when seen against his failure to see the bearing of that work on Kant's philosophy.

54. Oxford: Clarendon Press, 1986. In the whole book cosmology covers only six pages (281-88). Pais, who quotes Mach's claim that inertial motion is an abbreviated reference to the mutual influence of all bodies "in the entire universe" (p. 284), fails to note that it is Einstein's work that provided scientific basis for talking about the universe. Pais failed in the same way (p. 332) in connection with a remark of Uhlenbeck who in 1926 felt, in a mood of ecstasy, that "now one understands the world" on hearing the report (incorrect) that Einstein succeeded in incorporating not only electromagnetism but also quantum mechanics into General Relativity.

55. In terms of his famed telegram to Rabbi Herbert S. Goldstein, reported in the *New York Times*, April 25, 1929, p. 60, col. 4. An early study of Einstein's advocacy of Spinozean pantheism is L. Schlesinger, "Spinoza und Einstein," *Scientia* 42 (1927), pp. 253-62. A recent study is by R. de Ritis and S. Guccione,

"Albert Einstein: The Scientific Monism," *Fundamenta Scientiae* 5 (1984), pp. 103-15.

56. A. Einstein, *The World as I See It* (New York: Covici Friede, 1934), p. 263. For Einstein's antagonism to a personal God and his inability to see the problems such antagonism implies even for scientific research, see my *The Road of Science*, p. 194.

57. *Lettres à Maurice Solovine* (Paris: Gauthier-Villars, 1956), p. 115.

58. J. Jeans, *Astronomy and Cosmogony* (Cambridge: University Press, 1928).

59. The papers of the panelists were published in *British Association for the Advancement of Science. Report of the Centenary Meeting. London Sept. 27-30, 1931* (London: Office of the British Association, 1932), pp. 573-610. For further discussion, see my *Cosmos and Creator*, pp. 7-14.

60. Lemaître ignored the question of the universe in his *The Primeval Atom: An Essay on Cosmogony*, tr. B. H. & S. A. Korff (New York: Van Nostrand, 1950), a collection of lectures and essays less technical and more philosophical and theological.

61. He did so in his Gifford Lectures (Aberdeen, 1927-29), published as *Scientific Theory and Religion: The World Described by Science and Its Spiritual Interpretation* (Cambridge: University Press, 1933), p. 49.

62. W. Temple, *Nature, Man and God* (London: Macmillan, 1934), p. 53.

63. Letter of July 16, 1942, to Dorothy Emmet, quoted in her contribution, "The Philosopher," to F. A. Iremonger, *William Temple, Archbishop of Canterbury: His Life and Letters* (London: Oxford University Press, 1948), pp. 537-38.

64. Especially his Riddell Lectures, *The Beginning and End of the World* (Oxford University Press, 1942) and his Donnellan Lectures, *Space and Spirit: Theories of the Universe and Arguments for the Existence of God* (Hinsdale, IL.: Henry Regnery, 1948).

65. The total absence of any reference to the universe in scholastic cosmologies is exemplified by D. Nys, *Cosmologie ou étude philosophique du monde inorganique* (4th ed.; Louvain: Em. Warny, 1928) and F. Renoirte, *Cosmology: Elements of a Critique of the Sciences and of Cosmology*, tr. J. F. Coffey from 2nd rev. ed. of the French original (New York: Joseph F. Wagner,

1950). Examples with not sufficiently strong references to the universe are P. Hoenen, *Cosmologia* (5th ed.: Rome: Gregorian University, 1956) and Ph. Selvaggi, *Cosmologia* (2nd ed.: Rome: Gregorian University, 1962). In the latter see, for instance, the references to Kant and Einstein (pp. 382 and 387).

66.   For the full text in English translation, see the brochure, "The Proofs for the Existence of God in the Light of Modern Natural Science. Address of Pope Pius XII to the Pontifical Academy of Sciences" (Washington: National Catholic Welfare Conference, 1951), 18 pp.

67.   Under the caption, "Pope says universe was created by God 5 to 10 billion years ago." *New York Times* Nov. 23, 1951, p. 1. Much of p. 6 is taken up by excerpts from the Pope's address.

68.   *Lettres à Maurice Solovine*, p. 115.

CHAPTER TWO

1.   H. A. Lorentz *et al, The Principle of Relativity*, tr. W. Perrett and G. B. Jeffrey (1923; New York: Dover, n.d.), p. 188.

2.   In a conversation with G. Gamow around 1947. See G. Gamow, *My World Line* (New York: The Viking Press, 1970), p. 44.

3.   See note 1 above, p. 188.

4.   G. Lemaître, "Un univers homogène de masse constante et de rayon croissant, rendant compte de la vitesse radiale des nébuleuses extragalactiques," *Annales de la Société scientifique de Bruxelles, Série A, Sciences mathématiques*, 47 (1927), pp. 49-59. No more effective in calling attention to Lemaître's article was its almost simultaneous publication in *Mathesis*. Although Lemaître sent a reprint of his article to his former teacher, Eddington, the latter overlooked its significance until he himself came to a similar conclusion in 1930. Then, to atone for his oversight, he had Lemaître's article appear in English translation in the *Monthly Notices of the Royal Astronomical Society*.

5.   E. P. Hubble and M. L. Humason, "Velocity-Distance Relation among Extra-galactic Nebulae," *Astrophysical Journal* 74 (1931), pp. 43-80. Most memorably, a hitherto unknown physical process, other than recessional velocity, was suggested as

late as 1934 by E. P. Hubble in his Silliman Lectures at Yale. See his *The Realm of the Nebulae* (London: Oxford University Press, 1935), pp. 122-23.

6. His first communication to that effect appeared in *Nature* 127 (1931), p.106. Several of his further, and in part popular, elaborations of the idea appeared in his *L'hypothèse de l'atome primitif* (1946) which also appeared in English translation, *The Primeval Atom: An Essay on Cosmogony* (New York: Van Nostrand, 1950).

7. For details, see my *Chesterton, a Seer of Science* (Urbana, I..: University of Illinois Press, 1986), pp. 19-20.

8. G. K. Chesterton, *Orthodoxy* (London: John Lane, 1909), p. 115.

9. A. S. Eddington, *New Pathways in Science* (Cambridge: University Press, 1934), p. 217.

10. For various statements of Herschel concerning stellar evolution and the role of that "nebulosity" there, see my work, *The Milky Way: an Elusive Road for Science* (New York: Science History Publications, 1972; paperback reprint 1976), pp. 238-43.

11. For details, see my *Planets and Planetarians: A History of Theories of the Origin of Planetary Systems* (Edinburgh: Scottish Academic Press; New York: John Wiley Inc, 1978), pp. 122-26.

12. The popularity of the theory received a major boost through the publication of Herbert Spencer's "Recent Astronomy and the Nebular Hypothesis," in *Westminster Review* 70 (July 1858), pp. 185-225.

13. The difficulty can be overcome only by assuming a most finely tuned collision that involves two stars and a gaseous cloud. For details, see my *Planets and Planetarians*, pp. 236-39.

14. On the clash between Napoleon and Laplace, Herschel offered the judicious comment: "Mons. De la Place wished to shew that a chain of natural causes would account for the construction and preservation of the wonderful system [of planets]. This the first Consul rather opposed. Much may be said on the subject; by joining the arguments of both we shall be led to Nature and to nature's God." Quoted in *The Herschel Chronicle*, ed. C. A. Lubbock (New York: Macmillan Company, 1933), p. 310.

15. The story, first recorded by Sextus Empiricus, is used by W. Whewell in his *Astronomy and General Physics considered with*

Reference to Natural Theology (London: William Pickering, 1833), p. 209.

16. Ibid., p. 207. Whewell's reference was, of course, to a phrase in the famed Scholium appended by Roger Cotes to the 2nd edition of the *Principia* in 1713.

17. Chapters vii-xvii, that deal in Herbert Spencer's *Autobiography* (London: Williams and Norgate, 1904) with his years 13-24, are a proof of this in his very narrative. He could receive no help from a certain Mr. Stephenson, his boss in a civil engineering bureau, about whom he wrote: "He had no special discipline fitting him for engineering — very little mathematical training or allied preparation" (vol. 1, p. 131).

18. See *The Autobiography of Charles Darwin 1809-1882*, with original omissions restored, edited with an appendix and notes by his granddaughter, Nora Barlow (New York: W. W. Norton, 1969), pp. 108-09.

19. H. Spencer, *First Principles* (4th ed.; New York: D. Appleton, 1882), p. 426.

20. Ibid.

21. Ibid., p 405.

22. Spencerian cosmogony as the foundation of the social applicability of Darwinism is ignored in R. Hofstadter's *Social Darwinism in American Thought* (1944; rev. ed.: Boston: Beacon Press, 1955).

23. H. G. Wells, *First and Last Things: Confession of Faith and Rule of Life*, definitive edition (London: Watts & Co., 1929), p. 30.

24. A. S. Eddington, *The Expanding Universe* (Cambridge: University Press, 1933), p. 57.

25. J. S. Rigden, *Rabi: Scientist and Citizen* (New York: Basic Books, 1987), p. 15.

26. R. Dawkins, *The Blind Watchmaker* (New York: W. W. Norton, 1986), pp. 14-15.

27. Such final "simple" sets were believed to be on hand around 1932 when the counterparts of electron and proton were discovered in the positron and neutron, and again in the late 1950s when the discovery of the omega particle seemed to put the finishing touch on the "eightfold way".

28. The plausibility of the eventual finding of a single formula applicable to all forces and interactions in nature is derived in part from past successes of physics in unifying apparently different physical forces, and even more so from convictions that

are metaphysical and religious in ultimate analysis. Particularly noteworthy in this connection is the impact made through many centuries by the verse in the Book of Wisdom that God "arranged all things according to measure, number, and weight (11: 20).

29.   S. Weinberg, *The First Three Minutes*, (London: André Deutsch, 1977), p. 132.

30.   The reason for this is the 'infinity catastrophe" implied in the fact that in the eternal universe of the steady-state theorists an infinite amount of matter has to pile up "outside" the visible universe. The steady-state theory is in fact a replay of that schizophrenic partition of the universe into two units (one puny, the other infinite) which cosmologists naively endorsed half a century earlier.

31.   See Weinberg, *The First Three Minutes*, pp. 122-23.

32.   G. Gamow, *The Creation of the Universe* (New York: Viking Press, 1952). Author's note to the second printing, August 1952 (p. vii).

33.   Quoted in *Time*, Oct. 27, 1980 (p. 75) in connection with their being awarded the Nobel Prize.

34.   At present, quarks are classed into three generations, the first being made up of *up* and *down* quarks, the second denoted by the words *charm* and *strange*, the third called *top* and *bottom*. There are as yet no extensive speculations about the constituent particles of the quarks themselves.

35.   See J. S. Trefil, *The Moment of Creation* (New York: Colllier Books, 1983), pp. 21-22.

36.   See J. Trainer and M. Kaku, "John Schwarz's Quest for the Theory of Everything," *Harvard Magazine* 89 (March-April, 1987), p. 21.

37.   Ibid., p. 26.

38.   Ibid., p. 25. It is indicative of the philosophical insensitivity of the practicing physicist that no reference to the startling specificities of "strings" appear in such major accounts of them as *Superstrings: The First 15 Years of Superstring Theory*, ed. J. H. Schwarz (Singapore: World Scientific, 1985) and *Superstrings, Supergravity and Unified Theories: Proceedings of the Summer Workshop on High Energy Physics and Cosmology: Trieste, Italy, 10 June-19 July, 1985*, ed. G. Furlan *et al* (Singapore: World Scientific, 1986).

39.   Trefil, *The Moment of Creation*, p. 220.

40.   E. P. Tyron, "Is the Universe a Vacuum Fluctuation?" *Nature* 246 (Dec. 14, 1973), p. 397.

41.   "To see a World in a Grain of Sand/ And Heaven in a Wild Flower,/ Hold Infinity in the palm of your hand/ And Eternity in an hour," or the first four lines in Blake's "Auguries of Innocence," in *Blake. Complete Writings*, ed. G. Keynes (Oxford: University Press, 1959), p. 431.

42.   Quoted in A. Moszkowski, *Conversations with Einstein*, tr. H. L. Brose (1921; New York: Horizon Books, 1970), p. 202.

43.   V. F. Weisskopf, "Of Atoms, Mountains, and Stars: A Study in Qualitative Physics," *Science* 187 (1975), pp. 605-12.

44.   L. Thomas, who in his *The Lives of a Cell* (Penguin Books, p. 132) gives that detail, does not name the physicist in question. For the statement of Juliana of Norwich, see ch. 5 in her *Revelations of Divine Love*, tr. J. Walsh (London: Burns and Oates, 1961), p. 53. That the essence of the vision in question is the cohesiveness of the universe, as graphically revealed in its "small" appearance is made very clear in ch. 11, where in another vision God is seen "in a point". The point then is made in the same breath that because of God's utter simplicity "nothing is done by hap or chance, but all by the foreseeing wisdom of God". And, as if to leave no room for any equivocation about chance, Juliana adds: "If a thing be hap or chance according to man's judgment, the cause is our blindness and lack of foreknowledge" (p. 66). No less an unfolding of the Christian vision of the cosmos are the concluding remarks in that vision which show the remarkable extent of medieval awareness about a passage from the Book of Wisdom, quoted above in note 28.

45.   Claims made by E. W. Hobson, Professor of Pure Mathematics at Cambridge University, in his Gifford Lectures, *The Domain of Natural Science* (1923; New York: Dover, 1968), pp. 487-88.

46.   A. Huxley, *Grey Eminence: A Study in Religion and Politics* (London: Chatto and Windus, 1942), p. 13.

47.   My slightly revised version of a ditty by Mr John E. Keyes that appeared in *Princeton Alumni Weekly* (January 26, 1981, p. 8) as his reaction to the article, "Cosmology at Princeton," published in the October 20, 1980, issue. In his version the last two lines are as follows: "Should place at Singularity/ A slight irregularity".

48. Statement attributed to Bishop Creighton in M. Demiaskevich, *The National Mind: English, French, German* (New York: American Book Co., 1938), p. 155.
49. See the main caption on the cover of *Newsweek*, June 13, 1988.
50. See E. Waugh, *The Life of the Right Reverend Ronald Knox* (London: Chapman and Hall, 1959), p. 214.
51. Bohr's intense reading of Kierkegaard relates to the Spring of 1911 when he wrote his doctoral dissertation on the electron theory of metals which had nothing to do with the revolutionary theory of the hydrogen atom he had worked out in England in 1913. Moreover, Bohr most explicitly disavowed Kierkegaard's theological ideas (see the reminiscences of J. Rud Nielson, Bohr's colleague as professor of physics at the University of Copenhagen, "Memories of Niels Bohr," in *Physics Today*, October 1963, pp. 27-28). In view of this, rather unconvincing should seem Russell Stannard's suggestive question, "Could it be that twentieth-century physics owes a modest debt to a nineteenth-century theologian's contemplation of a fourth-century Christian creed?" in *The Times*, Dec. 3, 1983, quoted in *Niels Bohr: A Centenary Volume*, ed. A. P. French and P. J. Kennedy (Cambridge: Harvard University Press, 1985), p. 303.
52. A statement attributed to Kierkegaard by B. V. Schwarz in his introduction to a collection of essays in honor of Dietrich von Hildebrand, *The Human Person and the World of Values* (New York: Fordham University Press, 1960), p. xiii. Closely similar phrases are contained in Kierkegaard's reflections on all-embracing conceptual systems in his *Concluding Unscientific Postscript*, tr. D. F. Swenson and W. Lowrie (Princeton: University Press, 1968), pp. 105-08.

CHAPTER THREE

1. A. Einstein, "Principles of Research" (1918), in *Essays in Science* (New York: Covici-Friede, 1934), pp. 21-22. In the same context Einstein emphatically stated that modest as could be the scientist's effort, it deserved "to be called by the proud name of a theory of the Universe".

2. See A. Moszkowski, *Conversations with Einstein* (1922; New York: Horizon Press, 1970), pp. 127-30. Tellingly, in those conversations, that took place in 1920-21, Zöllner is referred to only as one involved in spiritist séances (p. 137) but not as one who wrote in some detail about the recasting of cosmology in a four-dimensional manifold and setting the total mass of the universe as strictly finite.

3. For instance, S. Weinberg, *Gravitation and Cosmology: Principles and Applications of the General Theory of Relativity* (New York: John Wiley and Sons, 1972), pp. 475 and 611. Ignored, throughout that excellent treatise, is the problem of an actually realized infinite quantity.

4. C. Kahn and F. Kahn, "Letters from Einstein to de Sitter on the Nature of the Universe," *Nature* 257 (Oct. 9, 1975), p. 454.

5. A. Einstein, "Autobiographical Notes," in P. A. Schilpp (ed.), *Albert Einstein: Philosopher-Scientist* (1949; New York: Harper Torchbooks, 1959), p. 5. On materialist versions of cosmogony, very popular in the latter half of the 19th century, see F. Gregory, *Scientific Materialism in Nineteenth Century Germany* (Dordrecht: D. Reidel, 1977), pp. 100-21.

6. B. Spinoza, *Ethics*, Part I, Prop. xxi, in *Works of Spinoza*, ed. R. H. M. Elwes (1883; New York: Dover, n.d.), vol. 2, p. 63.

7. Ibid., pp. 291-92.

8. Ibid., p. 409.

9. Details given about Friedmann's work and Einstein's first reaction to it in G. Gamow's autobiographical *My World Line* (New York: Viking Press, 1970), pp. 42-45, are all the more valuable because Gamow was at that time a student in Friedmann's class on cosmology.

10. Although in 1923 Einstein atoned for his earlier brushing aside of Friedmann's work with the remark that it was "valid and enlightening," it was not until 1931 that he gave serious thought to the idea of an oscillating universe in a memoir to the Prussian Academy of Sciences. For details, see my *Science and Creation: From Eternal Cycles to an Oscillating Universe* (2nd rev. ed.; Edinburgh: Scottish Academic Press, 1986), p. 357.

11. F. Engels, *Anti-Dühring or Herr Eugen Dühring's Revolution in Science* (1877) in *Karl Marx and Friedrich Engels. Collected Works* (London: Lawrence & Wishart, 1987), vol. 25, p. 56.

12. F. Engels, *Dialectics of Nature*, ibid., pp. 562-63.

13. V. I. Lenin, *Materialism and Empirio-Criticism* (New York: International Publishers, 1927), p. 352.

14. Prof. Ambartsumian arrived at the Congress in the last minute in the company of three Soviet citizens who sat in the front row while he read his paper. As a member of the panel I was able to observe them at close range and failed to gain the impression that they were intellectuals.

15. E. Littré, *La science au point de vue de philosophie* (3rd ed.; Paris: Didier, 1873), p. 322.

16. An illustration is the course, popularly dubbed "Guilt 33", taught by Prof. R. Coles at Harvard University.

17. Quoted in E. T. Mallove, *The Quickening Universe: Cosmic Evolution and Human Destiny* (New York: St. Martin's Press, 1987), p. 235. This statement of Einstein, which I was not able to verify, matches perfectly the lines jotted by him in 1953 on a letter whose writer, a licensed Baptist woman pastor, inquired about his belief in the immortality of the soul: "I do not believe in the immortality of the individual and I consider ethics to be an exclusively human concern with no superhuman authority behind it." Quoted in *Albert Einstein. The Human Side: New Glimpses from His Archives*, selected and edited by H. Dukas and B. Hoffman (Princeton: Princeton University Press, 1979), p. 39.

18. Reported in *The New York Times*, Feb. 24, 1929 p. 12. Nernst spoke in the Virchow House on "The Balance of Energy in the Universe".

19. A. Pais, *Subtle Is the Lord: The Science and Life of Albert Einstein* (Oxford: Clarendon Press, 1982), pp. 14 and 17.

20. E. R. Harrison quoted in *The New York Times*, Nov. 2, 1975, p. 56, col. 2. The occasion was the "neighborhood meeting "organized by the Center for Astrophysics in Cambridge, Mass."

21. The panel discussion took place on Sept. 29, 1931. The text of papers was published in *British Association for the Advancement of Science. Report of the Centenary Meeting. London, Sept. 23-30, 1931* (London: Office of the British Association, 1932), pp. 573-610. See especially pp. 577 and 597. Six years earlier W. D. MacMillan, of the University of Chicago, explicity proposed the spontaneous emergence of new matter in the universe in support of his view that "the Universe does not change always in any one direction. Using figurative language — the uni-

verse is not like a stream which flows steadily from one unknown region to another, it is like the surface of the ocean, never twice alike and yet always the same." For details see my *The Paradox of Olbers' Paradox* (New York: Herder & Herder, 1969), pp. 230-31.

22. As witnessed by four talks on cosmology, sponsored by BBC and published as *Rival Theories of Cosmology* (London: Oxford University Press, 1960). In fact the talks were slanted in favor of the steady-state theory inasmuch as the latter was presented by its chief protagonist, H. Bondi, wheres at least one, W. B. Bonnor, of the three other speakers was sympathetic to it, and neither of the remaining two, R. A. Lyttleton and G. J. Whitrow, was really critical of it.

23. *The New York Times*, May 24, 1952, pp. 1 and 17, under the headline, "British Astronomer Royal Supports Theory that Creation Is Continuous".

24. H. Dingle, "Science and Modern Cosmology," *Monthly Notices of the Royal Astronomical Society* 113 (1953), p. 406.

25. H. Bondi, *Cosmology* (Cambridge: University Press, 1952), p. 144.

26. This is certainly true of the best of them, "Creation and the 'New' Cosmology," by M. K. Munitz, in *British Journal for the Philosophy of Science* 5 (1954-55), pp. 32-46.

27. F. Hoyle, *Astronomy Today* (London: Heinemann, 1975), p. 165.

28. F. Hoyle and C. Wickramasinghe, *Evolution from Space: A Theory of Cosmic Creationism* (New York: Simon and Schuster, 1981), p. 143.

29. A. Einstein, *Out of My Later Years* (New York: Philosophical Library, 1950), p. 59.

30. D. C. Stove, *Popper and After: Four Modern Irrationalists* (Oxford: Pergamon Press, 1982), p. 19.

31. Stove himself conveniently if not naively assumes that the origins of the irrationalist movement in present-day philosophy of science are "*principally* intellectual" (ibid., p. 45).

32. The year when W. Baade published his results about the recalibration of the Hubble constant. One can easily guess Hoyle's feelings as he had to admit, in writing three years later Baade's obituary, that "perhaps his most famous piece of work was his re-assessment . . . of the distance scale of the universe." *Monthly Notices of the Royal Astronomical Society* 114

(1955), p. 370. Hoyle had no right to use the qualifying adverb, perhaps.

33.　F. von Weizsäcker, *The Relevance of Science: Creation and Cosmogony* (New York: Harper and Row, 1964), p. 151.

34.　F. Hoyle, *From Stonehenge to Modern Cosmology* (San Francisco: W. H. Freeman, 1972), p. 2.

35.　A phrase of M. Disney, *The Hidden Universe* (London: J. M. Dent & Sons, 1984), p. 202.

36.　F. Hoyle, *Astronomy and Cosmology: A Modern Course* (San Francisco: W. H. Freeman, 1975), p. 680.

37.　Particularly prolific was H. Seeliger in suggesting changes of the inverse square law as a solution of the gravitational paradox. For details, see my *The Paradox of Olbers' Paradox* (New York: Herder and Herder, 1969), pp. 189-94.

38.　Quoted in M. Disney, *The Hidden Universe*, p. 174.

39.　Quoted in *The New York Times*, April 29, 1980, p. C1.

40.　P. Hut and S. D. M. White, "Can a Neutrino Dominated Universe Be Rejected?" *Nature* 310 (Aug. 23, 1984), p. 637.

41.　V. Trimble, "Dark Matter in the Universe: Where, What, and Why?" *Contemporary Physics* 29 (1988), p. 389.

42.　I. D. Novikov and Ya. B. Zel'dovich, "Physical Processes near Cosmological Singularities," *Annual Review of Astronomy and Astrophysics* 11 (1973), p. 401.

43.　Oxford: Clarendon Press. Reprinted in 1946, 1949, 1950, 1958, 1962, and 1966.

44.　P. C. W. Davis, *The Physics of Time Asymmetry* (Berkeley: University of California Press 1976), p. 191.

45.　See J. S. Trefil, *The Moment of Creation* (New York: Macmillan, 1983), pp. 216-17.

46.　See the first six chapters of my *Science and Creation*, dealing respectively with science in ancient China, India, pre-Columbian America, Egypt, Babylon, and Greece.

47.　Unfortunately, this ideological point is overlooked in D. Gasman, *The Scientific Origins of National Socialism* (New York: American Elsevier, 1971) and A. D. Beyerchen, *Scientists under Hitler: Politics and Physics in the Third Reich* (New Haven: Yale University Press, 1977).

48.　On Engels' advocacy of a cyclic cosmos, see my *Science and Creation*, pp. 311-14.

49.　Duhem's pioneer findings on the medieval origins of Newton's first law is not, of course, to the liking of those historians of science who view the rise of science in its Enlightenment-perspective, namely, as a radical break with the Christian ingredients of Western culture. For details, see ch. 10 in my *Uneasy Genius: The Life and Work of Pierre Duhem* (2nd. ed.; Dordrecht; Martinus Nijhoff, 1988).

50. S. Hawking, *A Brief History of Time* (Toronto: Bantam Books, 1988), p. 47.

51. D. Hilbert, "On the Infinite," in *Philosophy of Mathematics*, ed. P. Benacerraf and H. Putnam (Englewood Cliffs, NJ.: Prentice-Hall, 1964), p. 151.

52. The opposite position is argued by W. L. Craig in his *The Kalam Cosmological Argument* (London: Macmillan, 1979) where the argument of al-Ghazzali, Saadia, and Bonaventure is set forth in modern form. Concerning Aquinas, whose argument to the contrary is found by Craig "singularly unconvincing" (p. 152), Craig fails to survey the exposition of Aquinas's arguments by Gilson although he mentions Gilson as the author of a monograph on Bonaventure (p. 55).

53. As I argued in my article, "The Intelligent Christian's Guide to Scientific Cosmology," *Faith and Reason* 12 (1986), pp. 124-36.

54. See J. N. Wilford's report, "Novel Theory Challenges the Big Bang," in *The New York Times*, Feb. 28, 1989, p. C1.

55. Ibid., p. C11.

56. Ibid., p. C1.

57. Ibid., pp. C1-C11.

58. H. Dicke and P. J. E. Peebles, "The Big Bang Cosmology — Enigmas and Nostrums," in S. W. Hawking and W. Israel (eds.), *General Relativity: An Einstein Centenary Survey* (New York: Cambridge University Press, 1979), p. 510.

59. "On the Reconcentration of the Mechanical Energy of the Universe," in *W. J. M. Rankine. Miscellaneous Scientific Papers*, ed. W. J. Millar (London: Charles Griffin, 1891), p. 202.

60. L. Boltzmann, *Lectures on Gas Theory*, tr. S. G. Brush (Berkeley: University of California Press, 1964), pp. 446-48.

CHAPTER FOUR

1. As emphatically stated in the Manifesto of the Vienna Circle. Quoted in R. Carnap, *The Unity of Science*, tr. M. Black (London: Paul, 1934), pp. 10-11.

2. C. P. Snow, who in his "The Moral Un-neutrality of Science" (*Science* 133 [1961], p. 257) reported Rutherford's words and added that "scientists have sneaking sympathy for Rutherford."

3. See my essay, "The Reality Beneath: The World View of Rutherford," in M. Bunge and W. R. Shea (eds.), *Rutherford and Physics at the Turn of the Century* (New York: Dawson and History of Science Publications, 1979), pp. 110-123.

4. For a survey and analysis of Aristotle's various references to physical processes as expressive of volitions, see my *The Relevance of Physics* (Chicago: University of Chicago Press, 1966), pp. 19-28.

5. E. T. Whittaker, *From Euclid to Eddington: A Study of Conceptions of the External World* (Cambridge: University Press, 1949), p. 65.

6. There is, from the viewpoint of scientific method, something much more ominous than what meets the eye in Plotinus' warning in *The Enneads* (III, 2) that "to linger about the parts is to condemn not the Cosmos but some isolated appendage of it; in the entire living Being we fasten our eyes on a hair or a toe neglecting the marvelous spectacle of the complete Man; we ignore all the tribe and kinds of animals except for the meanest; we pass over an entire race, humanity, and bring forward —Thersites." Such warning, being the sequel to one of his many emphatic declarations that "the world is a product of Necessity, not of deliberate purpose," reveals the logical reluctance of necessitarian and emanationist cosmic philosophers to dwell on particular specific details of the real world, the very heart of scientific research. It was therefore no coincidence that, as Porphyry recalled, Plotinus "had a thorough theoretical knowledge of Geometry, Mechanics, Optics, and Music, though it was not in his temperament to go practically into these subjects" and that "he paid some attention to the principles of Astronomy though he did not study the subject very deeply on the mathematical side," where, as Rutherford would add, quantitatively exact statements must replace vague utterances exuding "hot air". See *Plotinus. The Enneads*, tr. S. McKenna (2nd rev. ed.; London: Faber and Faber, 1956), pp. 10 and 173.

7. See G. Scholem, *Kabbalah* (New York: The New York Times Books Co., n.d.), pp. 88-122 and 128-35.

8. As set forth in detail in my article, "The Universe in the Bible and Modern Science," in *Ex Auditu*, 3 (1987), pp. 137-47, and in my *The Savior of Science* (Washington: Regnery-Gateway, 1988), pp. 54-66.

9. Giordano Bruno, *The Ash Wednesday Supper (La cena de le ceneri)*, tr. Stanley L Jaki with introduction and notes (The Hague: Mouton, 1975), p. 165.

10. Ibid., p. 156.

11. M. Mersenne, *Quaestiones celeberrimae in Genesim* (Paris: sumptibus Sebastiani Cramoisy, 1623), cols. 714-16. See also F. A. Yates, *Giordano Bruno and the Hermetic Tradition* (Chicago: University of Chicago Press, 1964), pp. 406 and 437-38.

12. Spinoza, *Ethics*, Part I, Prop. xxix, in *Works of Spinoza*, tr. R. H. M. Elwes (1883: New York: Dover, n. d.), vol. 2, p. 68.

13. The great defects, from the viewpoint of physics, of Spinoza's treatment of the rainbow are acknowledged by M. J. Petry, editor and translator of the treatise, *Spinoza Algebraic Calculation of the Rainbow & Calculation of Chances* (Dordrecht: Martinus Nijhoff, 1985), pp. 9 and 143.

14. For details, see my *The Relevance of Physics* (Chicago: University of Chicago Press, 1966) ch. 1, and *The Road of Science and the Ways to God*, (Chicago: University of Chicago Press, 1978) ch. 8.

15. On Marx and Engels, see ch. 13 in *The Relevance of Physics*; Blanqui's dicta on science are discussed in my *Science and Creation: From Eternal Cycles to an Oscillating Universe* (2nd enlarged ed.; Edinburgh: Scottish Academic Press, 1986), pp. 314-18.

16. Examples of those various meanings cover two densely printed quarto pages (905-06) in volume IV.

17. Reported from personal interview with Dirac by H. F. Judson, "Where Einstein and Picasso Meet," *Newsweek*, Nov. 17, 1980, p. 23.

18. Reported from personal interview with Hawking by J. L. Wilhelm, "A Singular Man," *Quest*, April 1979, p. 39.

19. Ibid.

20. S. Hawking, *A Brief History of Time: From the Big Bang to Black Holes* (Toronto: Bantam Books, 1988), p. 175.

21. Hawking quotes Wittgenstein, "The sole remaining task for philosophy is the analysis of language" (ibid.).

22. Ibid.

23.   A succinct but devastating proof of this is that, according to Thomas, it is from experience that man derives his knowledge even of the indemonstrable first principles. See his *Quaest. disp. de Anima*, un., art. 5, and his *Summa contra Gentiles*, II, 78.
24.   Hawking, *A Brief History of Time*, p. 175.
25.   Quoted in *Time*, Feb. 8, 1988, p. 60.
26.   From B. Appleyard's interview, "A Master of the Universe," with the Hawkings, in *Sunday Times Magazine*, June 19, 1988, pp. 26-30, for quotation see p. 29. A year later, in an interview with the *Star Tribune* (Minneapolis) following his lecture in the Northrop Auditorium of the University of Minnesota, Hawking gave a categorical Yes to the question: "In earlier interviews, you have said you don't believe in a personal God. Is that true?" May 17, 1989, p. A15.
27.   Ibid.
28.   Hawking, *A Brief History of Time*, p. 174.
29.   Ibid.
30.   Ibid.
31.   Quoted in *Star Tribune* (Minneapolis), April 4, 1988, p. 8E, in an article with a title, "Key to Universe may be in Mind of Scientist," that credits journalism insofar as it wants to serve as an accurate receiving and transmitting antenna of some prevailing moods among cosmologists.
32.   On being asked what would have been his reaction had the 1919 solar eclipse disproved his theory, Einstein replied: "Then I would have been very sorry for the dear Lord — the theory is correct." Quoted by G. Holton, "Mach, Einstein, and the Search for Reality," in *Thematic Origins of Scientific Thought: Kepler to Einstein* (Cambridge: Harvard University Press, 1973), p. 237.
33.   Quoted in G. Holton's review of R. Clark's *Einstein: The Life and Times*, in the *New York Times Book Review*, Sept. 5, 1971, p. 20. col. 2.
34.   According to E. Straus, who worked with him at the Institute for Advanced Study, Einstein often spoke in that vein whenever a "simple" solution was the result of his investigations. See B. Hoffman, *Albert Einstein: Creator and Rebel* (New York: The Viking Press, 1972), pp. 227-28.
35.   In the wake of the disputes that arose about the reliability of the measurement of the bending of light around the sun by the British scientific expedition to West Africa, Einstein re-

marked in a lecture given in Prague in 1920 that without experimental verification his General Relativity would turn "into mere dust and ashes". A personal recollection of H. Feigl, who as a "young student" attended that meeting. See his "Beyond Peaceful Coexistence," in R. H. Stuewer (ed.), *Historical and Philosophical Perspectives of Science* (Minneapolis: University of Minnesota Press, 1970), p. 9.

36.   A non-technical account of Eddington's Fundamental Theory is given in A. Vibert Douglas, *The Life of Arthur Stanley Eddington* (London: Thomas Nelson, 1957), ch. 11, and J. Singh, *Modern Cosmology* (Pelican Book, 1970), ch. 11.

37.   E. T. Whittaker, "Eddington's Theory of the Constants of Nature," *The Mathematical Gazette* 29 (1945), pp. 137-44.

38.   J. R. Oppenheimer, *The Constitution of Matter* (Eugene: Oregon State System of Higher Education, 1956), p. 2.

39.   Quoted in G. Holton, "The Mainsprings of Discovery — The Great Tradition," *Encounter*, April 1974, p. 91.

40.   S. Weinberg, "Where We Are Now," *Science* 180 (20 April 1973), p. 278.

41.   S. Weinberg, *The First Three Minutes: A Modern View of the Origin of the Universe* (London: André Deutsch, 1970), p. 154.

42.   C. Misner, K. S. Thorne, and J. A. Wheeler, *Gravitation* (San Francisco: W. H. Freeman, 1973), p. 1208.

43.   Ibid.

44.   Leibniz's statement, "Further, suppose that things must exist, we must be able to give a reason why they *must exist so* and not otherwise," in his *Principles of Nature and Grace* (1714) (see *Leibniz Selections*, ed. P. P. Wiener [New York: Charles Scribner's Sons, 1951], p. 527) is weakened by two factors. One is its touch of apriorism, evident also by its being followed by Leibniz's declaration that the actually existing world must be the best of all possible worlds. The other is that in the same context he presents "nothing" as "simpler and easier than something". Leibniz was an idealist even when he came close to a most incisive formulation of the true contingency of actual existents.

45.   Misner, *Gravitation,* p. 1208. The same puzzlement about the difference between mathematical equations and real existence is in evidence in Hawking's remark: "My work indicates

that God wouldn't have a choice in making the universe as it is. That doesn't explain why it exists. You can still blame God for that if you like." Quoted in *Star Tribune* (Minneapolis), May 16, 1989, pp. B1-2.

46. J. A. Wheeler, "Hermann Weyl and the Unity of Knowledge," *American Scientist* 74 (1986), p. 374.

47. Ibid.

48. Ibid.

49. See reference 45 in ch. 1.

50. As told by Carnap in his "Intellectual Autobiography," in P. A. Schilpp (ed.), *The Philosophy of Rudolf Carnap* (La Salle, IL.: Library of Living Philosophers, 1963), pp. 37-38.

51. The papers read at the symposium were published as *The Nature of the Physical Universe: 1976 Nobel Conference*, ed., D. Huff and O. Prewett (New York: John Wiley & Sons, 1979).

52. The members of the panel were, in addition to M. Gell-Mann and myself, F. Hoyle, V. F. Weisskopf, S. Weinberg, and H. Putnam.

53. Wisdom 11: 20.

54. "From the intrinsic evidence of his creation, the Great Architect of the Universe now begins to appear as a pure mathematician" (p. 144 in the first edition, New York: Macmillan Co., 1930). Typically, in the same concluding chapter, entitled "Into Deep Waters," Jeans becomes lost in the shallows of idealism as he presents modern scientific cosmology as incompatible with "the old dualism of mind and matter" (p. 158) and speaks of the act of creation as an act of thought (p. 154) instead of the act of a Being whose essence is to exist.

55. In their book-length pharaphrasis of Gödel's paper, *Gödel's Proof* (New York: New York University Press, 1958). E. Nagel and J. R. Newman failed to exploit their felicitous remark about the meta-mathematical proofs of the consistency of sets of mathematical propositions, namely, that "it would be irresponsible to claim that these formally indemonstrable truths established by meta-mathematical arguments are based on nothing better than bare appeals to intuition" (p. 101). Perhaps the empiricist Nagel was afraid that he might have cast an unwitting vote for realist metaphysics had he tried to specify the true nature of those truths.

56. H. Weyl's remark in his *The Philosophy of Mathematics and Natural Science* (1949; New York: Atheneum, 1963), p. 219.

57. The topic of E. P. Wigner's "The Unreasonable Effectiveness of Mathematics in the Natural Sciences," *Communications in Pure and Applied Mathematics* 13 (1960), pp. 1-12.

58. Weyl, *The Philosophy of Mathematics*, p. 108.

59. As reported by K. R. Popper, an "informal" member of the Vienna Circle, in his *Conjectures and Refutations: The Growth of Scientific Knowledge* (New York: Harper and Row, 1968), p. 270.

60. *The Relevance of Physics* (Chicago: University of Chicago Press, 1966; reprinted 1969), pp. 127-29; *The Road of Science and the Ways to God* (Chicago: University Chicago Press; Edinburgh: Scottish Academic Press, 1978), pp. 426-27; *Cosmos and Creator* (Edinburgh: Scottish Academic Press, 1980), pp. 49-51; and "The Chaos of Scientific Cosmology," in *The Nature of the Physical Universe* (see note 51 above).

61. Thus, for instance, F. J. Tipler, "The Omega Point Theory: A Model of An Evolving God," in *Physics, Philosophy and Theology: A Common Quest for Understanding*, ed. R. J. Russell, W. R. Stoeger, and G. V. Coyne (Vatican City State: Vatican Observatory, 1988), p. 330. Without reconstructing my argument, Tipler dismisses it, a fact that may be understandable in an essay aimed at demonstrating God's evolving character. For if the Ultimate in intelligibility and being is subject to change, there remains no stable ground for any rational discourse, not even for a discourse about Gödel's theorems. Contrary to Tipler, Gödel's theorems apply at any non-trivial set of arithmetic propositions and not merely at the complete set of arithmetic propositions. No less importantly, it remains to be shown that it is possible to construct a physical theory about the real universe without relying on a non-trivial set of arithmetic propositions, unless, of course, the proponents of that theory abdicate the task of measuring and counting the quantitatively specific parameters of physical reality.

62. Attributed to A. Weil by P. Rosenblum in his *The Elements of Mathematical Logic* (New York: Dover, 1950), p. 72.

63. P. Benacerraf, "God, the Devil, and Gödel," *The Monist* 51 (1967), p. 10.

64. The antidote, as formulated by Gödel, was responsible for his denial of the reality of time as well as of free will.

65. For instance, K. Gödel, "An Example of a New Type of Cosmological Solution of Einstein's Field Equations of Gravitation," *Reviews of Modern Physics*, 21 (1949), pp. 447-50. For a brief discussion of Gödel's rotating universe cosmology, see S. W. Hawking and G. F. R. Ellis, *The Large Scale Structure of Space-Time* (Cambridge: University Press, 1973), pp. 168-70.

CHAPTER FIVE

1. This version is taken from R. Wright's report, "Did the Universe just Happen?" on the ideas of E. Fredkin, a champion of artificial intelligence, in *Atlantic Monthly*, April 1988, p. 41.

2. W. Heisenberg, "Zur Quantentheorie des Atomkernes," *Zeitschrift für Physik* 51 (1928), pp. 204-12. Heisenberg's communication was mailed on 29 July and published in the October issue.

3. G. Gamow, "The Quantum Theory of Nuclear Disintegration," *Nature* 122 (1928), pp. 805-06. Gamow's letter was dated, Copenhagen, Sept. 29, 1928, and published in the November 24 issue.

4. R. W. Gurney and E. V. Condon, "Wave Mechanics and Radioactive Disintegration," *Nature* 122 (1928), p. 439. Their letter, dated Princeton, July 30, 1928, was published in the Sept. 22 issue.

5. Ibid.

6. And were taken for such, for instance, by those psychologists — behaviorists as well as Gestaltists — who launched about that time the idea of a psychology modelled on physics. For details, see my *Brain, Mind and Computers* (3rd enlarged ed.; Washington: Regnery-Gateway, 1989), ch. 3.

7. Quoted by D. E. Thomsen, "Going Bohr's Way in Physics," *Science News* Jan. 11, 1986, p. 27. No less expressive is Bohr's other remark: "It is more difficult to write in one's own language; for there one knows precisely what the words mean. In a foreign language one doesn't quite know so well, and so one can let the words mean just what one wants them to mean." A recollection of J. R. Nielson, Bohr's colleague in the physics department of the University of Copenhagen, in his "Memories of Niels Bohr," *Physics Today*, October 1963, p. 25.

8.   *The Scientific Papers of James Clerk Maxwell*, ed. W. D. Niven (Cambridge: University Press, 1890), vol. 2, p. 775.

9.   G. Gamow, *My World Line: An Informal Autobiography* (New York: Viking Press, 1970), p. 70. The same preposterousness appears in quantitative paraphernalia in J. D. Barrow's claim that "according to quantum mechanics if you drive your car up to Mount Snowdon 10^{30} times, once you should actually go all the way through it." "The New Cosmology," *Beshara*, Summer 1988, p. 25.

10.   *The Scientific Papers of James Clerk Maxwell*, vol. 1, p. 759.

11.   A. Einstein, *The World as I See It* (New York: Covici Friede, 1934), p. 29.

12.   I refer to the novel, *Egri csillagok* ("The Stars of Eger"), by Géza Gárdonyi (1863-1922), first published in 1901.

13.   *Letters on 'Wave Mechanics: Schrödinger, Planck, Einstein, Lorentz*, ed. K. Przibram (New York: Philosophical Library, 1967), p. 36.

14.   C. A. Hooker, "The Nature of Quantum Mechanical Reality: Einstein versus Bohr," in R. G. Colodny (ed.), *Paradigms and Paradoxes: The Philosophical Challenge of the Quantum Domain* (Pittsburgh: University of Pittsburgh Press, 1972), pp. 67-302. *The Philosophy of Niels Bohr: The Framework of Complementarity* by H. J. Folse (Amsterdam: North Holland, 1985) is a lengthy effort aimed at saving Bohr from the charge of being a sheer phenomenologist, wholly unconcerned about ontological reality as existing independently of the observer. It is admitted by Folse that "unfortunately, Bohr never makes clear in what sense we can have knowledge of the reality which causes our experiences" (p. 241). Folse takes lightly the fact that Bohr skirted that issue over many years, although on many occasions he was challenged to come clean philosophically. Quite unsatisfactory is the appraisal of ontology in *The Metaphysics of Quantum Theory* (Oxford: Clarendon Press, 1987) by H. Krips, which begins with a chapter aimed at showing the "realist" nature of Bohr's philosophy of quantum mechanics. Krips agrees (p. 27) with Bohr that "indeterminacy is not merely due to lack of measurement" and fails to see that a realism which is truly ontological is incompatible with partial affirmations of reality. As to *Speakable and*

Unspeakable in Quantum Mechanics (Cambridge: University Press, 1987), a collection of essays by J. S. Bell, ontology is not spoken of there at all.

15. W. Heisenberg, "Uber den anschaulichen Inhalt der quantentheoretischen Kinematik und Mechanik," *Zeitschrift für Physik* 43 (1927), p. 197.

16. Ibid. "The invalidity or at least the meaninglessness of the law of causality seems to be firmly established through recent developments in atomic physics," so Heisenberg stated in his more popular article, "Uber die Grundprinzipien der Quantenmechanik," *Forschungen und Fortschritte* 3 (10 April, 1927), p. 83. Two years later, in his Chicago Lectures, Heisenberg argued that "the resolution of the paradoxes of atomic physics can be accomplished only by further renunciation of old and cherished ideas. Most important of these is the idea that natural phenomena obey exact laws — the principle of causality." *Physical Principles of the Quantum Theory* (Chicago: University of Chicago Press, 1930), p. 62.

17. P. Frank, *Das Causalgesetz und seine Grenzen* (Schriften zur wissenschaftliche Weltauffassung, Band 6; Vienna, 1932). H. Bergmann, *Der Kampf um das Kausalgesetz in der jüngsten Physik* (Sammlung Vierweg, Heft 98; Braunschweig, 1929). An earlier phase of the disputes, provoked by the wave theory of matter, is reflected in the writings of A. Gatterer, *Das Problem des statistischen Naturgesetzes in Philosophie und Grenzwissenschaften* (Innsbrucker Institut für scholastische Philosophie. 1 Band, 1 Heft; Innsbruck, 1924) and of V. F. Lenzen, "The Philosophy of Nature in the Light of Contemporary Physics," *University of California Publications in Philosophy* 5 (1924), pp. 24-48.

18. This detail is given on p. 105 in the heavily documented study of P. Forman, "Weimar Culture, Causality and Quantum Theory 1918-1927. Adaptation by German Physicists and Mathematicians to an Hostile Intellectual Environment," *Historical Studies in Physical Science* 3 (1971), pp. 1-115. The weakness of Forman's study lies in his inability to see that questions of philosophy cannot be settled by a sociological or historical narrative. Precisely because Forman looks at ontology as a form of mysticism, he is unable to see the fallacy of the antiontological interpretation given by Heisenberg to his principle of uncertainty. Consequently, Forman becomes

guilty of the same failure for which he takes to task most leading German physicists of the period in question: "Far from engaging in any critical analysis of the concept of causality, directed toward the relaxation of determinism without renouncing *a priori* the comprehensibility of nature, these physicists actually reveled in that consequence, stressed the failure of analytical rationality, implicitly repudiated the cognitive enterprise in which physics had theretofore been engaged" (p. 112). And this failure of theirs had run its course before they saw Heisenberg's paper in print!

19. W. Heisenberg, *Physics and Beyond: Encounters and Conversations*, tr. A. J. Pomerans (New York: Harper & Row, 1971), p. 27.

20. W. Wien, *Aus der Welt der Wissenschaft: Vorträge und Aufsätze* (Leipzig: J. A. Barth, 1921), pp. 16-40.

21. A. Einstein, "Uber die gegenwärtige Krise der theoretischen Physik," *Kaizo* (Tokyo) 4 Dec. 1922), 1-8. This address by Einstein, delivered in August 1922, is not listed in the bibliography of Einstein's publications in *Albert Einstein: Philosopher Scientist*, ed. A. P. Schilpp (1949; New York: Harper and Brothers, 1959). Forman (art. cit., p. 62) cites half a dozen other prominent German physicists who also sounded alarm about the crisis of physics during 1921-22.

22. M. Born, "Raum, Zeit und Schwerkraft," *Frankfurter Zeitung*, Nov. 23, 1919, pp. 1-3. A month later, Einstein remarked in a letter to Born (see p. 18 in work quoted in note 26 below) on the discomfiture of "the established Church of Kantians."

23. E. Mach, *The Analysis of Sensations and the Relation of the Physical to the Psychical*, tr. from the 5th German edition (1905) by S. Waterlow (New York: Dover, 1959), p. 89.

24. Ibid., p. 90.

25. Beginning with a lecture delivered at the University of Leiden on December 9, 1908, on "The Unity of the Physical Universe". See M. Planck, *A Survey of Physics* tr. R. Jones and D. H. Williams (London: Methuen, 1925), pp. 1-41.

26. *The Born-Einstein Letters: Correspondence between Albert Einstein and Max and Hedwig Born from 1916 to 1955 with Commentaries by Max Born*, tr. Irene Born (New York: Walker and Co., 1971), pp. 82, 101, 158, and 259.

27. Ibid., pp. 221-24.

28. Ibid., p. 223.

29. Such as that for a proof he can raise only his little finger.

30. See Hooker's essay, referred to in note 14 above.

31. "No hint of metaphysics, but God speaks, *causa finita est*, and Exodus lays down the principle from which henceforth the whole of Christian philosophy will be suspended." E. Gilson, *The Spirit of Medieval Philosophy* (New York: Charles Scribner's Sons, 1936), p. 56.

32. Such as Max Jammer, *The Conceptual Development of Quantum Mechanics* (New York: McGraw-Hill, 1966) and Banesh Hoffman, *The Strange Story of the Quantum* (2nd ed.; New York: Dover, 1959).

33. A. Landé, *From Dualism to Unity in Quantum Physics* (Cambridge: University Press, 1960), pp. 55-56.

34. A. McRobert, "Beyond the Big Bang," *Sky and Telescope* (March 1983), p. 211.

35. J. S. Trefil, *The Moment of Creation: Big Bang Physics from before the First Millisecond to the Present* (New York: Macmillan, 1983), p. 79. What is suggested in that passage about the production of matter would appear in its true light as soon as one imagined the quantum mechanical creation of matter of a stock market where solvency would be assured, credit maintained, inflation checked, interest rates stabilized by a quantum mechanical creation of bonds, stocks, banknotes, silver certificates, coins, and gold bullions, while the actual existence of none of these items could be registered and counterchecked.

36. For instance, J. C. Polkinghorne, *The Particle Play: An Account of the Ultimate Constituents of Matter* (Oxford: W. H.Freeman, 1979).

37. I first gave this rephrasing of Trefil's passage in a lecture, "Cosmologia e religione," given at the Gregorian University in Rome, March 13, 1989, and, the following week, in Bologna, Padova, Pavia, Brescia, and Milano. It will see publication in KOS (Milano). The English version will appear in *Atheism and Dialogue* (Rome).

38. S. W. Hawking, "Black Hole Explosion," *Nature* 248 (1974), pp. 30-31.

39. A. H. Guth, "Inflationary Universe: A Possible Solution to the Horizon and Flatness Problems," *Physical Review* D23 (1981), pp. 347-51.

40. G. W. Gibbons, S. W. Hawking, and S. T. C. Siklos (eds.), *The Very Early Universe: Proceedings of the Nuffield Workshop. Cambridge, 21 June to 9 July, 1982* (Cambridge: University Press, 1983), p. 6.

41. Ibid., p. 476.

42. A. McRobert, "Beyond the Big Bang," p. 212.

43. D. Atkatz and H. Pagels, "Origin of the Universe as a Quantum Tunneling Event," *Physical Review* D25 (1982), pp. 2065-73.

44. See *The New York Times*, Feb. 2, 1989, p. C24.

45. J. S. Trefil, *The Moment of Creation*, p. 177.

46. J. D. Barrow, "The New Cosmology," p. 24.

47. Guth's dictum received further publicity by being quoted in Hawking's *A Brief History of Time*, p. 129. In his article, "The Inflationary Universe," co-authored with P. J. Steinhardt, *Scientific American*, April 1984, pp. 116-28, Guth repeatedly asserted the physicist's ability to create universes "literally" and "absolutely" out of nothing.

48. "Ten years ago, we couldn't have even posed the question of whether a man-made universe would be possible. But physics has progressed a long way since then, and today we can ask this and related questions in the real hope of finding scientifically testable answers. We are working in a new and exciting environment," stated A. H. Guth in an interview to *The New York Times*, April 14, 1987, p. C4. Such statements are all the more effective in polluting the intellectual environment, because the scientific community, lacking philosophical sensitivity, fails to disavow them.

49. E. Farhi, and A. H. Guth, "An Obstacle to Creating a Universe in the Laboratory," *Physics Letters*, B183 (8 Jan., 1987), pp. 149-54.

50. Quoted in Trefil, *The Moment of Creation*, pp. 205-06.

51. Quoted in A. Petersen, "The Philosophy of Niels Bohr," in A. P. French and P. J. Kennedy, *Niels Bohr: A Centenary Volume* (Cambridge, MA.: Harvard University Press, 1985), p. 305.

52. As I argued in ch. 13, "The Horns of Complementarity," in my Gifford Lectures, *The Road of Science and the Ways to God* (3rd printing: Chicago: University of Chicago Press, 1987).

53. Quoted by Petersen, see note 51 above, p. 305. For examples of the cultivation of basic ambiguities by protagonists of artifi-

cial intelligence, see ch. 5, "Language, Logic, Logos," in my *Brain, Mind and Computers.*

54. See *Washington Post*, Nov. 8, 1988, p. C11.

55. Quoted in Trefil, *The Moment of Creation*, p. 208.

56. Lindé quoted by A. F. Mallove, "The Self-Reproducing Universe," *Sky and Telescope*, Sept. 1988, p. 256.

57. D. Hume, *Dialogues concerning Natural Religion*, ed. N. K. Smith (Edinburgh: Thomas Nelson and Sons, 1947), pp. 180-81.

CHAPTER SIX

1. "Fire and water — so they say — all owe their being to nature and chance, none of them to art. . . . They had been produced not, so they say, by the agency of mind, or any god, or art, but, as I tell you," says the Athenian, "by nature and chance . . . All these views, my friends, come from men who impress the young as wise, prose writers and poets who profess that indefeasible right mean whatever a man can carry with the high hand . . . hence the factions created by those who seek, on such grounds, to attract men to the 'really and naturally right life,' that is, the life of real domination over others, not of conventional service to them." *The Laws* 889b-890a, quoted from *The Collected Dialogues of Plato*, ed., E. Hamilton and H. Cairns (New York: Pantheon Books, 1963), pp. 1444-45.

2. "It never entered my head that a man," Socrates declares in reference to his disillusion with Anaxagoras' book on the mind, "who asserted that the ordering of things is due to mind would offer any other explanation for them than that it is best for them to be as they are." *Phaedo* 98a, quoted from *The Collected Dialogues of Plato*, p. 79.

3. Mostly in the Third Part of *Timaeus*.

4. As amply revealed from the reconstruction of Anaxagoras' system by D. E. Gershenson and D. A. Greenberg, *Anaxagoras and the Birth of Physics* (New York: Blaisdell, 1964).

5. Quoted from *Ancilla to the Pre-Socratic Philosophers. A Complete Translation of the Fragments in Diels, Fragmente der Vorsokratiker*, by Kathleen Freeman (Oxford: Basil Blackwell, 1956), p. 33.

6. For a good discussion, see J. B. McAllister, "Chance in Aristotle and Aquinas," in *Philosophical Writings in Honor of the Very Reverend Ignatius Smith, O.P.*, ed. J. K. Ryan (Westminster, Md.: The Newman Press, 1952), pp. 76-91.

7. Counting the pseudo-Aristotelian *De Melisso, Xenophane et Gorgia disputationes*, 975a. The two genuine passages are in *Metaphysics* 1075b, and in *De coelo* 298b.

8. *Summa theologica*, I, Qu, 45, art. 5, "Whether it belongs to God alone to create?"

9. A remark of J. Polkinghorne in his *Science and Creation: The Search for Understanding* (London: SPCK, 1988), p. 77, in reference to Aquinas' argument that only an immaterial organ can carry on with the act of understanding. When a Christian clergyman does not see why this has to be so, he obviously can but be disturbed by the age-old Christian belief that the soul survives bodily death.

10. J. Polkinghorne, "The Quantum World," in *Physics, Philosophy, and Theology: A Common Quest for Understanding*, ed. R. J. Russell *et al.*, (Vatican City State: Vatican Observatory, 1988), pp. 333-42.

11. For details, see my article, "Thomas and the Universe," to be published in *The Thomist*, October 1989.

12. In particular in his commentary to the teaching of Lateran IV, "In Decretalem. Expositio ad Archidiaconum Tridentinum," in *Opera*, vol. XVI, pp. 303-04.

13. J. J. Bossuet, *Discours sur l'histoire universelle*, Partie III, ch. viii. See modern English translation by E. Forster, *Discourse on Universal History* (Chicago: University of Chicago Press, 1981), p. 374.

14. Such is the starting note in Section VI, "Of Probability," in D. Hume, *An Enquiry concerning Human Understanding* (Chicago: Henry Regnery, 1956), p. 55.

15. Voltaire, *Dictionnaire philosophique*, in *Oeuvres complètes de Voltaire* (Paris: Garnier Frères, 1877-85), vol. 17, p. 478.

16. Voltaire, *Zadig*, in *Oeuvres*, vol. 21, p. 90.

17. Helvetius, *De l'homme*, Sec. I, ch. viii, in *Oeuvres complètes* (Paris: Lepetit, 1818), vol. 2, p. 33.

18. From T. H. Huxley's reminiscences on the publication of Darwin's *Origin of Species*, in *The Life and Letters of Charles Darwin*, ed. F. Darwin (New York: Basic Books, 1959), vol. 1, pp. 553-55.

19.   Letter to J. Hooker, 1870, in *More Letters of Charles Darwin: A Record of His Work in a Series of Hitherto Unpublished Letters*, ed. F. Darwin and A. C. Seward (New York: D. Appleton, 1903), vol. 1, p. 321.

20.   C. S. Peirce, "The Probability of Induction," *Popular Science Monthly* 12 (April 1878), p. 714.

21.   C. S. Peirce, "The Order of Nature," *Popular Science Monthly* 13 (June 1878), p. 205.

22.   Ibid., p. 207.

23.   The first was, of course, by the editor of *Monist*, P. Carus, "Mr Charles S. Peirce's Onslaught on the Doctrine of Necessity," *The Monist* 2 (1891-92), pp. 560-82.

24.   C. S. Peirce, "The Doctrine of Necessity Examined," *The Monist* 2 (April 1892), pp. 321-37; for quote see p. 336.

25.   As illustrated by his collection of essays, *The Will to Believe*.

26.   Its true merits may be gathered from a brief reflection on the title, *Values in a Universe of Chance*, a selection from the writings of Peirce, edited with an introduction and notes by P. P. Wiener (Garden City, N.Y.: Doubleday & Company, 1958).

27.   P. Delbet, *La science et la réalité* (Paris: Flammarion, 1913), p. 238. Actually, Delbet did not do full justice to Poincaré. To be sure, in chapter iv, "Chance," in his *Science and Method* (1908), tr. F. Maitland (New York: Dover, n. d.), Poincaré begins with references to the standard view of chance as being a word for our ignorance of true causes. But for Poincaré this is a mere background to his view on chance as "an assemblage of complex causes" (p. 89). What he argued was the idea "rediscovered" in recent studies on chaos that "small differences in the initial conditions produce very great ones in the final phenomena" (p. 68).

28.   Delbet, *La science et la réalité*, p. 238.

29.   Rutherford's letter to Bohr, March 20, 1913, quoted from A. S. Eve, *Rutherford: Being the Life and Letters of the Rt. Hon. Lord Rutherford, O. M.* (Cambridge: University Press, 1939), p. 221.

30.   Dirac did so at the 1927 Solvay Conference as he challenged Heisenberg. See *Electrons et photons. Rapports et discussions du Cinquième Conseil de Physique tenu à Bruxelles du 24 au 29 Octobre 1927 sous les auspices de l'Institut International de Physique Solvay* (Paris: Gauthier-Villars, 1928), p. 262.

31.   D. Bohm, *Quantum Theory* (Englewood Cliffs, N. J.: Prentice Hall, 1951), pp. 614-19.

32.   A. Einstein, B. Podolsky, and N. Rosen, "Can Quantum-mechanical Description of Physical Reality Be Considered Complete?" *Physical Review* 47 (1935), pp. 770-80.

33.   "I cannot seriously believe in it [the statistical approach] because the theory cannot be reconciled with the idea that physics should represent a reality in time and space, free from spooky actions at a distance," wrote Einstein to Born on March 3, 1947. See *The Born-Einstein Letters. Correspondence between Albert Einstein and Max and Hedwig Born from 1916 to 1955 with commentaries by Max Born*, tr. Irene Born (New York: Walker and Company, 1971), p. 158. Five years earlier, in a letter to C. Lanczos, Einstein wrote: "It seems hard to look in God's cards. But I cannot for a moment believe that He plays dice and makes use of 'telepathic' means (as the current quantum theory alleges He does)." Quoted in A. Pais, *'Subtle is the Lord . . .' The Science and the Life of Albert Einstein* (Oxford: Clarendon Press, 1982), p. 440.

34.   A phrase of A. Shimony, quoted in M. W. Browne, "Quantum Theory: Disturbing Questions Remain Unsolved," *The New York Times*, Feb. 11, 1986, p. C3.

35.   Oversight of this in the English-speaking world implies wilful ignorance since the publication in three volumes of *Hegel's Philosophy of Nature* (London: George Allen and Unwin, 1970) in the translation of M. J. Petry, who in his introduction and explanatory notes tries in vain to gloss over the long chain of Hegel's monumental counterscientific utterances.

36.   A. Pais, "Einstein and the Quantum Theory, *Reviews of Modern Physics* 51 (1979), p. 863.

37.   Pais, *'Subtle is the Lord . . .'*, p. 5.

38.   W. Heisenberg, "Development of the Interpretation of the Quantum Theory," in *Niels Bohr and the Development of Physics*, ed. W. Pauli (New York: McGraw-Hill, 1955), pp. 12-29.

39.   Ibid., p. 24.

40.   They still have to realize the obvious, put by E. Gilson with elementary force: "The first step on the realist path is to recognize that one has always been a realist; the second is to recognize that, however hard one tries to think differently, one will never manage to; the third is to realize that those who claim they think differently, think as realists as soon as they forget to act a part. If one then asks oneself why, one's own conversion to realism is all but complete." The opening phrase in

chapter v, "The Realist Beginner's Handbook," in *Methodical Realism*, tr. P. Trower, with an introduction by S. L. Jaki, to be published by Christendom Press, Front Royal, Va.

41. W. Heisenberg, "Development of the Interpretation of the Quantum Theory," pp. 24-25.

42. Ibid., p. 26.

43. W. R. Thompson, *Science and Commonsense* (London: Longmans, Green and Co., 1937), p. 218.

44. P. Jordan, "Quantenphysikalische Bemerkungen über Biologie und Psychologie," *Erkenntnis* 4 (1934), p. 228.

45. M. W. Browne, "Quantum Theory," p. C3.

46. W. Heisenberg, "Development of the Interpretation of the Quantum Theory," p. 73.

47. As indirectly shown by Sir Thomas Heath in his *Mathematics in Aristotle* (Oxford: Clarendon Press, 1949), p. 107, where it is recalled that Aristotle explicitly rejected the application of potentiality to infinity.

48. W. Heisenberg, "Development of the Interpretation of the Quantum Theory," p. 28.

49. Ibid.

50. J. R. Newman in his review of D. Bohm's *Causality and Chance in Modern Physics* (Princeton: Van Nostrand, 1957) in *Scientific American* 198 (Jan. 1958), p. 116.

51. B. S. De Witt, "Quantum Mechanics and Reality," in B. S. De Witt and N. Graham (eds.), *The Many World Interpretation of Quantum Mechanics* (Princeton: University Press, 1973), pp. 161-63.

52. As reported by M. W. Browne, "Quantum Theory".

53. K. R. Popper, *The Open Universe: An Argument for Indeterminism* (Totowa, N. J.: Rowman and Littlefield, 1982), p. 7.

54. As discussed in Chapter 5.

55. L. Boltzmann, *Lectures on Gas Theory*, tr. S. G. Brush (Berkeley: University of California Press, 1964), p. 446.

56. G. Wald, "The Origin of Life," in *The Physics and Chemistry of Life. A Scientific American Book* (New York: Simon and Shuster, 1955), p. 12.

57. See chapters 1-6 in my *Science and Creation: From Eternal Cycles to an Oscillating Universe* (2nd enlarged edition; Edinburgh: Scottish Academic Press, 1986).

58.   I. Prigogine and E. Stengers, *Order out of Chaos: Man's New Dialogue with Nature* (Boulder, Colorado: New Science Library, 1984).,

59.   V. F. Weisskopf, "Of Atoms, Mountains, and Stars: A Study in Qualitative Physics," *Science* 187 (1975), pp. 605-12.

60.   Quoted in D. E. Thomsen, "As God's Dice Fall," *Science News* 129 (Jan. 1986), p. 28.

61.   A remark which explains the full depth of Bohr's choice, ten years after his visit in China in 1937, of the Chinese symbol of *yin* and *yang* for his coat of arms and his pleasure on hearing the Japanese physicist, Hideki Yukawa, explain the Orientals' receptivity to the idea of complementarity with the remark: "You see, we in Japan have not been corrupted by Aristotle." See A. P. French and P. J. Kennedy (eds.), *Niels Bohr: A Centenary Volume* (Cambridge: Harvard University Press, 1985), p. 325. One, however, may wonder whether the real corruption does not lie in the refusal to be "corrupted" by Aristotle's insistence on the fundamental character of the principle of identity and contradiction.

62.   See P. A. M. Dirac, "The Versatility of Niels Bohr," ibid., p. 309.

63.   Bohr never tried to reconcile this remark of his with his statements that "There is no quantum world. There is only an abstract quantum physical description. It is wrong to think that the task of physics is to find out how nature is. Physics concerns what we can say about nature" (ibid., p. 305) and that "mathematical formalism of quantum mechanics . . . merely offers rules of calculation" (*Atomic Theory and the Description of Nature* [Cambridge: University Press, 1934], p. 60).

64.   J. R. Nielson, "Memories of Niels Bohr," *Physics Today*, October 1963, p. 27.

65.   In the *Born-Einstein Letters* alone the phrase occurs at least four times, pp. 91, 149, 155, 199.

66.   See A. Einstein, *Out of My Later Years* (New York: Philosophical Library, 1950), p. 60.

67.   The statement prominently graces the first page in D. E. Knuth, *The Art of Computer Programming. Volume 2. Seminumerical Algorithms* (Reading, Ma.: Addison-Wesley, 1969), p. 1.

68.   Quoted in J. Gleick, *Chaos: Making a New Science* (New York: Viking, 1987), p. 5.

69.   That is, Gleick, ibid., p. 269.

70.   Ibid., pp. 314 and 197. The first of the two phrases is Gleick's comment on J. Ford's claim that "evolution is chaos with feedback," which, at best, is a linguistic acrobatics.

71.   Quoted by Gleick, ibid., p. 314.

72.   According to Gleick, (ibid., p. 121) the story has been connected with at least four other physicists.

73.   J. Monod, *Chance and Necessity: An Essay on the Natural Philosophy of Modern Biology* (New York: Vintage Books, 1971), p. 144.

74.   I. Prigogine and E. Stengers, *Order out of Chaos*, pp. xxix-xxvi.

75.   Ibid., p. 313. The Talmudic passage, which the authors do not separate from their own reflections, is not among the hundreds of quotations from the Talmudic literature relating to Genesis 1, that fill 88 quarto pages in *Encyclopedia of Biblical Interpretation, Genesis: Volume 1*, by M. M. Kasher (New York: American Biblical Encyclopedia Society, 1953). Most likely the number is 24, the number of letters in the Hebrew alphabet. The authors fail to note the contradictory character of the fact that they claim to know with no trace of uncertainty their final statement, namely, that all cosmic and human history is "branded with the mark of radical uncertainty."

76.   As amply shown by the section on God and Creation in *Kabbalah* by Gershom Scholem (New York: Quadrangle/The New York Times Book Co., n. d.), pp. 88-122.

77.   A. Koestler, *Darkness at Noon* (New York: Bantam Books, 1941), p. 149.

78.   J. H. Newman, Letter of May 22, 1868, to J. Walker, in *Letters and Diaries of John Henry Newman* (Oxford: Clarendon Press, 1971-   ), vol. XXIV, p. 77.

79.   J. Monod, *Chance and Necessity*, p. 180.

80.   K. R. Popper, *The Open Universe*, p. 130..

81.   See *Times* (London), Aug. 25, 1988, p. 3.

82.   K. R. Popper, *The Open Universe*, p. 143.

CHAPTER SEVEN

1.   A. Einstein, "Physics and Reality," (1936), in *Out of My Later Years* (New York, Philosophical Library, 1950), p. 60.

2.   Quoted in *National Geographic* 167 (May 1985), p. 662.

3.   See G. S. Kirk and J. E. Raven, *The Presocratic Philosophers: A Critical History with a Selection of Texts* (Cambridge: University Press, 1962), p. 134.

4.   Ibid., p. 135.

5.   Ibid., p. 411.

6.   As reported by Simplicius, a famed sixth-century commentator of Aristotle; see ibid., p. 389.

7.   Ibid., p. 391.

8.   This Socratic turn, vividly described by Plato in *Phaedo*, was a classic in misunderstanding, whatever its noble motivations. Its chief lure was that of a simple, all-cure medicine that in the long run could only aggravate the symptoms to be remedied. Instead of securing "the best," lopsided pre-occupation with "values" inevitably blocked man's access to those quantitative methods without which he could not achieve control of physical processes.

9.   The most memorable (and influential) of those ratios was the one in *Timaeus* (36C-D), where the Demiurgos is described as having divided the space between the celestial sphere and the earth "in six places into seven unequal circles, severally corresponding with the double and triple intervals, of each of which there were three." For comments, made in classical Antiquity, on this passage, see F. M. Cornford, *Plato's Cosmology* (New York: The Liberal Arts Press, 1957), pp. 79-81.

10.   Unfortunately, the important thesis of R. M. Bentham, "The Fragments of Eratosthenes" (University of London, 1948), remains unpublished.

11.   As memorably noted by H. Butterfield, the first Horblit lecturer at Harvard University, on March 24, 1959, "The History of Science and the Study of History," *Harvard Library Bulletin* 13 (1959), pp. 329-47.

12.   This is sadly true even of the standard study by Sir Thomas Heath, *Aristarchus of Samos, the Ancient Copernicus: A History of Greek Astronomy to Aristarchus together with Aristarchus's Treatise on the Sizes and Distances of the Sun and Moon. A New Greek*

Text with Translation and Notes (Oxford: Clarendon Press, 1913).

13. See *Aristotle. On the Heavens*, with an English translation by W. K. C. Guthrie (Loeb Classical Library: Cambridge, MA.: Harvard University Press, 1939), pp. 65 and 143.

14. The essence of the method consisted in assuming no separation between the spheres that carried the planets in their courses around the earth. See *Hypothèses et époques des planètes de C. Ptolemée et hypotyposes de Proclus Diadochus*, ed. Halma (Paris, Merlin, 1820), pp. 145-46.

15. W. H. McCrea, "Astronomer's Luck," *Quarterly Journal of the Royal Astronomical Society* 13 (1972), p. 508.

16. Chief among those features are the automatic rotation of the sun, the formation of successive separate rings as it cools, and the marked diminution in each case of the sun's angular momentum without a corresponding increase in the sun's speed of rotation.

17. It was actually shown by F. R. Moulton in 1900. For details, see my *Planets and Planetarians: A History of Theories of the Origin of Planetary Systems* (Edinburgh: Scottish Academic Press, 1978), p. 188.

18. See ibid., ch. 7 "Collisions Revisited."

20. H. Spencer, *An Autobiography* (London: Williams and Norgate, 1904), vol. 2, p. 470.

21. G. H. Darwin, "On the Precession of a Viscous Spheroid, and on the Remote History of the Earth" (1879) in *Scientific Papers by Sir George Howard Darwin*, vol. 2, *Tidal Friction and Cosmogony* (Cambridge: University Press, 1908), pp. 36-139.

22. H. Jeffreys, "The Amplitude of Tidal Resonances," *Monthly Notices of the Royal Astronomical Society* 91 (1930), pp. 169-73.

23. His work, originally published in Russian in the 1940s and early 1950s became available in English as a set of four lectures, *A Theory of Earth's Origin* (Moscow: Foreign Languages Publishing House, 1958). For a discussion, see my *Planets and Planetarians*, pp. 236-37.

24. W. M. Kaula, quoted by J. Gleick, "Moon's Creation Now Attributed to Giant Crash," *The New York Times*, June 3, 1986, p. C7.

25. See W. K. Hartmann *et al* (eds.) *Origin of the Moon* (Houston: Lunar and Planetary Institute, 1986), p. viii.

26. Printed as *Origin of the Moon* as quoted above.

27.   D. J. Stevenson, "Origin of the Moon — The Collision Hypothesis," *Annual Review of Earth and Planetary Sciences* 15 (1987), p. 271.

28.   W. K. Hartmann and D. R. Davis, "Satellite-Sized Planetesimals," *Icarus* 24 (1975), pp. 504-15, and A. G. W. Cameron and W. R. Ward, "The Origin of the Moon, *Lunar and Planetary Science* 7 (1976), pp. 120-22.

29.   Quoted by J. Gleick, see note 24 above.

30.   For several sets of computer-simulated images of the various stages of the collision, see W. Benz, W. L. Slattery, and A. G. W. Cameron, "The Origin of the Moon and the Single-Impact Hypothesis," *Icarus* 66 (1986), pp. 515-35, and 71 (1987), pp. 30-45.

31.   Quoted by J. Gleick, see note 24 above.

32.   W. K. Hartmann and D. R. Davis, "Satellite-sized Planetesimals," *Icarus* 24 (1975), p. 513.

33.   See *Origin of the Moon*, p. 581.

34.   As documented throughout in my *Planets and Planetarians*.

35.   Geological evidences about the flipping of the Earth's magnetic poles began to be recognized from the early 1950s on. The role which the impact of large asteroids on the Earth can play in the process was the topic of the conference held on "Global Catastrophes in Earth History" in October 1988 at Snowbird, Utah, under the sponsorship of the Lunar and Planetary Institute (Houston) and the National Academy of Sciences. See report by W. Sullivan in *The New York Times*, Nov. 1, 1988, pp. C1 and C6.

36.   See McCrea, "Astronomer's Luck," p. 508.

37.   *The Nemesis Affair: A Story of the Death of Dinosaurs and the Ways of Science* by D. M. Raup (New York: W. W. Norton, 1986) gives the story from the viewpoint of one of the first proponents of the Nemesis-theory. More recently, a team lead by E. Anders of the University of Chicago concluded that a global fire was triggered by a huge meteorite impact about 65 million years ago, the transition time from the Cretaceous to the Tertiary period.

38.   Such was the word Darwin penned on the margin of the reprint of Wallace's article, "Geological Climates and the Origin of Species," *Quarterly Review* 126 (1869), pp. 359-94.

39.   See report by F. Golden, "New Proposals Bolster Search for

Life in Space," *The New York Times*, Aug. 10, 1988, pp. C1 and C12.

40.   Ibid., p. C12.

41.   L. Eiseley, *The Immense Journey* (New York: Vintage Books, 1959), p. 162.

42.   Such an advice has more to recommend itself than the opinion that radio-contact with extraterrestrial civilizations may be man's last hope of avoiding global self-destruction.

43.   Letter to Editor, *The New York Times*, Jan. 9, 1983, p. E22.

44.   The lack of rigor in experiments aimed at proving the existence of linguistic ability in apes has been amply exposed in the collection of essays, *Speaking of Apes* (New York: Plenum, 1980).

45.   See ch. 5, "Language, Logic, Logos," in my *Brain, Mind and Computers* (3rd enlarged edition; Washington, DC: Regnery-Gateway, 1989).

46.   See T. Ferris' review of J. D. Barrow and F. J. Tipler, *The Anthropic Cosmological Principle* (Oxford: Clarendon Press, 1986) in *The New York Times Book Review*, Feb. 16, 1986 p. 20.

47.   Ibid., p. ix.

48.   Fortunately, Sagan's deploring such editorials was not effective enough to put an end to them.

49.   "If they existed, they would be here," goes the version given by Barrow and Tipler, *The Anthropic Cosmological Principle*, p. 578.

50.   E. Purcell, "Radioastronomy and Communication through Space," Brookhaven Lecture Series, Number 1, November 16, 1960, p. 11.

51.   See, especially, ch. 9, "The Space-Travel Argument against the Existence of Extraterrestrial Intelligent Life," which is offered by the authors of *The Anthropic Cosmological Principle* as a complement "of the earlier arguments we presented in Chapters 3-8 [or over 400 pages] regarding the improbability of other forms of local (that is, within range of communication with us) extraterrestrial life. We have developed the general theory of exploration and colonization using self-reproducing robots, the theory of whose existence is already known to us although at present we lack the level of computer technology to implement it in practice. This theory was then used to demonstrate the ease with which advanced Galactic civilizations

could reveal their presence and the difficulty they would have concealing it. These arguments are based upon technological considerations and an analysis of the collective features necessary to support an advanced technological civilization. Finally, we have demonstrated how the non-observation of other life-forms in our Galaxy allows one to rule out a large class of otherwise quite possible steady-state cosmologies having infinite ages" (pp. 607-08). Underlying all that largely mistaken enterprise is the authors' failure to realize that no amount of mathematics or physics can decide the essentially philosophical status of the question about intelligence embodied in personal consciousness.

52.   In reviewing the pros and cons of the story, R. S. Westfall, Newton's foremost modern biographer, concludes: "There is every reason to believe that the fall of an apple gave rise to it [namely, to Newton's realization that a centripetal acceleration keeps the moon in its orbit]." *Never at Rest: A Biography of Isaac Newton* (Cambridge: Cambridge University Press, 1980), p. 155.

53.   One of the dozen or so students who witnessed Oersted's historic experiment emphatically asserted, years later, its accidental character. This is indirectly supported by Oersted himself, who in an article prepared for the *Edinburgh Encyclopedia* in 1830, or almost ten years after the experiment, wondered over the fact that he had not repeated the experiment for another three months and that those present had not at all been impressed with it. Equally accidental was Galvani's observation that the calf-muscles of a frog, suspended on a metallic support, contract under the effects of an electric spark produced in their vicinity. It was further purely accidental that Volta was on hand to note the most significant feature of an in itself very complicated process. Many other examples could, of course, be listed. See ch. vii in R. Taton, *Reason and Chance in Scientific Discovery*, tr. A. J. Pomerans (New York: Science Editions, 1962).

54.   See my Gifford Lectures, *The Road of Science and the Ways to God* (Chicago: University of Chicago Press, 1978), pp. 188-92.

55.   As one would expect, non-believing or agnostic historians of medieval science do their best to underplay the theological roots of Buridan's epoch-making discovery.

56. The topic of the first six chapters of my *Science and Creation: From Eternal Cycles to an Oscillating Universe* (1974; 2nd enlarged edition, Scottish Academic Press, 1986).

57. H. S. Harrison, "Evolution in Material Culture," *Report of the British Association for the Advancement of Science* (London: Office of the British Association, 1931), p. 140.

58. J. Monod, *Chance or Necessity* (New York: Vintage Books, 1971), pp. 174-75.

59. Monumental as well as heroic. See ch. 10 in my *Uneasy Genius: The Life and Work of Pierre Duhem* (1984; 2nd ed., Dordrecht, London, Boston: Martinus Nijhoff, 1987).

60. For details, see my *Cosmos and Creator* (Edinburgh: Scottish Academic Press, 1980), p. 153.

61. An unjustified projection into 17th-century thought by S. Dick, *Plurality of Worlds: The Origins of Extraterrestrial Life: Debate from Democritus to Kant* (New York: Cambridge University Press, 1982), p. 89.

62. See my article, "The Universe in the Bible and in Modern Science," *Ex Auditu. Volume III* (Pittsburgh: Pickwick Publications, 1988), pp. 137-47.

CHAPTER EIGHT

1. Published posthumously in 1918. References will be to the Modern Library edition, New York, 1931.

2. H. Adams, *The degradation of the Democratic Dogma* (New York: Macmillan, 1290; reprinted, New York: Peter Smith, 1949).

3. Henry Adams turned to Pearson's book after he had heard a friend say that Willard Gibbs esteemed it greatly. See *The Education of Henry Adams*, p. 449.

4. K. Pearson, *The Grammar of Science* (1892; London: Walter Scott, 1895), p. 214.

5. *The Education of Henry Adams*, p. 430.

6. Ibid., p. 429.

7. Ibid., p. 430.

8. Ibid.

9. In his *The Concepts and Theories of Modern Physics* (1881), Stallo upheld both the infinity and the finitude of the universe. He claimed, on the one hand that physical laws are applicable only to finite agglomerates, and, on the other, that the gravitational and optical paradoxes do not invalidate the idea of an infinite universe which "is the background of all material actions and forms; no system of elements or foces can exist without it, or is cognizable without reference to it; and in this sense, and in this sense only, the universe is necessarily infinite in mass as well as in space and in time." See the re-edition by P. W. Bridgman (Cambridge: Harvard University Press, 1960), p. 285. While this solution of the finitude versus the infinity of the universe could satisfy Stallo's Hegelianism, it could readily appear to Henry Adams as a grave threat to the unity of the universe. On Stallo's Hegelianism, see L. D. Easton, *Hegel's First American Followers: The Ohio Hegelians: John B. Stallo, Peter Kaufmann, Moncure Conway, and August Willich, with Key Writings* (Athens: University of Ohio Press, 1966). Stallo's first publication was a long summary of Naturphilosophie of Schelling, Hegel, and Oken.

10. See note to chapter 2.

11. In all such efforts there is a marked oversight of the Koran's overemphasis on Allah's will as distinct from his intellect.

12. T. H. Huxley, *Lay Sermons: Addresses and Reviews* (5th ed.; London: Macmillan, 1874), p. 274.

13. "Eadem sancta mater Ecclesia tenet et docet, Deum, rerum omnium principium et finem, naturali humanae rationis lumine e rebus creatis certo cognosci posse." *Constitutio dogmatica de fide catholica.* cap. 2. De revelatione. Although half a dozen Catholics (five of them priests) were among the contributors to *Physics, Philosophy and Theology: A Common Quest for Understanding*, edited by R. J. Russell, W. R. Stoeger, and G. V. Coyne (Vatican City State: Vatican Observatory, 1988) or the volume containing eighteen papers read at the Castelgandolfo Conference (September 1987) on science and faith, none of them seemed to have been convinced about the capital importance of that dogmatic declaration to the point of making mention of it in that context. This is another illustration of an "ecumenical discussion" in which the solemnly defined Catholic position cannot be voiced, whereas other

kinds of voices, especially very liberal Protestant positions, can be given full hearing.

14. "In fact, whatever can be known about God is clear to them; he himself made it so. Since the creation of the world, invisible realities, God's eternal power and divinity, have become visible, recognized through the things he has made." Rom 1: 19-20.

15. A. Moszkowski, *Conversations with Einstein* tr. H. L. Brose (New York: Horizon Press, 1970), pp. 129-30.

16. Ibid., p. 129.

17. Emphasis on the empirical untestability of the universe plays a key part in M. K. Munitz's rejection of the cosmological argument, as for instance, in his "The Logic of Cosmology," *British Journal for the Philosophy of Science* 13 (1962-63), pp. 34-50, and "The Use of the 'Universe' in Cosmology," *The Monist* 118 (1964), pp. 185-94.

18. B. Bosanquet, *The Principle of Individuality and Value* (London: Macmillan, 1912), pp. 37-38.

19. Ibid., p. 43.

20. Ibid., p. 34.

21. C. S. Lewis, "The Personal Heresy in Criticism," *Essays and Studies by Members of the English Association* 19 (1933-34), p. 28.

22. J.-P. Sartre, *Nausea*, tr. L. Alexander (New York: New Direction Books, 1964), p. 177.

23. G. K. Chesterton, *St Francis of Assisi* (1924; Garden City, NY: Doubleday, 1957), p. 49.

24. Saint Augustine, *Confessions*, tr. R. S. Pine-Coffin (Penguin Books, 1961), p. 212.

25. J. G. Frazer, *The Golden Bough: A Study in Magic and Religion*, I Volume abridged edition (New York: Macmillan Company, 1922), p. 712.

26. Ibid., p. 713.

27. A recollection of M. Barrès in his *Mes Cahiers* (Paris: Plon, 1929-57), vol. 10, p. 145.

28. M. Esslin, *Absurd Drama* (Harmondsworth: Penguin Books, 1965), p. 12.

29. M. Esslin, *The Theatre of the Absurd* (rev. ed.; London: Eyre Methuen, 1974), p. 364.

30. Quoted, ibid., p. 313.

31. Ibid., p. 375.

32.   These words of Rousseau were recalled by D'Escherny, who eulogized him on behalf of the Revolution in 1796, as his favorite utterance. See P.-M. Masson, *La religion de Rousseau* (Paris: Garnier, 1916), vol. 2, p. 270.

33.   Quoted by J. Maritain, *The Peasant from the Garonne*, tr. M. Cuddihy and E. Hughes (New York: Holt, Rinehart and Winston, 1968), p. 21.

34.   "Ebauche d'un serpent," in P. Valéry, *Charmes commentés par Alain* (Paris: Gallimard, 1926), p. 179. The gist of the poem consists in the logic that leads from a resentment about the alleged irresolubility of evil to the denial of the reality of the universe itself.

35.   "The Principles of Nature and of Grace, Based on Reason," in *Leibniz Selections*, ed. P. P. Wiener (New York: Charles Scribner's Sons, 1951), p. 527.

36.   M. Heidegger, *Was ist Metaphysik?* Öffentliche Antrittsvorlesung 24 juli 1929, Universität Freiburg in Breisgau (3rd ed.; Bonn: F. Cohen, 1931), p. 27.

37.   H. Bergson, *Creative Evolution*, tr. A. Mitchell (New York: The Modern Library, 1944), p. 324. The price of Bergson's attack on the notion of nothing is a universe whose future is undefined by its past. A similar price is paid by Popper who, in this connection too, is much more indebted to Bergson than generally realized.

38.   H. Bergson, *The Two Sources of Morality and Religion*, tr. R. A. Audra and C. Brereton (Garden City, NY: Doubleday, 1954), p. 317.

39.   *Creative Evolution*, p. 263. Bergson continues: "It [the universe] is growing, perhaps indefinitely, by the addition of new worlds." Bergson's reputed originality will lose much of its lustre if one recalls the declaration of his predecessor, V. Cousin: "God, in creating the universe, draws it not from nothing, which exists not, which cannot exist, which is a mere word; he draws it from himself; . . . it follows, not only that creation is possible, but that it is necessary." *Course of the History of Modern Philosophy*, tr. O. W. Wight (New York: D. Appleton, 1852), vol. 1, pp. 93-94.

40.   Quoted in L. Eiseley, *Darwin and the Mysterious Mr. X: New Light on Evolutionists* (New York: Harcourt, Brace, Jovanovich, 1979), p. 228.

41. *Dernières pages d'Anatole France*, publiées par Michel Corday (3rd ed.: Paris: Calman Lévy, 1935), pp. 50-51.
42. A. France, *La vie littéraire* (Paris: C. Lévy, 1888-92), vol. 3, p. 212.
43. D. A. Wilson, *Carlyle on Cromwell and Others* (London: Kegan Paul, Trench, 1925), vol. 3, p. 177.
44. D. A. Wilson and D. W. MacArthur, *Carlyle in Old Age (1865-1881)* (London: K. Paul, Trench, Trubner, 1934), p. 177.
45. The opening statement in J. Narlikar's *The Structure of the Universe* (Oxford: University Press, 1978), p. 1. See also, P. Davies, *Other Worlds: A Portrait of Nature in Rebellion. Space, Superspace and the Quantum Universe* (New York: Simon and Schuster, 1980), pp. 134-35.
46. J. Narlikar, *The Structure of the Universe*, p. 104.
47. Psalm 11: 5. No less appropriate are verses 9-10 from Psalm 72: "They have set their mouths in heaven and their tongues dictate to the earth." See also Ps. 74: 6 and 93: 4.
48. R. C. Tolman, *Relativity, Thermodynamics, and Cosmology* (Oxford: Clarendon Press, 1934), p. 488.
49. See his obituary by J. Gleick in *The New York Tiimes* Feb. 17, 1988, p. D27, cols. 1 and 6. "I don't feel frightened by not knowing things, by being lost in a mysterious universe without any purpose, which is the way it really is, so far as I can tell."
50. "The universe is just there, and that's all," was Bertrand Russell last-ditch stance in his radio-debate with F. Copleston on the existence of God. See *The Existence of God. Readings selected, edited, and furnished with and introductory essay* by J. Hick (New York: Macmillan Company, 1964), p. 174.
51. A recollection of L. Rosenfeld; quoted in R. V. Jones, "Complementarity as a Way of Life," in A. P. French and P. J. Kennedy, *Niels Bohr: A Centenary Volume* (Cambridge: Harvard University Press, 1985), p. 323.
52. A. Toynbee, *A Study of History*, Vol. XII, *Reconsiderations* (New York: Oxford University Press, 1964), pp. 9-10.
53. H. Reichenbach, *The Rise of Scientific Philosophy* (Berkeley: University of California Press, 1951), p. 268.
54. A. Camus, *The Myth of Sisyphus and Other Essays*, tr. J. O'Brien (New York: A. Knopf, 1955), p. 6.
55. Ibid., p. 123.
56. Ibid.

57. C. S. Lewis, *Surprised by Joy: The Shape of My Early Life* (London: Bles, 1955), pp. 65 and 193.

58. C. S. Lewis did indeed recognize that debt in glowing terms, ibid., pp. 180 and 211.

59. For details, see ch. 2 in my *Chesterton. A Seer of Science* (Urbana: University of Illinois Press, 1986).

60. G. K. Chesterton, *Heretics* (London: John Lane, 1911), p. 15.

61. "Ecclesiastes," in *The Collected Poems of G. K. Chesterton* (London: Methuen, 1933), p. 326.

62. J. H. Newman, "Holy Scripture in Its Relation to the Catholic Creed," in *Discussions and Arguments on Various Subjects* (new ed.; London: Longmans, Green, and Co., 1897), p. 233.

63. Especially in his "On the Nature and the Limitations of Cosmical Inquiries," *Scientific Monthly* 37 (1933), pp. 385-97.

64. "There is but one thought greater than that of the universe, and that is the thought of its Maker," *The Idea of a University* (London: Longmans, Green, and Co., 1888), p. 462.

65. A story related to me by Mr. Robert Wills, President of Farmington Institute for Christian Studies.

66. *The Life of Saint Claire ascribed to Fr. Thomas of Celano*, translated and edited from the earliest mss. by Fr. Paschal Robinson (Philadelphia: Dolphin Press, 1910), p. 70.

67. Psalm 138: 16.

INDEX OF NAMES

INDEX OF SUBJECTS

284

Note on the Author

Stanley L. Jaki, a Hungarian-born Catholic priest of the Benedictine order, is Distinguished Professor at Seton Hall University, South Orange, New Jersey. With doctorates in theology and physics, he has for the past thirty years specialized in the history and philosophy of science. The author of twenty-five books and over seventy articles, he served as Gifford Lecturer at the University of Edinburgh and as Fremantle Lecturer at Balliol College, Oxford. He has lectured at major universities in the United States, Europe, and Australia. He is *membre correspondant* of the Académie Nationale des Sciences, Belles-Lettres et Arts of Bordeaux, and the recipient of the Lecomte du Nouy Prize for 1970 and of the Templeton Prize for 1987.